REACTION DYNAMICS
Recent Advances

Springer-Verlag
  Berlin
  Heidelberg
  New York
  London
  Paris
  Tokyo
  Hong Kong
  Barcelona

Narosa Publishing House
  New Delhi
  Madras
  Bombay
  Calcutta

REACTION DYNAMICS
Recent Advances

EDITED BY
N. SATHYAMURTHY

Springer-Verlag

Narosa Publishing House

Editor
N. Sathyamurthy
Professor of Chemistry
Indian Institute of Technology
Kanpur-208016
India

Exclusive distribution in North America (including Canada and Mexico) and Europe by
Springer-Verlag Berlin Heidelberg New York

For all other countries exclusive distribution by
Narosa Publishing House, New Delhi

ISBN 81–85198–37–3 Narosa Publishing House, New Delhi
ISBN 3–540–53360–5 Springer-Verlag Berlin Heidelberg New York
ISBN 0–387–53360–5 Springer-Verlag New York Berlin Heidelberg

Printed in India at Rajkamal Electric Press, Delhi 110 033

"One amusing characteristic of
Chemists is their tendency to
talk as if they can really 'see'
atoms and molecules as clearly
as objects in the everyday world."

—I.W.M. Smith
Nature, 343, 691 (1990)

Preface

The award of the Nobel Prize in chemistry for the year 1986 to Professors D.R. Herschbach, Y.T. Lee and J.C. Polanyi could be considered an indication of the field of molecular reaction dynamics coming of age. That does not mean to say that there have not been much development after 1986. On the contrary, the activity has flourished much more intensely. Much more refined state-to-state information has become available on the most fundamental $H + H_2$ reaction; "dynamical stereochemistry" has gotton into the parlance of the dynamicists; the shift from scalar to vector observables is noticeable; photodissociation has gotten beyond the state-to-state level; gas-surface scattering has benefitted from the developments in molecular beam and laser techniques; and more recently, the femtosecond transition state spectroscopy is being used to probe the transition state and "to observe molecular vibration and rotation". Fully converged three dimensional quantum mechanical calculations using accurate ab initio potential-energy surfaces have definitely become "practicable" if one has access to Cray or any of its cousins. Classical trajectories are being computed merrily for anything ranging from $H + H_2$ collisions to protein dynamics. It has been shown that chaos is not all that chaotic, that it has far reaching implications to intra- as well as inter-molecular processes and that some of it might be "observed". Present day detailed dynamical studies are not confined to gas phase only. Some of the barrierless isomerization reactions have become amenable to time-resolved laser spectroscopy. Theory has kept pace with experiments.

To review all the developments in the field of molecular reaction dynamics would be an undertaking we could not venture into. Instead we have highlighted some of them which fall right in our alley.

I am grateful to all the contributors for their valuable contributions and co-operation. But for the referees who took the time out to critically examine the earlier versions of the manuscripts, this volume would not be in its present form. I am grateful to all of them. It is a pleasure to place on record the fact that this volume emerged as a consequence of the two Winter Schools on Molecular Reaction Dynamics organized at IIT Kanpur and to acknowledge the continued support from the Department of Science and Technology, New Delhi. Finally, we thank Mr. N.K. Mehra of Narosa Publishing House for encouraging us into this exercise, gently reminding us of the deadlines and finally bringing the volume in the form seen by the readers.

N. Sathyamurthy

Contents

REACTION DYNAMICS
Recent Advances

1. Molecular Beams and Clusters

P.K. Chakraborti

M.D.R.S., Physics Group
Bhabha Atomic Research Centre
Bombay, India

Abstract

Precise knowledge of intermolecular potential, which is at the heart of understanding macroscopic properties of matter, is most directly probed through measurements of scattering cross sections. High resolution differential elastic cross section data along with bulk properties can determine inert gas potentials to within 1% precision. Comparable precision in atom-diatom potential is achievable through high resolution differential cross section measurement and accurate evaluation of quenching of the diffraction structure. Rotationally inelastic differential cross section measurements provide direct information on potential anisotropy.

Supersonic expansion of pure and mixed gases lead to formation of pure and mixed clusters of various composition and sizes. Identification and characterization of clusters which provide linkage between gaseous phase and solid phase, is achieved through mass spectrometry, laser spectroscopic techniques, scattering measurements and a combination of all of them.

1. INTRODUCTION

Thermal energy atomic and molecular beam techniques are playing a very important role in the investigation of physical and chemical properties of matter. First important application of the atomic beam technique was the famous Stern-Gerlach experiment where atoms of silver were separated in an inhomogenous magnetic field depending on their spin state. Subsequently atomic beams found wide application in magnetic resonance studies [1]. Chemical application of molecular beams in a sustained manner has come into existence from sixties onwards. It is now a major and sensitive tool for probing intermolecular forces, energy transfer dynamics, biomolecular reaction dynamics, ultrasensitive spectroscopy and molecular structure, surface structure and surface reactions, catalysis, intramolecular processes, photodissociation dynamics, microelectronics and many other aspects of immense interest in chemistry and chemical physics. Precise knowledge of intermolecular forces is at the heart of understanding macroscopic properties of matter. Traditional sources of information on intermolecular forces are the bulk properties like virial coefficients, transport properties of dilute gases etc. which provide information on the "averaged" potential. In contrast, scattering of two atoms or molecules provides a direct method for determination of interaction potentials between colliding partners. Several reviews [2–8] in this field bring out the developments in the field over the initial fifteen years or so. Theoretical developments in many of these aspects have kept pace with the experimental progress.

An important spin-off of molecular beam research is the development of supersonic jets and supersonic beams. In view of their special characteristics, they could foster the generation of van der Waals clusters, metal and semiconductor clusters of various sizes and compositions. The study of such clusters is of prime importance because they serve as a definitive approach to the study, at a molecular level, of what is frequently referred to as the aggregated or "fifth state" of matter [2] having properties between gaseous and solid (or liquid) state. It is one of the challenging problems in chemical physics to elucidate factors which influence the variation in electronic and thermochemical properties, spectroscopic features, reactivity and other properties of matter during its course of change from gaseous to condensed phase.

In view of limitation of space and time, we will presently restrict ourselves to the discussion of only certain aspects of molecular beam chemistry. Our present discussion will concern with the latest developments in molecular beam elastic and inelastic scattering studies for precise determination of intermolecular potentials and the study of van der Waals clusters.

2. MOLECULAR BEAM SCATTERING AND INTERMOLECULAR FORCES

2.1 Elastic Scattering

Body of literature on intermolecular forces is presently far too large. Existing reviews and books [8–17] cover different facets of this complex subject. The reviews by Buck and Pauly are in particular useful for knowing about the quality and quantity of information on intermolecular forces contained in scattering data of different types (diffraction, rainbow etc.) and also about methods of extracting such information the best way. For inert gases such two body potentials are known very accurately (~ 1%) from use of multiproperty analysis [20, 21]. Further, all the rare gas systems [17] have the same reduced functional form (within ~ 1%) of the potential. A decisive contribution to the present knowledge of van der Waals interaction comes from atomic and molecular beam measurements of scattering cross sections [8, 17–19]. A direct inversion procedure, which leads from scattering results to intermolecular potential energy curves, has been attempted only in a few particularly favourable cases [21], where isotropic atom-atom interactions are involved and high resolution conditions in angle and energy are obtained in the experiments. However, if for a given system in addition to scattering results other properties sensitive to the potential, e.g. spectroscopic and thermophysical data are available, a combined analysis of all these data can extend the range of validity of the potential energy function and improve its reliability [11, 22–23].

In general, two kinds of scattering measurements are made—differential and integral cross sections. The former (DCS) for two colliding atoms provides detailed information on the interaction potential of van der Waals systems. The rainbow scattering angle provides probably the most direct and unique measure of the potential well depth ε, while the diffraction oscillations give a direct measure of the diameter σ of the repulsive wall (and thus the location of the potential minimum r_m). Typically, rainbow oscillations are easily observable for heavy systems and diffraction oscillations for light ones. The observation of both types of oscillations in the thermal energy range for rare gas-rare gas systems has so far presented a challenge to the experimentalists because of resolution problems. While most of the rare gas potentials are known within 1% of the true potentials in the attractive and low repulsive regions, there are still discrepancies concerning some unlike rare gas pairs e.g. Ne-heavier rare gas systems.

For atom-diatom scattering non-spherical part of the potential can significantly alter the observed cross sections e.g. quenching of total DCS and the glory amplitudes in integral cross sections. However, an approach similar to that used for rare gases can be extended to atom-diatom systems. The precise measurement of total DCS and accurate evaluation of quenching of diffraction structure within the framework of infinite order sudden (IOS) approximation, coupled to absolute integral cross sections and second virial coefficients also lead for systems like He interacting with N_2, O_2 and NO [24], Ar interacting with N_2 and O_2 [25] and NO scattered by Ar and Kr [26] to rather precise determination of potential energy surfaces (PES). In particular the absolute position of the repulsive wall of the spherical potential has been determined with a precision of about 1% and well depth to within 5% uncertainties, comparable to those achieved for the corresponding He-Ar system [20]. Further, rotational anisotropy has been found to agree with the results obtained from rotationally inelastic DCS data [27]. However, while for spherical systems the determination of the potential can be very accurate and conclusive [28, 29], for non-spherical systems its validity remains confined within the limits of the approximate schemes of analysis employed, since it is still impracticable to perform exact quantum calculations for potential fitting purposes [24].

2.1.1 Experimental technique

The study of differential cross section involves measurement of the spatial distribution of the particles around the scattering centre while in integral cross section study one measures the attenuation of the incident beam by the scattering medium (e.g. a scattering chamber or a second molecular beam). Further, it is often necessary to characterize the pre-collision and post-collision state of the interacting atomic or molecular species either by use of mechanical devices, electric and magnetic fields or lasers. In modern molecular beam scattering machines one almost invariably uses supersonic beam sources for reasons of better beam intensity and better beam quality.

In order to perform crossed molecular beam scattering experiments we have to look for beam detectors sensitive to flux $< 10^9$ molecules/s. Properties of a number of currently used detectors are listed in Table 1. Ions are easily detected with multipliers where they trigger secondary electron generation. Most of the neutral particle detection techniques, therefore, depend on their conversion to ions. With the availability of intense and tunable laser sources, two-photon ionization [30] and resonance enhanced multiphoton ionization [31] methods are also used. Both methods can be made state and species selective and two photon ionization efficiency of 20% is very promising.

Table 1.   Properties of molecular beam detectors

Detector	Detected molecules	Detection efficiencies (cts./molecule)	Detector length	Response time
Open secondary electron multipliers	Ions, metastables	≤ 1	1 mm	ns
Surface ionization	Alkali halides and alkali metals	< 0.1–1	1 mm	µs to ms
Electron bombardment ionization	All	~10^{-4}	1 cm	µs
Laser induced fluorescence	Na_2, LiH, NO etc.	0.02	1 cm to 1 µm	ns[b]
Bolometer and tunable ir laser	HF, CO, NH_3 etc.	10^{5a}	—	s[b]
cw two photon and pulsed multiphoton ionization	Na_2, K_2, large organic molecules	0.2 (TPI) 10^{-4} (MPI)	—	ns[b]

[a]Noise equivalent estimated for 2 s averaging time and 0.2 eV/molecule.
[b]Species and state selective.

Typical experimental systems for differential and integral cross section studies are shown in Figs.1 and 2. The necessary corrections required to take into account non-ideal experimental conditions are discussed in the literature. The geometric arrangement used in recent precision measurement of DCS by the Italian group [24] has the following characteristics: the collision volume is always contained in the detector viewing angle, which for a point collision zone is 0.5°, narrow divergence in angle (0.4 to 1.8°) and velocity spread (FWHM 3.5 to 20%) of the colliding beams.

2.1.2 Rare gas data

Rare gases offer the simplest systems for precise determination of interaction potential. Only when the two body potential is known precisely at all internuclear distances can serious work on problems of three body forces in dense phases can be initiated. Study of elastic scattering in inert gas systems has come a long way since the early sixties. The quality of DCS data available then and now are shown in Figs. 3 to 5. It is apparent from Fig. 5 that the high degree of instrumental sophistication allows us to resolve experimentally the fine features of the quantum scattering theory and thus derive the intimate details of the potential energy curves.

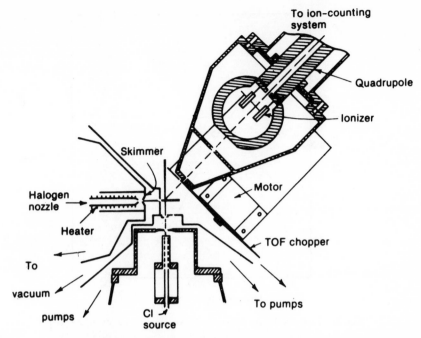

Fig. 1. Schematic diagram of crossed molecular beam apparatus showing arrangement for differential pumping for detector and source chambers and beam geometry (from J.J. Valentini et al, J. Chem. Phys. **67**, 4866, (1977)).

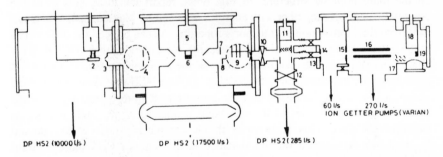

Fig. 2. Schematic diagram of apparatus used to measure integral cross section using crossed molecular beams : 1. liquid N_2 cold trap, 2. nozzle, 3. skimmer, 4. collimator, 5. liquid He/H_2 cryostat, 6. multichannel source for secondary beam, 7. shutter, 8. chopper, 9. velocity selector, 10. butterfly valve, 11. liquid N_2 cold trap, 12. VAT valve, 13. straight through valve, 14 and 15. collimators, 16. quadrupole mass filter with electron impact ion source, 17. multiplier (off axis), 18. liquid He cryostat and 19. beam trap (apparatus used in Goettingen).

For low B ($B = 2\mu\varepsilon r_m^2/\hbar^2 < 300$) values no pronounced rainbow structure is expected. As B increases in going from He$_2$ to Xe$_2$ angular spacing and amplitude of identical particle oscillations progressively decrease and finally disappear due to finite apparatus resolution but rainbow structures do survive. In recent experiments with crossed molecular beams very high resolution elastic DCS

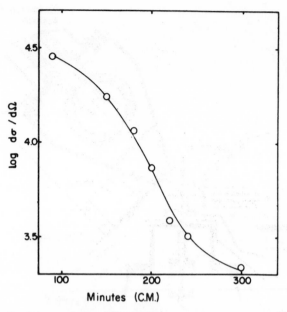

Fig. 3. Low resolution differential cross section for Ar on Ar [10].

data have been obtained [28] at thermal energies for Ne-He, Ne-Ar, Ne-Kr and Ne-Xe scattering in which diffraction quantum oscillations were superimposed on the main rainbow structure. In Fig. 6 we report the three best available potentials for Ne-Xe together with energies obtained by Maitland and Wakeham [33] from direct inversion of transport properties. As can be seen the differences in the potentials are very small (a few percent). Nevertheless, these DCS data are able to discriminate between them. None of the available potentials provides a good fit to the experimental data (see Fig. 5). The NLB (Ng, Lee and Barker) potential [34] gives the diffraction oscillations which are increasingly shifted towards too large angles with increasing scattering angle with respect to experimental data. This is because the low repulsive wall is too inward ($r_m = 3.745$ Å) located on the distance scale. The CPV (Candori, Pirani and Vecchiocattivi) potential [22] gives diffraction oscillations almost perfectly in phase having the correct r_m ($r_m = 3.90$ Å), but the location of the rainbow and general slope of the cross section curve is not in agreement with the experiment, because of too shallow a well ($\varepsilon = 6.05$ meV) and of incorrect slope of the outer potential wall in the region of the inflection point, just the domain of rainbow scattering. The prediction of the A (Aziz) potential having the correct r_m ($r_m = 3.872$ Å) follows rather closely in phase and period the experimental data. However, it does not predict the general fall off of the rainbow as well, indicating that the shape of the outer wall and/or the well depth is not correctly accounted for. The inverted energies of Maitland and Wakeham [33] give a σ value of 3.502 ± 0.009 Å which is slightly out of bounds of the direct determination (σ = 3.47 ± 0.02 Å) of the Perugia group. Clearly, presently available DCS data permit sophisticated refinement of

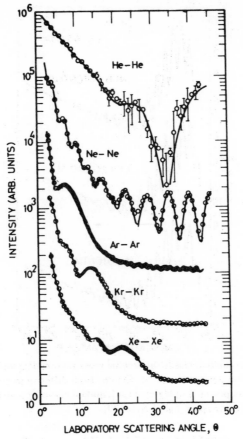

INTENSITY (ARB. UNITS)

LABORATORY SCATTERING ANGLE, θ

Fig. 4. High resolution differential cross section of like inert gas partners(after Y.T. Lee).

the unlike inert gas pair potential by simultaneously analysing them with other properties.

2.1.3 Atom-diatom systems

It is possible to extend to some simple atom-diatom systems the same approach used for the rare gas systems. Precise measurements of total DCS and accurate evaluation of the quenching of the diffraction structure within the framework of infinite order sudden (IOS) approximation, coupled to total integral cross sections, second virial coefficients and semiempirical long range coefficients, also lead for systems like He and other rare gases interacting with N_2, O_2 and NO to rather precise determination of some aspects of the PES. In particular, the absolute position of the repulsive wall of the spherical potential has been determined with a precision of 1% and the well depth of about 5%. These uncertainties are comparable to those achieved for He-Ar isotropic system.

As seen from Figs. 7 and 8, a pronounced quenching of the diffraction structure occurs in $He-O_2$, $He-N_2$ and He-NO cases with respect to corresponding isotropic

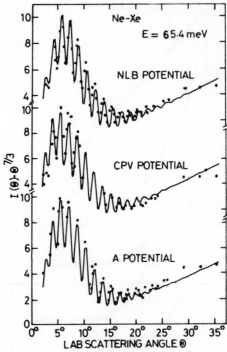

Fig. 5. Very high resolution elastic differential cross section data multiplied by $\theta^{7/3}$ for Ne-Xe system compared with predictions from different interatomic potentials. Upper curve: potential of Ng et al [34], middle curve: potential of Candori et al [22], lower curve: potential of Aziz [20].

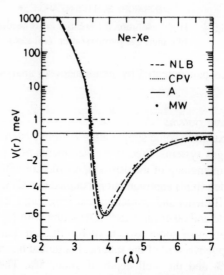

Fig. 6. Various interatomic potentials for Ne-Xe system as quoted in Fig. 5. Dots represent energy values obtained by Maitland and Wakeham [33].

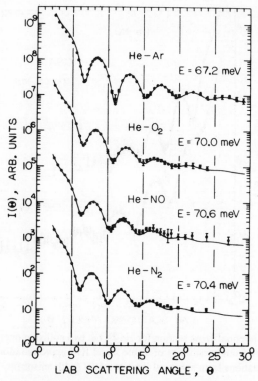

Fig. 7. Total differential cross section data for scattering of He off O_2, NO and N_2 and elastic differential cross section data of He-Ar. Curves for He-diatom are calculated from best fit anisotropic potential data of Table 2 in the IOS approximation [24].

He-Ar system. This is a manifestation of the anisotropy of the underlying potential energy surface. Pack [35] has shown that quenching of the rainbow and the diffraction oscillations in total DCS is directly related to potential well depth (ε) and minimum position (r_m) anisotropy respectively. An accurate evaluation of the quenching of the diffraction structure provides indirect estimate of the potential anisotropy.

It has been shown that for atom-molecule systems different from rare gas-H_2 (and hydrogen isotopes) the usual expansion of the potential in terms of Legendre polynomials converges very slowly. A model proposed by Pack [35] and recently widely applied consists of making potential parameters angle dependent

$$V(r, \gamma) = \varepsilon(\gamma) \cdot f(x), \qquad x = r/r_m(\gamma) \qquad (1)$$

where

$$\varepsilon(\gamma) = \varepsilon[1 + A_2 P_2 (\cos \gamma)] \qquad (2)$$

$$r_m(\gamma) = r_m[1 + B_2 P_2(\cos \gamma)] \qquad (3)$$

the reduced potential curve, $f(x)$, is chosen to be the piecewise analytic exponential-spline-Morse-spline-van der Walls (ESMSV) form. The spherical limit

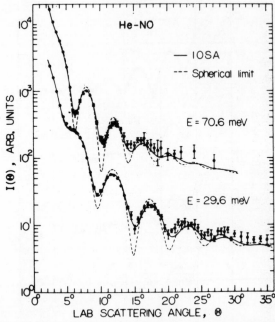

Fig. 8. Total differential cross section for He-NO at two collision energies. Continuous curves are from parameters of Table 2 and IOS approximation. Dashed curves are calculations from spherical limit potential (with anisotropy parameters set to zero).

$V_a(r)$ of such potential forms, obtained by setting to zero the anisotrophy parameters in $\varepsilon(\gamma)$ and $r_m(\gamma)$ is not the same as $V_0(r)$ term (the spherical average of PES) in a Legendre series expansion of PES [$V(r, \gamma, r') = \sum_{\lambda} V_{\lambda}(r, r')P_{\lambda}(\cos \gamma)$].

In particular, $V_a(r)$ is a much better effective spherical potential than $V_0(r)$, i.e. the scattering properties of $V_a(r)$ are closer to those of $V(r, r')$ than $V_0(r)$. It is interesting to note in the parametrization of $\varepsilon(\gamma)$ and $r_m(\gamma)$ that V_a corresponds to the potential at the "magic" angle (54.73°) where the second Legendre polynomial $P_2(\cos \gamma)$ vanishes.

The DCSs were calculated in the c.m. system for each orientation angle, γ, by partial wave analysis with JWKB phase shifts. A 32-point Gauss-Legendre quadrature was used to average the c.m. differential cross section $\sigma(\theta, \gamma)$ over $\cos \gamma$ according to IOS prescription:

$$\sigma(\theta) = \frac{1}{2} \int_{-1}^{+1} \sigma(\theta, \gamma) \, d(\cos \gamma) \tag{4}$$

For comparison with experimental $I(\Theta)$, the $\cos \gamma$ weighted total (elastic + inelastic) c.m. $\sigma(\theta)$ were transformed into laboratory frame using elastic Jacobian and then averaged over velocity distributions of the two beams and over beam and detector geometries. Potential parameters so determined are presented in Table 2. Potential for parallel ($\gamma = 0°$) and perpendicular ($\gamma = 90°$) configuration for He-O$_2$ is shown in Fig. 9.

Table 2. Potential parameters [24]

System	He-N$_2$	He-NO	He-O$_2$	He-Ar
$\bar{\varepsilon}$ (meV)	2.42 ± 0.12	2.69 ± 0.19	2.69 ± 0.16	2.57 ± 0.13
A_2	−0.456	− 0.518	− 0.425	
$\bar{r}_m$(Å)	3.65 ± 0.04	3.63 ± 0.04	3.49 ± 0.04	3.48 ± 0.04
σ(Å)	3.24 ± 0.03	3.21 ± 0.03	3.09 ± 0.03	3.10 ± 0.02
B_2	0.125 ± 0.010	0.140 ± 0.010	0.125 ± 0.010	
A	0.5229	0.5229	1.3208	
α	14.8783	14.8783	12.46	
β	6.20	6.00	6.00	
C_6 (meVÅ^6)	6093	5963	6574	
C_8 (meVÅ^8)	30962	29487	28941	
C_{10} (meVÅ^{10})	204372	177920	166299	
x_1	0.50	0.50	0.61	
x_2	0.80	0.80	0.80	
x_3	1.1117980	1.1155245	1.1155245	
x_4	1.55	1.55	1.45	

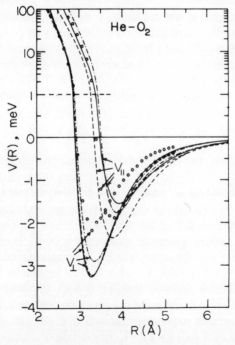

Fig. 9. Best fit He-O$_2$ anisotropic potential (continuous curve) for parallel $(V_\parallel)$ and perpendicular $(V_\perp)$ configurations. Also shown are the potentials of Keil et al, Faubel and ab initio potential of Jaquet and Staemmler [24].

2.2 Rotationally Inelastic Scattering and Potential Anisotropy

The anisotropy of molecular potentials is of great interest for understanding crystal structure [13] and also the solid, liquid and gaseous equations of state [38]. The anisotropy of molecules also has a direct effect on gas dynamic transport coefficients and rotational relaxation times [98]. Scattering experiments provide a direct tool for the determination of the interaction forces of vdW molecules. As we have already seen in the earlier section elastic scattering experiments essentially probe the isotropic potential whereas rotationally inelastic processes are due to angle dependent noncentral forces. Recently developed molecular beam experiments of essentially two types, in which: (1) the cross section anisotropy of polarized molecular beams [39] and (ii) the rotationally inelastic differential cross sections are measured [40] have made possible a rather precise measurement of the anisotropy of the vdW potential. The later category of experiments have been carried out for H_2 and its isotopomers scattered from He [41], Ne [42–44] and Ar [45], for Na_2 scattered from He [46], Ne [47–48] and Ar [47, 49] for N_2, O_2 and CO scattered from He [50] and for CH_4 scattered from He [50], Ne [51] and Ar [51]. Among these, the hydrogen molecule-rare gas interactions are the best studied. In addition, these small systems are well suited to perform highly reliable calculations of the ab initio type with configuration interaction included [52–54] or of the model type where dispersion attraction is added to the SCF repulsion with suitable corrections for the overlap region [55–57].

Theoretical analysis of the rotationally inelastic transition of HD and D_2 molecules scattered from rare gas atoms in the energy range from 30 to 90 meV gave results as follows: (i) the inelastic cross sections are peaked in the backward direction, i.e. the coupling essentially occurs in the repulsive part of the anisotropy, (ii) if we expand the interaction potential $V(r, r')$ with r as atom-molecule separation and r' as interatomic separation in a diatomic molecule in Legendre polynomials

$$V(r, r') = V_0(r) + V_2(r) P_2 (\cos \gamma) \tag{5}$$

two terms are sufficient to describe the scattering process for the homonuclear species, (iii) the $0 \rightarrow 2$ transitions of D_2 are directly related to the repulsive $V_2(r)$ term. Since the coupling is weak it was possible to construct an inversion procedure based on exponential distorted wave approximation which directly gives $V_2(r)$ once $\sigma(0 \rightarrow 2, \theta)$ is known [58, 59]. The magnitude of coupling is determined by V_2, where σ depends quadratically on V_2. However, the range is given by the elastic wavefunctions which can be approximated by the classical turning point r_0 of V_0. Thus, V_0 also has to be known for data analysis. Combining rotationally inelastic transitions with the total differential cross sections, it is possible to derive reliable interaction potentials. Early vibrationally state resolved scattering experiments at collision energies of a few eV were reported by David et al [60] for Li^+-H_2. Resolution of rotational states [25] was achieved first for Li^+-H_2 and for H_2-rare gas scattering [42, 61].

2.2.1 Experimental results

A typical apparatus used by the Goettingen group [40] is shown schematically in Fig. 10(a) and to scale in the side view machine assembly drawing in Fig. 10(b). Two nearly monochromatic molecular beams, a monatomic (He, Ne, Ar) primary beam and the diatomic (H_2 and its isotopes, Na_2, CO, N_2 etc.) secondary beam are formed by nozzle expansion. After collimation by skimmers and additional differentially pumped collimators the two beams intersect at the centre of the apparatus. Scattered rare gas atoms (most often He) are detected by mass

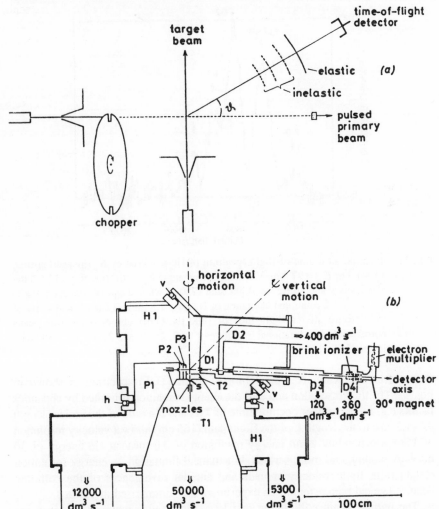

Fig. 10. (a) Schematic illustration of the crossed beam time-of-flight apparatus principle. (b) The actual system design with six differential pumping stages and two well collimated supersonic beam sources. A helium partial pressure of 10^{-16} torr in the mass spectrometer detector is sustained by four additional differential vacuum stages. Horizontal and vertical scattering angles are selected by motion of ball bearing supporting flanges "*v*" and "*h*" [40].

spectrometer detector at the right hand side of Figs. 10(a) or (b) respectively. The scattering angle is changed by rotating the detector part of the machine with respect to the vertical axis indicated in Fig. 10(b). For observing individual rotational transitions at a given scattering angle the flight time and thus the energy change of the scattered molecules is measured. To do this a 12 cm chopper wheel with four 1 mm wide slots is rotated through the He beam at 24,000 rpm. The count rate of the scattered particles arriving at the detector is then recorded as a function of time delay from the passage of a chopper slit

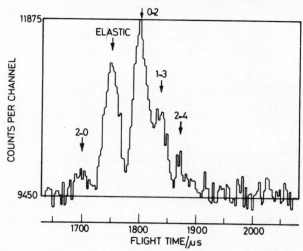

Fig. 11. Example of a time-of-flight spectrum of He scattered by N_2 (measuring time 14 hr). For $E_{cm} = 27.3$ meV and scattering angle $\theta_{lab} = 20°$ (i.e. $\theta_{cm} = 17.5°$) the elastically scattered He has flight time 1750 μs while the peak corresponding to $j_i = 0$ to $j = 2$ rotational excitation of N_2 loses 1.5 meV (12 cm^{-1}) and arrive at the detector after a flight time of 1800 μs. Other observed inelastic peaks corresponding to rotational transitions $1 \rightarrow 3$, $2 \rightarrow 0$ and $2 \rightarrow 4$ are marked by arrows [40].

through the He beam. A typical time-of-flight (TOF) spectrum is shown in Fig. 11. The time resolution and thus the energy resolution is limited by apparatus factors e.g. finite chopper opening time of 7 μs and the ratio of the ionizer length ΔL (1.5 cm) to the length L of the flight path (165 cm) allow a velocity resolution of 1% corresponding to an energy resolution of 0.6 meV at He energy of 30 meV. A second, and more serious, kinematical limitation on energy resolution results from finite velocity spreads and angular divergences of the colliding beams. Typical parameters in an experiment are summarised in Table 3.

The narrow beam collimation and long flight paths drastically reduce the scattered intensity. The He partial pressure in the detector had, therefore, to be lowered to less than the signal pressure of 10^{-16} torr. As shown in Fig. 10(b) the detector vacuum is sustained against main chamber pressure of 10^{-6} torr by four stages of differential pumping. With an estimated He detection efficiency of 10^{-5} the average detector count rate was 10 s^{-1} and measuring times of typically 10 to 30 hours were required to obtain spectra of Figs. 11 and 12.

Table 3. Typical experimental parameters [40]

Component	Nozzle condition		Spreads (fwhm)	
He primary beam	Pressure : $p_0 = 100$ bar Diameter : $D = 100$ μm Temperature: $T_0 = 88$ K		Velocity: $v/v_0 = 0.7\%$ at $v_0 = 950$ m/s Angular: $\Delta\alpha = 0.75°$ in-plane $\Delta\beta = 2.0°$ out-of-plane	
N_2 target beam	Pressure : $p_0 = 8$ bar Diameter : $D = 100$ μm Temperature: $T_0 = 300$ K		Velocity: $\Delta v/v_0 = 5\%$ at $v_0 = 750$ m/s Angular: $\Delta\alpha = 2°$ $\Delta\beta = 2°$ Rotational population $j_i = 0 : 50\%$ $j_i = 1 : 33\%$ $j_i = 2 : 15\%$	
Detector			Velocity: $\Delta v/v = \Delta L/L = 1\%$ at $L = 165$ cm Angular: $\Delta\alpha = 0.4°$ $\Delta\beta = 0.2°$	

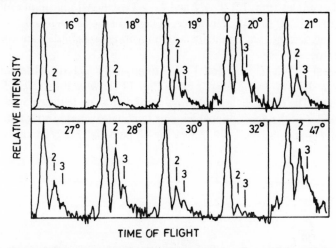

Fig. 12. Time-of-flight spectrum for He-N_2 scattering at $E_{cm} = 27.3$ meV for different scattering angles. The largest peak amplitude is normalized to unity [40].

The procedure to derive cross section ratios from such data has been described in detail in [38]. Briefly, as a first step the distribution functions in the final velocity space are calculated by a Monte Carlo procedure for the elastic and possible inelastic transitions using angular and velocity spreads of the two intersecting beams and the transmission function of the TOF analyser. As for the second step, the measured spectra are fitted to the calculated distribution functions. If the half-width of the distribution function is smaller than the corresponding energy loss due to the inelastic transition, the problem is relatively simpler. The fitted amplitude A_{if} is directly related to the cross section $\sigma_{if}(\bar{\theta}, \bar{g})$ by

$$A_{if} = K p_i \bar{J}_{if} \sigma_{if}(\bar{\theta}, \bar{g}) \tag{6}$$

where K is a constant with respect to velocity variables and it depends only on the laboratory deflection angle $\bar{\theta}$, p_i is the relative population of the initial state, $\bar{J}_{if}$ is the Jacobian for the transformation from the c.m. to the laboratory frame, $\bar{g}$ is the relative velocity and θ c.m. scattering angle. If we normalize these values to elastic contribution we can derive cross section ratios. To obtain absolute inelastic cross sections the total differential is used together with suitable calibration based on calculations.

The experimental data of Figs. 11 and 12 correspond to c.m. energy $E = 27.3$ meV. The spectrum of Fig. 12 corresponding to laboratory angle 20° shows a fast peak of elastically scattered He atoms at flight times of 1750 µs. At 1800 µs an even larger second peak is found with an energy loss of 1.5 meV equal to level spacing between the $j = 0$ and $j = 2$ rotational levels of ortho-N_2. The shoulder on the right hand side of $0 \rightarrow 2$ transition peak results from $1 \rightarrow 3$ transition of para-N_2. Also observed are the much weaker $2 \rightarrow 0$ and $2 \rightarrow 4$ rotational transitions of $j_i = 2$ state of ortho-N_2 which accounts for 15% of all N_2 molecules. Higher rotational transition probabilities are estimated to be < 3%.

At most angles (Fig. 12) $0 \rightarrow 2$ and $1 \rightarrow 3$ rotational transition probabilities are quite small, 10 to 20%. However, at certain specific angles $\theta_{lab} = 20°$, 28° and 47° and at larger angles the inelastic transition probabilities are comparable to the elastic.

The total and the $0 \rightarrow 2$ and $1 \rightarrow 3$ rotationally inelastic differential cross sections in the c.m. frame, displayed in Fig. 13 show well-resolved diffraction oscillations. The shoulder in total cross section at angle between 5 and 10° is a last reminder of the conventional angular rainbow scattering structure which is expected there for the shallow ~ 2 meV He-N_2 potential, but is almost completely washed out by the widely spaced diffraction.

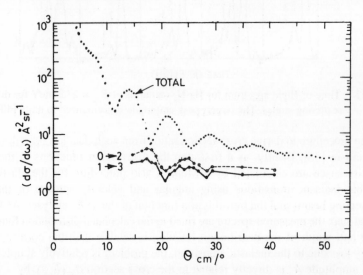

Fig. 13. Experimental centre-of-mass total (•), $0 \rightarrow 2$ (O) and $1 \rightarrow 3$ (●) rotationally inelastic cross sections for He-N_2 at $E_{cm} = 27.3$ meV [40].

The complete potential model for He-N$_2$ is written as

$$V(r, \gamma) = V_{SCF}(r, \gamma) + V_{Corr}(r, \gamma) + V_{Disp}(r, \gamma) \tag{7}$$

The repulsive part of the He-N$_2$ potential was obtained by calculating the SCF potential energies in the range $4 < r/a.u. < 8$ for orientation angles $\gamma = 0°$, $45°$ and $90°$. The SCF energy values were also fitted to a 3 term Legendre expansion in γ, each coefficient of which could be well approximated by Born-Mayer radial function

$$V_{SCF}(r, \gamma) = \sum_{\lambda} A_{2\lambda} \exp(-\beta_{2\lambda} \cdot r) P_{2\lambda}(\cos \gamma) \tag{8}$$

The asymptotic regions of the He-N$_2$ potential are joined together by the following prescription which takes into account the effect of electron overlap on the dispersion coefficients. This correction has been estimated semiclassically from the energy splitting induced in the Drude model molecules when coupled to each other by SCF interaction.

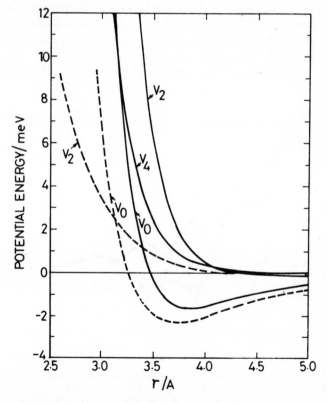

Fig. 14. Radial terms V_0, V_2 and V_4 of He-N$_2$ van der Waals potential by Tang-Toennis model (full curves). Dashed lines are the V_0 and V_2 terms of an experimental He-N$_2$ potential obtained by Keil et al from fitting total differential cross section only.

For computational purposes the standard representation of the total potential function in Legendre function is

$$V(r, \gamma) = V_0(r) + V_2(r)P_2(\cos \gamma) + V_4(r) P_4(\cos \gamma) + \dots \qquad (9)$$

and the first three radial potential functions $V_{2\lambda}(r)$ for He-N$_2$ are shown in Fig. 14. The spherical part V_0 of this potential has well depth $\varepsilon° = 1.62$ meV and an $r°_m = 3.83$ Å. Remarkably, in the region of the repulsive barrier, the $V_2(r)$ potential is considerably larger than the spherical term while the V_4 term has only a significant effect in the potential well region and at the beginning of the repulsive barrier. The figure also shows (dashed curve) the V_0 and V_2 terms derived by Keil et al [62] entirely from total differential cross section measurements at $E = 64$ meV. This is an effective potential in that it accounts indirectly for the quenching due to inelastic processes as well. There is a surprisingly large discrepancy between the two V_0 curves. Coupled-channels calculations of differential elastic and rotationally inelastic cross sections were carried out from these known potentials at an experimental collision energy of $E = 27.3$ meV using 25 coupled channels. Results of this calculation are shown in Fig. 15. Test calculations show that V_4 term of the potential influences the cross section by $< 10\%$ for angles $< 60°$. As seen from this figure all characteristic features of the experimental cross section, e.g. oscillatory decreasing total cross section, amplitude of inelastic cross sections and relative phases between diffraction oscillations of total and rotationally inelastic cross sections are well

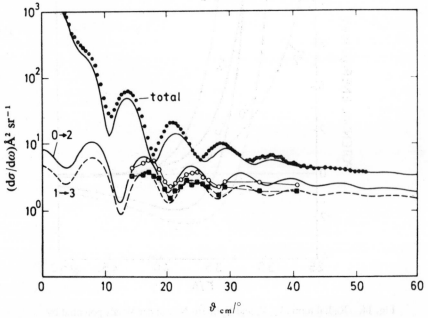

Fig. 15. Comparison of predicted theoretical (smooth curves) with measured total (•), $0 \rightarrow 2$ (O) and $1 \rightarrow 3$ (■) rotationally inelastic differential cross section for He-N$_2$ at $E_{cm} = 27.3$ meV [40].

predicted by theory. However, small deviations exist in the absolute magnitude and in positions of the diffraction maxima.

Because of the small V_2 term in it, Keil, Slankes and Kuppermann (KSK) potential, tends to underestimate the rotational inelastic cross sections by as much as a factor of 5. Nevertheless, the KSK effective V_0 potential gives approximately the same fit to the experimental total cross section as did the close coupling total cross section of Tang-Toennies (TT) potential [55]. This seems to indicate that with strongly asymmetric potentials the total scattering cross section structure is preferentially weighing the perpendicular orientation $(V(r, \gamma = 90°) = V_0(r) - (1/2) V_2(r))$ of the potential. As can be estimated from the TT potential, this potential is quite close to the effective KSK V_0 potential. Thus, the effective spherical potential derived from total cross section measurements is not always identical to the true spherical part $V_0(r)$ of the potential.

3. VAN DER WAALS CLUSTERS

Recent years have seen rapidly growing interest in the physics and chemistry of both neutral and ionized clusters. Recent progress in cluster ion research has been extensively reviewed elsewhere [63, 64]. The fundamental goal of cluster physics is to study the transition

$$\text{atom/molecule} \rightarrow \text{clusters} \rightarrow \text{solid/liquid}$$

The study of clusters serves as a positive and definitive approach to the study, at the molecular level, of what is frequently referred to as the aggregated or 'fifth' state of matter [65] having properties in between the gaseous and the solid (or liquid) states. It is a challenging problem in chemical physics to elucidate the factors influencing the electronic and thermochemical properties, spectral features, reactivity etc. as the transition takes place from the gas phase to the condensed. Clusters are relatively unexplored species and as such this field is full of astonishing discoveries. Due to limitations in space we will present some illustrative examples in selected domains of cluster physics as reported by different groups around the world.

3.1 Classification of Clusters

Clusters are entities comprising of a non-rigid assembly of components bound together by physical and/or chemical bonds [66]. Jortner [67] classified clusters on the basis of their bond strength (Table 4) into two categories: (i) weakly bound clusters (vdW clusters, molecular and hydrogen bonded clusters) and (ii) strongly bound clusters (e.g. ionic, valence and metallic clusters).

There are several ways of forming and studying clusters, that is, (i) gas phase clusters, (ii) clusters supported upon substrate surface, and (iii) clusters existing in liquids and solids. In this chapter we will mainly consider weakly bonded clusters existing in gas phase.

3.2 Transition State

Bulk values of melting temperature are reached only when considerably large size (radius > 100 Å) of a cluster is achieved (see Fig. 16 for gold) [67]. Considerable insight into solid-like or liquid-like cluster behaviour can be derived

Table 4.   Classification of clusters based on binding energy
(J. Jortner, Ber. Bunsenges. Phys. Chem. **88**, 188 (1984))

Cluster type	Typical cases	Binding force	Average binding energy (eV)
van der Waals	(rare gas)$_n$, (N$_2$)$_n$, (CO$_2$)$_n$ . . .	Dispersion + Weak electrostatic	≤ 0.3
Hydrogen bonded	(H$_2$O)$_n$, (NH$_3$)$_n$ etc.	H-bonding, electrostatic	~ 0.3 to 0.5
Ionic	(NaCl)$_n$ etc.	Ionic	~ 2 to 4
Valence	C$_n$, S$_8$	Conventional chemical bond	~ 1 to 4
Metallic	Na$_n$, Cu$_n$ etc.	Metallic bonds	~ 0.5 to 3

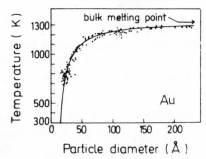

Fig. 16.   Size dependence of the melting temperature of gold clusters [68].

from recent numerical simulation of melting transition of very small Ar$_n$ clusters [69, 70]. Recently Scoles and collaborators [71, 72] have used optothermal (bolometer) detection method to obtain extremely interesting infrared spectra of Ar$_n$ clusters containing SF$_6$ molecules (Fig. 17). It may be observed that at the highest source pressure spectral features approach that of SF$_6$ spectra in Ar matrix [73]. A different approach is to study electron diffraction pattern to determine unit cell lattice parameters. For lead clusters [65] unit cell lattice parameters are shown in Fig. 18. The data are consistent with the model of a cluster having a crystallized core plus a surface layer which becomes progressively more liquid like as the cluster size gets smaller. Similar studies with Ar [74] and SF$_6$ clusters [75, 76] have been carried out by Farges et al and Bartell and his collaborators.

Study of metal clusters is being pursued actively and some of the findings have wide ranging application potential. An important enquiry is to identify the size of the metal atom clusters where bulk metallic properties are displayed. One approach to this is to study changing ionization energies, and hence work function/ or electron affinity of metallic clusters as a function of the degree of aggregation. Extensive study along these lines has been made by Smalley and co-workers [77-79] on copper clusters. Their work shows that the bulk value of ionization energy (4.4 eV) is not reached even for Cu$_{25}$ clusters.

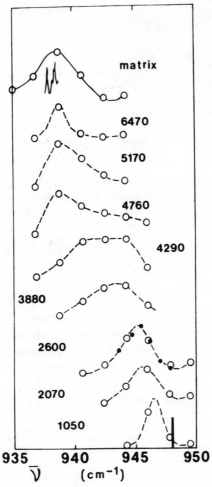

Fig. 17. Photodissociation spectra of $SF_6 \cdot (Ar)_n$ at different nozzle stagnation pressures (torr). Open circles correspond to laser induced attenuation of the molecular beam intensity for different CO_2 laser lines (laser power 7.5 W). Closed circles at 2600 torr are attenuation data with an N_2O laser (power 0.5 W). The gas mixture used was 1% SF_6 in Ar. The vertical bar indicates the SF_6 band centre in gas phase [71].

3.3 Generation of Clusters Through Supersonic Expansion

Neutral vdW clusters in gas phase are generally not available in equilibrium systems. The dynamic method of supersonic expansion of gases through a nozzle, frequently used for generating high intensity molecular beams, provides a very convenient means for generating gas phase neutral clusters of atoms and molecules [80–88]. The basic process involves adiabatic expansion of a gas or a gas mixture at high stagnation pressure (p_0) and temperature (T_0) through a small orifice (diameter D) into an evacuated (< 10^{-3} torr) volume (see Fig. 19). Molecular flow is characterized in terms of Knudsen number (K_n) which is the ratio of

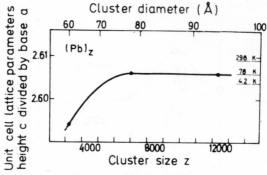

Fig. 18. The ratio of unit cell lattice parameters, height c to base a, for lead clusters plotted as a function of the cluster size z and the average cluster diameter (after Stein). Lines on rhs scale indicate the corresponding values in bulk crystalline materials at the given temperatures.

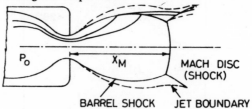

(a) Flow lines and shock fronts in expanding gas jet.

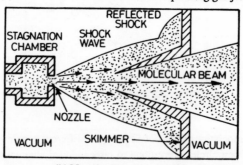

(b) Nozzle skimmer system.

Fig. 19. (a) Supersonic jet with associated shock waves. (b) Nozzle-skimmer system for collimated molecular beam generation.

escape orifice diameter (D) to the mean free path, λ, in the stagnation chamber. If $K_n \ll 1$, the flow is continuous and particles undergo a large number of collisions during the flow period. Expansion converts random motion into directed flow, thus reducing translational (T_{tran}), rotational (T_{rot}) and vibrational (T_{vib}) temperatures of the molecules to very low values. Translational and rotational temperatures as low as a few Kelvin can be routinely achieved [89, 90]. Extremely low temperatures coupled with a high number density environment lead to nucleation and condensation. By appropriate design of nozzle geometry and experimental parameters one can control [91] the degree of condensation.

Assuming ideal isentropic expansion, which neglects viscous and conduction effects, we write down the energy conservation equation as

$$h_0 = h + 1/2\ mu^2 \tag{10}$$

that is

$$C_{p_0} T_0 = C_{p_b} T_b + 1/2\ mu^2 \tag{11}$$

Subscripts 0 and b refer to stagnation condition and beam respectively and u is the flow velocity. Defining Mach number (M) as the ratio of the flow velocity to the local velocity of sound, $a = (\gamma kT/m)^{1/2}$ one derives

$$T_b/T_0 = [1 + 1/2 \cdot (\gamma - 1)M^2]^{-1} \tag{12}$$

and

$$p_b/p_0 = [1 + 1/2 \cdot (\gamma - 1)M^2]^{-1/(\gamma - 1)} \tag{13}$$

Axial (x) Mach number under continuum flow condition is given [92] by

$$M(x) = A(\gamma)\ [(x - x_0)/D](\gamma - 1) - 1/2\ (\gamma + 1)/(\gamma - 1)/A(\gamma)[(x - x_0)/D]^{\gamma - 1} \tag{14}$$

With progress of expansion, rarefaction sets in and the Mach number attains a terminal value (M_t) for a given expansion condition. Anderson and Fenn [93] derived the expression for the terminal Mach number as

$$M_t = 1.17\ K_n^{-0.4} \sim (p_0 D)^{0.4} \tag{15}$$

Formation of molecular aggregates requires at the minimum three body collisions which scale as $p_0^2 D$ whereas cooling in supersonic jet requires two body collisions scaling as $p_0 D$. Thus the three body to two body collision ratio is proportional to the stagnation pressure p_0, that is, the stagnation number

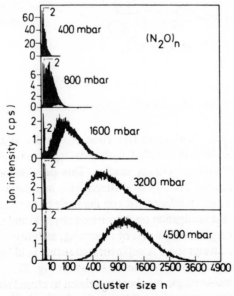

Fig. 20. Mass spectra of N_2O clusters produced by supersonic expansion (215 K nozzle temperature, 30 eV electron energy, 200 μm nozzle diameter) for different stagnation pressures (after Sattler).

density, n_0. It is seen that the terminal Mach number (M_t) and the terminal translational temperature (T_t) are functions of $p_0 D$. Keeping $p_0 D$ constant one can minimize the absolute value of p_0 and achieve a high degree of cooling without appreciable condensation. However, there is a technical limitation as regards pumping speed requirement which goes as $p_0 D^2$. For more details on scaling laws we refer to a recent review by Hagena [94]. Condensation evolves through statistical processes. It is therefore, difficult to obtain narrow size cluster distribution (see Fig. 20) unless some specifically devised source conditions are employed [86-88, 95].

Although it is not within the scope of the present discussion we would like to make a brief reference to the fast developing and extremely interesting field of metal and semiconductor clusters. Impressive series of advances has taken place in producing and studying such clusters [96]. A technique based on supersonic expansion of laser-evaporated metal vapour in a monatomic carrier gas is capable of synthesizing isolated clusters of any material. A schematic of the laser-evaporation pulsed nozzle set up is shown in Fig. 21. A laser beam is focussed on the side of the rotating metal rod and synchronized to fire synchronously with the peak density of the He carrier gas. Clusters of moderate size can now be routinely produced by this technique for almost all elements in the periodic table including the refractory metals.

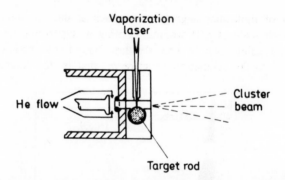

Fig. 21. Schematic diagram of gas phase metal cluster evaporation device.

3.4 Electron Impact Ionization Detection of van der Waals Clusters

Electron impact ionization coupled with mass spectrometric detection is the most universal method for cluster studies. This provides a direct method to distinguish and separate clusters of different size and composition (elemental, stoichiometric and non-stoichiometric) on the basis of their mass to charge ratio. It, therefore, allows investigation on the various physical and chemical properties e.g. appearance energies, enthalpies of clustering, stability, reactivity, transport coefficients etc. of cluster ions. A sophisticated sector field high resolution mass spectrometer set up for cluster studies is shown in Fig. 22.

Exceptionally stable magic numbers n_m related to closed shell phenomena for few-body self-bound systems is well known in atomic physics (electron shells of noble gas atoms) and nuclear structure ($n_m = 2,\ 8,\ 20,\ 28$ etc.). Recent

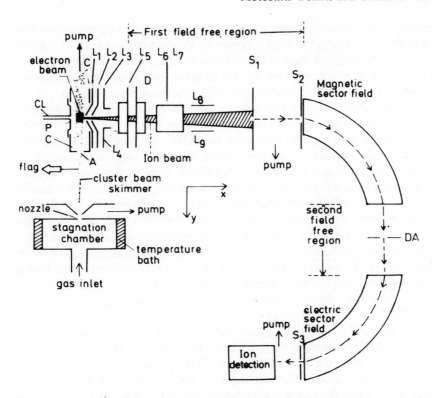

Fig. 22. Schematic view of molecular beam ionization mass spectrometer apparatus (after Mark [64]) P, pusher; C, collision chamber; CL, capillary leak gas inlet; A, aperture; nozzle: 20 μm nozzle for molecular beam gas inlet; L_1, collision chamber exit slit electrodes (L_1, P and C are at a common source potential of typically +3kV); L_2, penetrating field extraction electrodes; S_1, mass spectrometer entrance slit; S_2, entrance magnetic sector field; DA, defining aperture; S_2, mass spectrometer exit slit.

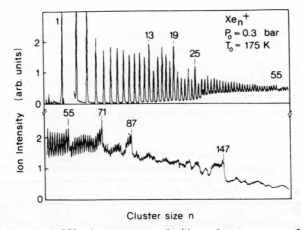

Fig. 23. Mass spectra of Xe clusters measured with an electron energy of 30 eV (after [97]). The most prominent abundance drops occur after magic numbers 13, 19, 25, 55, 71, 87 and 147 corresponding to shell closures of hard spheres in an icosahedral structure.

investigations in vdW clusters also reveal the presence of such magic numbers. In Fig. 23 we present the mass spectrum of Xe clusters recorded by Echt [97]. Pronounced abundance maxima and minima can be seen at certain magic numbers. Occurrence of magic numbers in case of other rare gases was subsequently confirmed by other investigators [98–101]. The most recent studies [98, 99] have shown that, at least for vdW clusters, evaporative stabilization after ionization process in the metastable time regime is the main reason, and the likely origin for the occurrence of these abundance anomalies. We may recall at this stage Klots' [102] observation that any ionized cluster of unusual abundance not accompanied by an abnormal life time (metastable decay rate) does not necessarily constitute a local stability, but is perhaps only an echo of some neutral precursor.

Ionic clusters of materials which form insulators in bulk undergo fragmentation. This, in other words, implies that a given ionized cluster size may have contributions from more than one neutral precursor size and the extent of ionization of a particular neutral size, in general, cannot be determined from the intensity of the corresponding ionized cluster within a cluster distribution. Furthermore, it has not been possible to generate neutral clusters of specific size at known number densities and as such hardly any quantitative information is available on cluster ionization process.

The physical reason for the fragmentation of vdW clusters can be understood in terms of their prototype, the rare gases. The binding between two neutral rare gas atoms is weak, e.g. 11 meV for argon. This changes by a factor of 100 if the dimer is singly ionized. The rearrangement energies are used to break up the cluster. Based on this fact and information gathered from a variety of solid state and cluster experiments, Haberland [103] proposed a model for charge localization on a dimer ion located on a cluster, e.g. an Ar_n^+ cluster should be more properly described as $Ar_2^+ Ar_{n-2}$. The concept of charge localization has recently been extended to other closed shell atoms and molecules forming insulators in bulk [104]. In all these cases it should be realized that one does not study transitions to a perfect solid in the limit of large cluster sizes, but to a solid containing positively charged defects.

The unknown cluster ion fragmentation pattern makes it extremely difficult to find any simple correlation between cluster ion signal and the corresponding neutral cluster distribution. A scattering method was used [86–88] to determine the nozzle operating condition for generating dimers alone. Very recently, Buck and coworkers [105–107] have used an elegant method to study cluster distribution by exploiting their kinematically different behaviours in a scattering experiment with a light atom. By measuring the angular and velocity distribution of the

Table 5. Measured fragmentation probabilities $f_{n,k}$ for Ar_n clusters appearing at Ar_k mass at different electron energies [105]

E_e (eV)	f_{21}	f_{22}	f_{31}	f_{32}	f_{33}
30	0.50	0.50	0.47	0.53	0.0
40	0.52	0.48	0.52	0.48	0.0
100	0.62	0.38	0.60	0.40	0.0

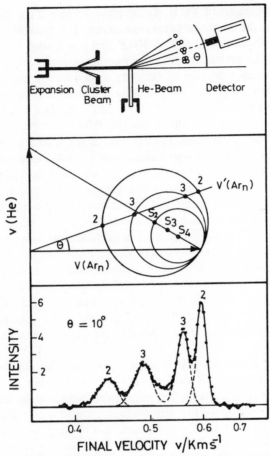

Fig. 24. The experimental method. *Upper part*: schematic view of the experimental set
up. Clusters of different masses are scattered at different angles. *Middle part*:
schematic kinematic diagram of the scattering process. The circles give the
positions of elastically scattered clusters in the centre-of-mass system. The
arrow marked v' (Ar$_x$) gives the angle and final velocity of the scattered clusters
in the laboratory system. *Lower part*: measured intensity distribution along the
arrow shown in the middle part. Dimers and trimers are clearly separated from
each other. The particles are detected at the dimer mass (after Buck [105]).

scattered clusters, different cluster species could be separated from each other
and their intensity determined independently from the subsequent detection
process. In this way fragmentation probabilities of Ar-dimers and trimers by
electron impact ionization have been measured as a function of electron energy.
For the dimer fragmentation probability varies between 50 and 62% while trimer
is completely fragmented into dimers and monomers (Table 5).

The principle of experimental method for the spatial isolation of clusters is
shown in Fig. 24. The upper part shows a schematic view of the apparatus.
Clusters (say of argon) are produced by expanding the gas through nozzles of
diameter $D = 40$ µm and 200 µm at stagnation pressures (p_0) from 0.13 to

4.0 bar at a temperature of 300 K. By sampling the core of the jet with an axially placed skimmer the molecular beam is generated. This beam is scattered by a He beam from a 30 μm nozzle at $T_0 = 300$ K and $p_0 = 30$ bar. In direct collisions clusters of smaller masses are deflected into larger angles so that they could be distinguished from each other by detecting them with a movable detector. This somewhat simplified picture is to be refined in a more accurate analysis. It is valid only for head-on collisions with impact parameter $b = 0$. For larger b values, smaller deflection results so that the deflection angle marked in Fig. 24 can only be a maximum value. For instance, at the angular position of trimers both monomers and dimers would be present as well. These contributions can also be separated from each other if, in addition to the deflection angle; the final velocity of the scattered clusters is also measured. Newton diagram which is based on conservation of energy and momentum relate the angles and velocities of elastically scattered clusters in the centre-of-mass frame (circles around different centres of mass, S_n) to those measured in the laboratory system (circles around crossing point of Ar_n and He velocities with radius $V'(Ar_n)$). The middle part of Fig. 24 shows such a diagram schematically (velocity of He not to scale). In the c.m. system the velocity of clusters of smaller masses is always larger than that of the heavier ones, so that in the laboratory system at a fixed angle they appear with a faster and a slower velocity component. If the velocity and angular resolution of the apparatus is good enough, these components can be separated from each other.

Experiments have been performed in a crossed molecular beam apparatus described in [108] which is similar to the one shown in Fig. 1. The two beams cross each other at right angles. The angular dependence of the scattered species is measured by rotating the two differentially pumped source chambers relative to the scattering centre and fixing detector unit in the plane of the two beams. The argon clusters are detected as multiples of monomer mass by electron impact ionization and mass analysed by a quadrupole mass filter which is operated in a doubly differentially pumped detection chamber at pressures lower than 10^{-10} mbar. The velocity distribution of the Ar-clusters shows about the same peak velocity of $v_1 = 570$ m/s with a slightly different velocity spread, $\Delta v/v = 5.2\%$ of monomer and $\Delta v/v = 4.1\%$ for dimer. The corresponding values for He beam are $v_2 = 1790$ m/s and $\Delta v/v = 2.1\%$. With these realistic values we get limiting deflection angles of 18° for dimer, 12° for trimer, 9° for tetramer and 7° for pentamer.

The lower part of the figure shows a measured velocity spectrum obtained at a deflection angle of 10° and detected on the Ar-dimer mass, $m = 80$ amu. At this angle only dimers and trimers could be detected. The experimental result shows clearly resolved contributions to the clusters, which correspond to marked intersection points in the middle part of Fig. 24. It is obvious from the figure that, at least for electron energy of 100 eV used in this experiment, considerable fragmentation occurs in the ion source, since the trimer contribution is measured at the dimer mass. The peak intensity of neutral clusters of size n, which are detected at mass k, is given by

$$N_{n,k}(\theta) = C\rho(Ar_n; T_0, p_0, D)\, \sigma_L(\theta, g)\, f_{n,k}(E_e)\, C_n(E_e) \qquad (16)$$

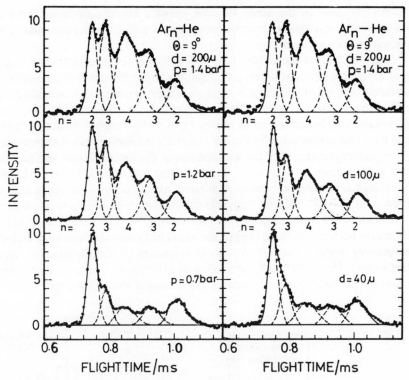

Fig. 25. Measured time-of-flight spectra for Ar_n-He scattering at three different source pressures and three different nozzle diameters (after Buck).

where ρ is the cluster density which depends on the source conditions; σ_L the laboratory differential cross section for elastic and inelastic Ar_n-He scattering at relative velocity g; $f_{n,k}$ the fragmentation probability that Ar_n appear at Ar_k, C_n the ionization probability of Ar_n and C a constant.

Typical results on cluster formation at different stagnation pressures and different nozzle diameters are shown in Fig. 25. The TOF spectra at $\theta = 9°$ correspond to measurements at dimer mass. At this location clusters upto $n = 4$ can be detected.

3.5 Study of Clusters Through Infrared Spectroscopic Techniques

Infrared absorption and photodissociation spectroscopy [109–132] have been extensively used to study vdW clusters, in particular dimers. Microwave and infrared spectroscopy of vdW molecules in a molecular beam electric resonance spectrometer provides extremely interesting results on dissociation energy, lifetime and structure of vdW dimers [133, 134]. Using a molecular beam electric resonance optothermal color-center-laser spectrometer, Pine and collaborators [135–138] have studied intramolecular vibrational energy transfer and unimolecular decomposition of vdW dimers. Recently Barth and Huisken have used Coherent Anti-Stokes Raman Scattering (CARS) to investigate NH_3 clusters [139–140] in supersonic jets. Other important spectroscopic techniques extensively used in the study of vdW clusters but not discussed here are fluorescence excitation spectroscopy, dispersed fluorescence and laser photoionization spectroscopy.

Study of NH_3 clusters [109–114, 133–134, 139–142] has attracted a great deal of interest in recent times. Investigations on the formation of ammonia and water clusters are of particular interest since they provide insight into the nature of hydrogen bonded systems existing not only in gaseous state but, more importantly, in liquid and solid phases [143, 144]. Further, ammonia clusters and their photochemical products are especially interesting because ammonia is an important constituent of the atmospheres of the Jovian planets and satellites and will condense into layers of clouds in some tropospheric levels [145–149]. Very high resolution conventional infrared spectroscopy of jet molecules has been used [84–88, 115] to study cluster formation in NH_3 jets using semi-conductor diode lasers (SDL) or color-center-lasers. Dimerization/cluster formation perturbs the force field of the individual molecular species in a cluster sufficiently strongly. These cluster species are, therefore, transparent to the narrow line width ($\sim10^{-3}$ to 10^{-4} cm^{-1}) laser radiation resonant to any given ro-vibrational transition of the monomeric species. The measured absorption coefficient will,

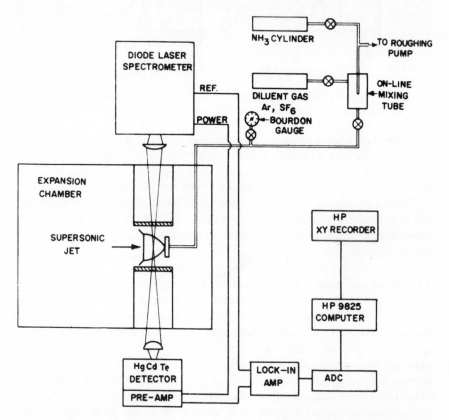

Fig. 26. Schematic diagram of the experimental set-up for SDL absorption spectroscopy (after Bajaj et al [114]).

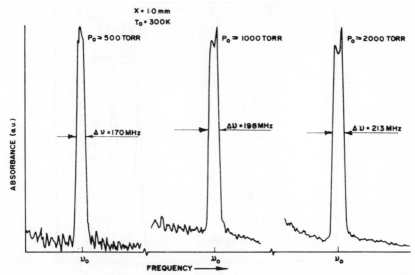

Fig. 27. Absorption line profile of aQ (1, 1) as a function of p_0 at $x = 1.0$ mm [114].

therefore, be proportional to the density of monomers only. Similarly, laser radiation tuned to dimer or higher cluster transition will probe only that particular species.

Bajaj et al [88] have used a circular nozzle of diameter 75 μm and a SDL spectrometer to investigate NH_3 cluster formation. The experimental set up is shown schematically in Fig. 26. Supersonic expansion results in extensive cooling, thus only the low lying levels of the jet molecules will be populated. With laser frequency tuned to aQ(1, 1) or aQ(2, 2) transition of the v_2-band of NH_3 a central dip (Fig. 27) in the absorption line profile appears at higher stagnation pressures. The magnitude of the dip and also the separation between the double peak (dp) structure increases with increasing stagnation pressure at a fixed location along the jet axis (Table 6). Under certain conditions of operation [141] absorption at the central frequency may disappear completely (Fig. 28). It is well known that ammonia clusters are easily formed in a supersonic expansion. Cluster formation will be most predominant at the jet axis, where collision probability is higher and temperature is lower. As a consequence, the density of the monomers will be lowest at this location and the absorption of the ir radiation tuned to monomer transition frequency will be lowest at this location. Thus, condensation will result in a general decrease of intensity of the absorption peak along with the appearance of a dp structure in the line profile.

The above interpretation about the origin of the double peak structure and the increase of separation between the peaks with increasing stagnation pressure has been further substantiated by the studies of Howard and co-workers [150] on N_2O system. They have observed in their study of spectral features as a function of p_0 that the dimer absorption spectrum initially appears as a narrow line indicating their presence in the narrow region around the jet axis only. With increasing pressure the linewidth of this absorption feature increases to cover the

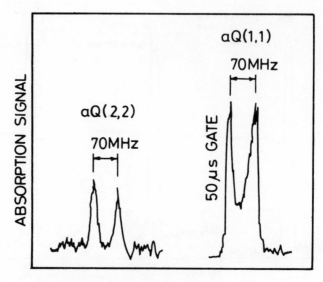

Fig. 28.   The absorption signals of aQ(1, 1) and aQ(2, 2) transitions show very pronounced dips at the central frequency. Experimental conditions: 5% NH_3 in He, $p_0 = 5$ bar, laser-nozzle distance 8 mm, Boxcar gate 50 μs [141].

entire spread of the jet diameter. Similar observation is made for trimer spectrum. These authors have further observed splitting in the dimer absorption feature, implying loss of dimers through formation of higher clusters. In the light of these experimental findings, the interpretation of Gaveau et al [151] about the origin of the double peak structure appear to be of doubtful validity.

Table 6.   Separation, Δv between the two peaks of the double structure (in MHz) of the aQ (1, 1) line of NH_3 [114]

Stagnation pressure p_0 of pure NH_3 in torr	Distance x from nozzle exit (in mm)	
	1.0	2.0
1000	105.0 (102.1)	74.0
1400	112.0 (107.2)	108.0
2000	128.0 (112.3)	126.0
3000	148.5	—

Figures in parentheses are simulated values.

The relative average number density corresponding to the integrated absorption across the jet and the relative number density on the jet axis corresponding to the central frequency absorption as a function of stagnation pressure at different locations, are shown in Figs. 29 and 30 respectively. These results [114] show that the measured number density always falls short of the expected number density [152] at higher p_0 values,

$$n/p_0 = (1/kT_0) \, [1 + (\gamma - 1)/2M^2]^{1/\Lambda 1 - \gamma} \qquad (17)$$

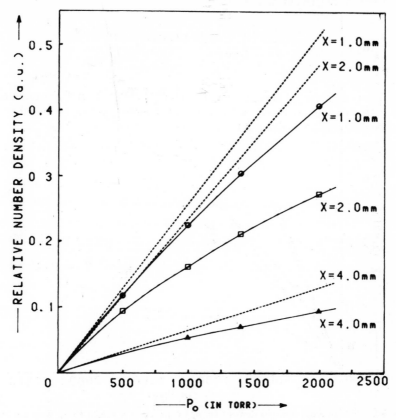

Fig. 29. Plots of average number density vs. p_0 for different x values along with the least square fitted curves: continuous curves correspond to least square fit to experimental points; dotted curves represent number density variations in absence of condensation [114].

The continuous curves in these figures represent least-square-fitted relative number densities. The dotted lines correspond to the situation when the number density increases linearly with pressure. From these plots, fractional condensation on the jet axis f_c, and the average fractional condensation across the jet, $\langle f_c \rangle$, are computed and shown in Fig. 31.

Coherent anti-Stokes Raman Scattering (CARS) has been shown to be a very powerful and versatile technique for spectroscopic studies in the expansion region of supersonic molecular jets. This technique has been used to investigate small clusters of HCN [118], CO_2 [153], H_2O [154] and large clusters of C_2H_4 [155] and NH_3 [140]. In Figs. 32 and 33 are shown CARS spectrum of NH_3 (5%) in jets seeded with He and Ne respectively [140] at $p_0 = 6$ bar and at various locations in the spectral range 3100 to 3500 cm^{-1} which covers v_1 vibration and $2v_4$ overtone. It is seen that the Q branch of v_1 vibration is rather narrow in both these figures which reflects efficient cooling in seeded jets. However, the most striking features are the appearance of broad features at 3204, 3294 and 3370 cm^{-1}. These new features grow in prominence at larger nozzle distances

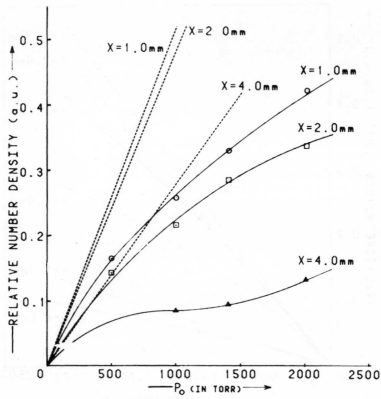

Fig. 30. Plot of axial number density vs. p_0 for different x values along with the least square fitted data: continuous and dotted curves have the same significance as in Fig. 29.

Table 7. Vibrational frequencies of ammonia in cm^{-1}

Vibration		v_1	$2v_4$	v_3
Solid	[156]	3223	3297	3378
	[157]	3213	3291	3375
	[158]	3200	3290	3370
	[159]	3220	3265	3365
Liquid	[159]	3218	3300	3373
	[160]	3220	3305	3388
Cluster	[140]	3204	3294	3370
Monomer		3337	3217	3444
		[135]	[136]	[135]
$\Delta v = v_{mon} - v_{clust}$		133	−77	74

and at higher dilution with heavier inert gases, which obviously correlate with progressive cooling in the beam [90]. These new spectral features are assigned to the growth of clusters which is substantiated by mass spectral results [140] at somewhat lower stagnation pressures (< 2 bar) as shown in Fig. 34. Helium as a carrier gas favours small size clusters while Ne favours large size clusters. Additional prominent spectral features in Ne seeded jets are believed to be due to clusters ranging in size from $n = 5$ to 50. Strongest support for this interpretation comes from infrared and Raman studies in solids [156–159] and liquids [159–160]. In Table 7 vibrational frequencies of NH_3 in solid and liquid phases are summarised along with the cluster results. It is noted that the band position of solid and liquid does not change. Presently observed new CARS frequency almost exactly coincides with these values. CARS spectra are similar to the liquid phase Raman spectra (Fig. 35) taken at $T = 182$ K. Intensity of the $2v_4$ band is subdued in the cluster spectra because these data correspond to a lower temperature ($T = 140$ K).

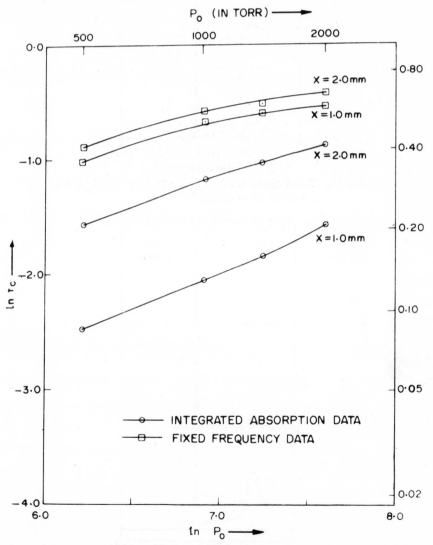

Fig. 31. Plot of $\ln f_c$ vs. p_0 for different x values for integrated and fixed frequency data [114].

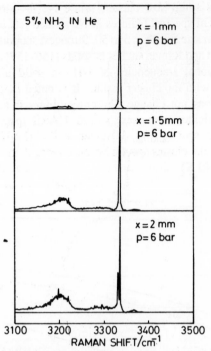

Fig. 32. CARS spectrum of NH_3 in a free jet of 5% NH_3 in He at various axial locations [140].

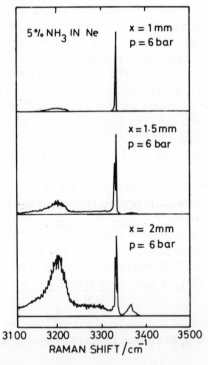

Fig. 33. CARS spectrum of NH_3 at various locations in 5% NH_3 in Ne jet [140].

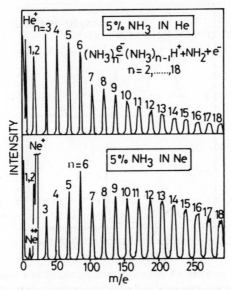

Fig. 34. Mass spectra for mixtures of 5% NH_3 in He and Ne [140].

It is worthwhile to note at this stage the interesting results on Ar clusters containing SF_6 molecules. Scoles and collaborators [71, 72] have developed and perfected the optothermal (bolometric) detection to study such clusters. The spectra at large cluster limit is remarkably similar (Fig. 17) to the infrared spectrum of the same molecule in an argon matrix.

Klemperer and coworkers [133, 134] have studied $(NH_3)_2$ and complexes of ammonia with other molecules using microwave and infrared-microwave double resonance in a molecular beam electric resonance apparatus. From these studies the dipole moment and the bond strength of the $(NH_3)_2$ complex are determined as 0.74 (2) D and < 990 cm^{-1} (2.8 kcal/mole) respectively. Further, high resolution microwave spectroscopy [134] results give support to the structure for $(NH_3)_2$ as shown in Fig. 36(c) which is different from the expected hydrogen bonded structure (Fig. 36(a)).

Weakly bonded vdW molecules provide model systems to study state-to-state intramolecular energy redistribution. In recent years infrared photodissociation of a variety of cluster systems [169–171] has been studied using mainly line tunable CO_2 lasers and a liquid He cooled bolometer or a mass spectrometer. Most convenient sources of clusters are the supersonic beams. In a photodissociation experiment a cluster beam is crossed with the radiation from an infrared source. The molecule in the cluster absorbs the radiation. The absorbed energy flows very fast into the vdW bond and since photon energy is larger than the bond strength the complex dissociates. The fragments of the dissociating vdW molecule are expelled from the beam and this appears in the detector as decrease in cluster signal (Fig. 37). Most polyatomic molecules display broad featureless spectra which correspond to lifetimes in the range of picoseconds [169–171]. It was, therefore, suggested that the broad linewidth is due to fast intramolecular relaxation and not due to predissociation rate [170]. Moreover, complicated

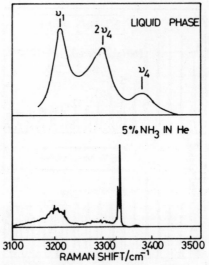

Fig. 35. Comparison between a CARS spectrum measured in a supersonic jet of 5% NH$_3$ in He (lower spectrum) and a Raman spectrum obtained by Schwartz and Wang in liquid NH$_3$ at $T = 182$ K (upper spectrum).

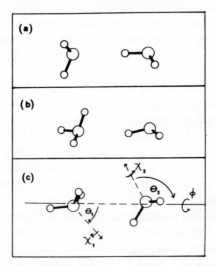

Fig. 36. (a) Theoretically predicted structure of (NH$_3$)$_2$. This structure is referred to as the "classical" structure in the text. (b) Nearest neighbour orientation which is observed in crystalline NH$_3$. (c) One possible experimental structure for (NH$_3$)$_2$. Also shown is the coordinate system used for structure analysis. The structure is drawn with $\theta_1 = 48.6°$, $\theta_2 = 115.5°$, $\varphi = 180°$, $\chi_1 = 180°$ and $\chi_2 = 180°$. The values of angles φ, χ_1 and χ_2 cannot be determined from these data. The average values of the other coordinates, though, are rigorously determined [134].

rotational structures [172] and also presence of clusters of various sizes [173, 174] in the beam may complicate the spectra and lead to broadening.

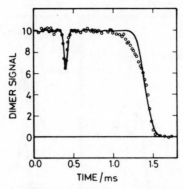

Fig. 37. Measured real-time spectrum of $(C_2H_4)_2$ dissociation. The laser is fired at $t = 0$. The solid line represents the computer simulation result (after Huisken).

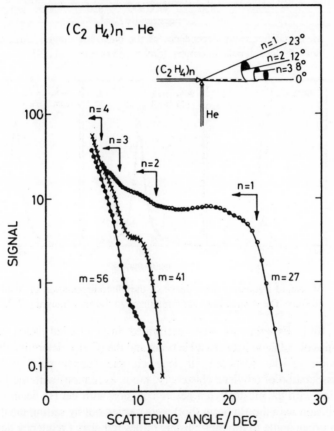

Fig. 38. Angular distribution of scattered $(C_2H_4)_n$ cluster beam measured at different mass settings of the mass spectrometer (after Huisken).

Recently developed technique of spatial isolation [79] of clusters of specific sizes has been gainfully employed to study ir predissociation [173, 174] of specific size clusters of ethylene, a molecular cluster widely studied

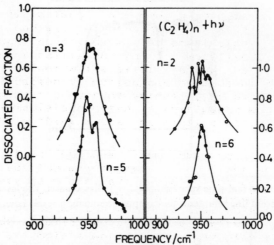

Fig. 39. Measured frequency dependence of the photodissociation cross section for 'hot' ethylene dimers, hexamers, trimers and pentamers [174].

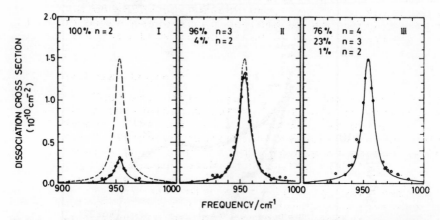

Fig. 40. Measured frequency dependence of the photodissociation of 'cold' ethylene clusters. The dashed lines are normalized to the same height [174].

earlier [109]. Experiments were performed in a crossed beam apparatus. Kinematics of collision between a He beam and the $(C_2H_4)_n$ determine the angular distribution of the scattered ethylene clusters (upper part of Fig. 38). Photodissociation of ethylene clusters (v_7 mode excitation) with the laser beam interacting with the cluster beam before collision with the He beam (cold) and after collision with the He beam (hot) were carried out by setting the detector at an appropriate angle to monitor clusters of desired size. Frequency dependence of the photodissociation spectra (Fig. 39) of ethylene clusters varies with cluster size. Prominent structures in the dimer spectrum almost completely disappear for the hexamer and approach 'cold' cluster features. Measured linewidth of 31 cm^{-1} for the dimer reduces to 12 cm^{-1} for the hexamer which is identical with the 'cold' spectrum (Fig. 40). The fact that the maximum of the spectra ($v_0 = 953$ cm^{-1}) and FWHM (12 cm^{-1}) remain unchanged in 'cold' spectra as we go from the dimer to the hexamer suggests that the parallel shifted structure found for the dimer [175] is continued for higher clusters so that the excitation of the v_7 (out of plane bending) mode, is not very much influenced [123, 125, 174] when another ethylene molecule is added on top of the cluster. Measured fractional dissociation of spatially isolated cold clusters is smaller than the earlier reported data on non-isolated clusters.

The observed features in 'hot' cluster dissociation spectrum is attributed to internal excitation of the cluster by collision with the He beam. Collisionally transferred energy is easily redistributed among the internal degrees of freedom so that in the limit of high cluster size (hexamer) internal excitation does not influence the dissociation spectra [174]. The observed structure in the dimer spectrum is assigned to excitation of the hot bands of the bending van der Waals motion.

4. CONCLUSION

Molecular beams have found a wide range of applications in a variety of fields in the broad domain of chemical physics. The most obvious application has been the thermal energy scattering studies and investigations on the details of intermolecular potential, both spherical and non-spherical. Differential elastic scattering data coupled with bulk properties provide the most precise (within 1%) information on the inert gas interaction potential. For atom-diatom systems also almost comparable accuracy could be achieved through precise measurement of differential scattering cross sections and accurate evaluation of the quenching of the diffraction structure. However, accuracy in this case is limited by the approximations used in the analysis. Anisotropy in van der Waals' potential is, however, more directly probed by rotationally inelastic differential cross section measurements which are relatively more complex and time-consuming. In recent times reasonable volume of data have been obtained for collisions of H_2, D_2, N_2 and O_2 with inert gas partners.

One of the fast emerging fields in chemical physics is the study of vdW clusters. Since it is a totally unexplored field it is full of surprises. Study of clusters has fundamental as well as applied implications. From the fundamental point of view, clusters provide a link between gaseous and bulk phases. In the study of clusters the primary task is to generate and characterise them. The most convenient source of pure and mixed clusters is the supersonic expansion of a gas through a nozzle. Electron impact ionization has played a very important role in the study of clusters. Recent developments in collision dynamics provide convenient means to study clusters of well defined size regardless of the detection technique.

5. ACKNOWLEDGEMENT

I am grateful to my colleagues, Dr. V.B. Kartha, Mr. P.N. Bajaj and Dr. R. Talukdar for their collaboration and many useful discussions. It is a pleasure to express my gratitude to Professor U. Buck for promptly responding to my request for his current reprints. I would like to thank Dr. P.R.K. Rao for his continued interest in molecular beam research. Finally, my sincere appreciation goes to

Professor N. Sathyamurthy, who has been the main driving force in the preparation of this volume.

REFERENCES

1. N.F. Ramsay, Molecular Beams, (Oxford University Press, London and New York (1956).
2. H. Pauly and J.P. Toennies, in Adv. At. Mol. Phys. 1, 195 (1965).
3. R.B. Bernstein, in Adv. Chem. Phys. 10, 75 (1966).
4. H. Pauly and J.P. Toennies, in Methods of Exptl. Phys. A7, 227 (1968).
5. Ch. Schlier, Ann. Rev. Phys. Chem. 20, 191 (1969).
6. J. P. Toennies, in Phys. Chem.—An Advanced Treatise VIA, 227 (1974).
7. H. Pauly, in Phys. Chem.—An Advanced Treatise VIB, 553 (1975).
8. U. Buck, Adv. Chem. Phys. XXX, 313 (1975).
9. C.R. Mueller, B. Smith, P. McGuire, W. Williams, P.K. Chakraborti and J. Penta, Adv. Chem. Phys. XXI, 369 (1971).
10. J. Penta, C.R. Mueller, W. Williams, R. Olson and P.K. Chakraborti, Phys. Letts. 25A, 658 (1967).
11. U. Buck in Atomic and Molecular Beam Methods, Vol. 1, ed. G. Scoles, Oxford University Press, Oxford (1988).
12. M. Faubel and J.P. Toennies, Adv. At. Mol. Phys. 13, 227 (1977).
13. T. Kihara, Intermolecular Forces, Wiley, New York (1978).
14. S. Stolte and J. Reuss, in Atomic and Molecular Collision Theory: A Guide for Experimentalists, ed. R.B. Bernstein, Plenum, New York (1979).
15. H. Pauly, in Atomic and Molecular Collision Theory : A Guide for Experimentalists, ed. R.B. Bernstein, Plenum, New York (1979).
16. H. Thuis, S. Stolte and J. Reuss, Comm. At. Mol. Phys. 8, 123 (1979).
17. G. Scoles, Ann. Rev. Phys. Chem. 31, 81 (1980).
18. U. Buck, Comm. At. Mol. Phys. 17, 143 (1986).
19. F. Vecchiocattivi, Comm. At. Mol. Phys. 17, 163 (1986).
20. R. Aziz, in Inert Gases, ed. M.L. Klein, Springer, Berlin (1984).
21. U. Lackschewitz, J. Maier and H. Pauly, J. Chem. Phys. 84, 181 (1986) and references therein.
22. R. Candori, F. Pirani and F. Vecchiocattivi, J. Chem. Phys. 84, 4833 (1986); Mol. Phys. 49, 551 (1983).
23. F.A. Gianturco, M. Venanzi, R. Candori, F. Pirani, F. Vecchiocattivi, A.S. Dickinson and M. S. Lee, Chem. Phys. 109, 417 (1986).
24. L. Beneventi, P. Casavecchia and G.G. Volpi, J. Chem. Phys. 85, 7011 (1986).
25. R. Candori, F. Pirani and F. Vecchiocattivi, Chem. Phys. Letts. 102, 412 (1983).
26. P. Casavecchia, A. Lagana and G.G. Volpi, Chem. Phys. Letts. 112, 445 (1984).
27. M. Faubel, J. Chem. Phys. 81, 5559 (1984); M. Faubel, K.H. Kohl, J. P. Toennies and F.A. Gianturco, J. Chem. Phys. 78, 5629 (1983).
28. L. Beneventi, P. Casavecchia and G.G. Volpi, J. Chem. Phys. 84, 4828 (1986).
29. L. Beneventi, P. Casavecchia and G.G. Volpi, in Structure and Dynamics of Weakly Bonded Molecular Complexes, ed. A. Weber, Reidel, Dordrecht (1987).
30. A. Hermann, S. Leutwyler, E. Schumacher and L. Woeste, Chem. Phys. Letts. 52, 418 (1977).
31. L. Zandee and R.B. Bernstein, J. Chem. Phys. 71, 1359 (1979).

32. L. Beneventi, P. Casavecchia and G.G. Volpi, XIth International Symposium on Molecular Beams, Univ. Edinburgh, July 13–17 (1987).
33. G.C. Maitland and W.A. Wakeham, Mol. Phys. **35**, 1429 (1978).
34. C.Y. Ng, Y.T. Lee and J.A. Barker, J. Chem. Phys. **61**, 1996 (1974).
35. R.T Pack, Chem. Phys. Letts. **55**, 197 (1978).
36. G.A. Parker and R.T Pack, J. Chem. Phys. **68**, 1583 (1978); D.J. Kouri, in Atom Molecule Collision Theory—A Guide to Experimentalists, ed. R.B. Bernstein Plenum, New York (1979).
37. J.O. Hirschfelder, C. F. Curtiss and R.B. Bird, Molecular Theory of Gases and Liquids, (Wiley, New York (1954).
38. J. Reuss, Adv. Chem. Phys. **30**, 389 (1976).
39. M. Faubel, Adv. At. Mol. Phys. **19**, 345 (1983).
40. M. Faubel, K.H. Kohl, J.P. Toennies, K.T. Tang and Y.Y. Yung, Faraday Disc. Chem. Soc. **73**, 205 (1982).
41. W.R. Gentry and C.F. Giese, J. Chem. Phys. **67**, 5389 (1977).
42. U. Buck, F. Huisken, J. Schleusner and H. Pauly, Phys. Rev. Letts. **38**, 680 (1977).
43. U. Buck, F. Huisken and J. Schleusner, J. Chem. Phys. **72**, 1512 (1980).
44. J. Andres, U. Buck, F. Huisken, J. Schleusner and F. Torello, J. Chem. Phys. **73**, 5620 (1980).
45. J. Andres, U. Buck, F. Huisken, J. Schleusner and F. Torello, in Electronic and Atomic Collisions, ed. N. Oda and K. Takayanagi, North-Holland, Amsterdam (1980), pp 531.
46. K. Bergmann, U. Hefter and J. Witt, J. Chem. Phys. **72**, 4777 (1980).
47. K. Bergmann, U. Hefter, A. Mattheus and J. Witt, Chem. Phys. Lett. **78**, 61 (1981).
48. U. Hefter, P.L. Jones, A Mattheus, J. Witt, K. Bergmann and R. Schinke, Phys. Rev. Letts. **46**, 915 (1981).
49. J.A. Serri, A. Morales, W. Moskowitz, D.E. Pritchard, C.H. Becker and J. L. Kinsey, J. Chem. Phys. **72**, 6304 (1980).
50. M. Faubel, K.H. Kohl and J.P. Toennies, J. Chem. Phys. **73**, 2506 (1980).
51. U. Buck, A. Kohlhase, T. Phillips and D. Seerest, Chem. Phys. Letts. **98**, 199 (1983).
52. W. Meyer, P.C. Hariharan and W.Kutzelnigg, J. Chem. Phys. **73**, 1880 (1980).
53. G.A. Gallup, Mol. Phys. **33**, 943 (1977).
54. J. Schaefer and W. Meyer, J. Chem. Phys. **70**, 344 (1979).
55. K.T. Tang and J.P. Toennies, J. Chem. Phys. **68**, 5501 (1978); ibid **74**, 1148 (1981).
56. R. Ahlrichs, R. Penco and G. Scoles, Chem. Phys. **19**, 119 (1977).
57. K.C. Ng, W.J. Meath and A.R. Allnatt, Mol. Phys. **37**, 237 (1979).
58. R.B. Gerber, V. Buch and U. Buck, J. Chem. Phys. **72**, 3596 (1980).
59. R.B. Gerber, V. Buch, U. Buck, G. Manake and J. Schleusner, Phys. Rev. Letts. **44**, 1397 (1980).
60. R. David, M. Faubel and J.P. Toennies, Chem. Phys. Letts. **18**, 87 (1973).
61. H.E. van den Bergh, M. Faubel and J.P. Toennies, Faraday Disc. Chem. Soc. **55**, 203 (1973).
62. M. Keil, J.T. Slankes and A. Kuppermann, J. Chem. Phys. **70**, 541 (1979).
63. T.D. Maerk and A.W. Castleman, Jr., Adv. At. Mol. Phys. **20**, 65 (1985).
64. T.D. Maerk, Int. J. Mass Spect. Ion Phys. **79**, 1 (1987).
65. G.D. Stein, Phys. Teacher 503 (1979).

66. T.D. Maerk, Adv. Mass Spect. 379 (1986).
67. J. Jortner, Ber. Bunsenges. Phys. Chem. **88**, 188 (1984).
68. D.A. Buffat and J.P. Borel, Phys. Rev. **A13**, 2289 (1976).
69. R.D. Etters and J. B. Kaelberer, J. Chem. Phys. **60**, 5112 (1977).
70. J. Jellinek, T.L. Beck and R.S. Berry, J. Chem. Phys. **84**, 2783 (1986).
71. T.E. Gough, D.G. Knight and G. Scoles, Chem. Phys. Letts. **97**, 155 (1983).
72. T.E. Gough, M. Mengeb, P.A. Rowntree and G. Scoles, J. Chem. Phys. **83**, 4958 (1985).
73. B.I. Swanson and L.H. Jones, J. Chem. Phys. **74**, 3205 (1981).
74. J. Farges, M. F. de Faraudy, B. Raoult and G. Torchet, J. Chem. Phys. **78**, 5067 (1983).
75. J. Farges, M.F. de Faraudy, B. Raoult and G. Torchet XIth International Symposium on Molecular Beams, Univ. Edinburgh, 13–17 July, 1987.
76. E.J. Valente and L.S. Bertell, J. Chem. Phys. **79**, 1458 (1983).
77. D.E. Powers, S.G. Hansen, M.E. Geusic, D.L. Michapoulos and R.E. Smalley, J. Chem. Phys. **78**, 2866 (1983).
78. M.D. Morse, J.B. Hopkins, P.R.R. Langridge-Smith and R.E. Smalley, J. Chem. Phys. **79**, 5316 (1983).
79. L.S. Zheng, C.M. Karner, P.J. Brucat, S.H. Yang, C.L. Pettiette, M.J. Craycraft and R.E. Smalley, J. Chem. Phys. **85**, 1681 (1986).
80. E.W. Becker, K. Bier and W. Henkes, Z. Phys. **146**, 333 (1956).
81. R.E. Leckenby, R.J. Robinson and P.A. Travalion, Proc. Roy. Soc. **A280**, 409 (1964).
82. D. Golomb, R.E. Good and R.F. Brown, J. Chem. Phys. **32**, 1545 (1970).
83. D. Golomb, R.E. Good, A.B. Bailey, M.R. Busby and R. Dawbarn, J. Chem. Phys. **57**, 3844 (1972).
84. T.A. Milne and F.T. Green, J. Chem. Phys. **47**, 4095 (1967).
85. T.A. Milne, A.E. Vandergriff and F.T. Green, J. Chem. Phys. **52**, 1552 (1970).
86. A. van Deursen, A. van Lumig and J. Reuss, Int. J. Mass Spect. Ion Phys. **18**, 129 (1975).
87. H. Vehmeyer, R. Feltgen, P.K. Chakraborti, M. Dueker, F. Torello and H. Pauly, Chem. Phys. Letts. **42**, 597 (1976).
88. P.K. Chakraborti, Pramana-J. Phys. **25**, 191 (1985).
89. D.H. Levy, Ann. Rev. Phys. Chem. **31**, 197 (1980).
90. P.K. Chakraborti, R. Talukdar, P.N. Bajaj, A. Joshi and V.B. Kartha, Chem. Phys. **95**, 145 (1985).
91. O.F. Hagena and W. Obert, J. Chem. Phys. **56**, 1793 (1972).
92. H. Ashkenhas and F.S. Sherman, Proceedings of the 4th Symp. on Rarefied Gas Dynamics, Vol. 2, 1966, pp. 84.
93. J.B. Anderson and J.B. Fenn, Phys. Fluids **8**, 700 (1965).
94. O.F. Hagena, Z. Phys. **D4**, 291 (1987).
95. R.S. Bowles, J.J. Kolstad, J.M. Calo and R.P. Andres, Surf. Sci. **106**, 117 (1981).
96. D.E. Powers, S.G. Hansen, M.E. Geusic, D.L. Michapoulos and R.E. Smalley, J. Chem. Phys. **78**, 2866 (1983); M.D. Morse, J.B. Hopkins, P.R.R. Langridge-Smith and R.E. Smalley, J. Chem. Phys. **79**, 5316 (1983); T.D. Dietz, M.A. Duncan, D.E. Powers and R.E. Smalley, J. Chem. Phys. **74**, 6511 (1981); D.E. Powers, S.G. Hansen, M.E. Geusic, A.C. Price, J.B. Hopkins, T.G. Dietz, M.A. Duncan, P.R.R. Langridge-Smith and R.E. Smalley, J. Phys. Chem. **86**, 2556 (1982); J.B. Hopkins, P.R.R. Langridge-Smith, M.D. Morse and R.E. Smalley, J. Chem. Phys. **78**, 1627 (1983); M.D. Morse and R.E. Smalley,

Ber. Bunsenges. Phys. Chem. **88**, 228 (1984); S.C. O'Brien, Y. Lin, Q. Zhang, J.R. Heath, F.K. Tittel, R.F. Curl and R.E. Smalley, J. Chem. Phys. **84**, 4074 (1986); V.E. Bondybey and J.H. English, J. Chem. Phys. **76**, 2165 (1982); V.E. Bondybey and J.H. English, J.Chem. Phys. **80**, 568 (1984); S.J. Riley, E.K. Parks, C.R. Mao, L.G. Pobo and S. Wexler, J. Phys. Chem., **86**, 3911 (1982); S.J. Riley, E.K. Parks, L.G. Pobo and S. Wexler, J. Chem. Phys. **79**, 2577 (1983); S.J. Riley, E.K. Parks, G.C. Nieman, L.G. Pobo and S. Wexler, J. Chem. Phys. **80**, 1360 (1984); E.A. Rohlfing, D.M. Cox and A. Kaldor, Chem. Phys. Letts. **99**, 161 (1983); E.A. Rohlfing, D.M. Cox and A. Kaldor, J. Chem. Phys. **81**, 3322 (1984); E.A. Rohlfing, D.M. Cox and A. Kaldor, J. Phys. Chem. **88**, 4497 (1984).

97. O. Echt, K. Sattler and E. Recknagel, Phys. Rev. Letts. **47**, 1121 (1981).

98. T.D. Maerk and P. Scheier, Chem. Phys. Letts. **137**, 245 (1987).

99. P. Scheier and T.D. Maerk, Chem. Phys. Letts. **136**, 423 (1987).

100. P.W. Stephens and J.G. King, Phys. Rev. Letts. **51**, 1538 (1983).

101. A. Ding and J. Hesslich, Chem. Phys. Letts. **94**, 54 (1983).

102. C.E. Klots, J. Chem. Phys. **83**, 5854 (1985).

103. H. Haberland, Surf. Sci. **156**, 305 (1985).

104. H. Haberland, Proc. Int. Symp. on Phys. Chem. of Small Clusters, Richmond, Virginia, 1986.

105. U. Buck and H. Meyer, Phys. Rev. Letts. **52**, 109 (1984); Surf. Sci. **156**, 275 (1985); J. Chem. Phys. **84**, 4854 (1986); Ber. Bunsenges. Phys. Chem. **88**, 254 (1984).

106. U. Buck, J. Phys. Chem. **92**, 1023 (1988); U. Buck, G. Hoffman, J. Kesper, D. Otten and M. Winter, Chem. Phys. **126**, 150 (1988); U. Buck, Ch. Lauenstein, R. Sroka and M. Tolle, Z. Phys. **D10**, 303 (1988); U. Buck, J. Kesper, Ch. Lauenstein, M. Tolle and M. Winter, Z. Phys. **D12**, 293 (1989).

107. U. Buck, H. Meyer, D. Nelsen, Jr., G. Fraser and W. Klemperer, J. Chem. Phys. **88**, 3028 (1988).

108. U. Buck, F. Huisken, J. Schleusner and J. Schaefer, J. Chem. Phys. **72**, 1512 (1980).

109. Y. Mizugai, H. Kuze, H. Jones and M. Takami, App. Phys. **B32**, 43 (1983).

110. G. Baldacchini, S. Marchetti and V. Montelatici, Nuovo Cimento Letts. **41**, 439 (1984).

111. K. Veeken and J. Reuss, App. Phys. **B34**, 149 (1984).

112. V.B. Kartha, V.A. Job and P.K. Chakraborti, J. Ind. Chem. Soc. **LXIII**, 22 (1986).

113. P.K. Chakraborti, R.K. Talukdar and P.N. Bajaj, XIth Int. Symp. Mol. Beams, Univ. Edinburgh (13–17 July, 1987).

114. P.N. Bajaj, R.K. Talukdar, P.K. Chakraborti and V.B. Kartha, J. Mol. Struc. **194**, 117 (1989).

115. R. Talukdar, P.N. Bajaj, P.K. Chakraborti and V.B. Kartha, to be published.

116. A.E. Barton, A. Chablo and B.J. Howard, Chem. Phys. Letts. **60**, 414 (1979).

117. K.W. Jucks, Z.S. Huang, D. Dayton, R.E. Miller and W.J. Lafferty, J. Chem. Phys. **86**, 4341 (1987).

118. M. Maroncelli, G.A. Hopkins, J.W. Nibler and T.R. Dyke, J. Chem Phys. **83**, 2129 (1985).

119. T.E. Gough, R.E. Miller and G. Scoles, J. Chem. Phys. **69**, 1588 (1978).

120. T.E. Gough, R.E. Miller and G. Scoles, J. Phys. Chem. **85**, 4041 (1981).

121. J. Geraedts, S. Setiadi, S. Stolte and J. Reuss, Chem. Phys. Letts. **78**, 277 (1981).

122. M.A. Hoffbauer, K. Lin, C.F. Giese and W.R. Gentry, J. Chem. Phys. **78**, 5567 (1983).

123. M.P. Casassa, D.S. Bomsey, J.L. Beauchamp and K.C. Janda, J. Chem. Phys. **72**, 6805 (1980); M.P. Casassa, D.S. Bomsey and K.C. Janda, ibid. **74**, 5044 (1981).

124. M.A. Hoffbauer, C.F. Giese and W.R. Gentry, J. Chem. Phys. **79**, 192 (1983).

125. M.A. Hoffbauer, K. Liu, C.F. Giese and W.R. Gentry, J. Chem. Phys. **79**, 2096 (1983).

126. M.J. Howard, S. Burdenski, C.F. Giese and W.R. Gentry, J. Chem. Phys. **80**, 4137 (1984).

127. M.A. Hoffbauer, C.F. Giese and W.R. Gentry, J. Chem. Phys. **80**, 181 (1984).

128. M.P. Casassa, D.S. Bomsey and K.C. Janda, J. Phys. Chem. **85**, 2631 (1981).

129. M.P. Casassa, C.M. Western, F.G. Celli, D.E. Brizza and K.C. Janda, J. Chem. Phys. **79**, 3227 (1983).

130. C.M. Western, M.P. Casassa and K.C. Janda, J. Chem. Phys. **80**, 4781 (1984).

131. J.M. Lisy, A. Trance, M.F. Vernon and Y.T. Lee, J. Chem. Phys. **75**, 4733 (1981).

132. M.F. Vernon, J.M. Lisy, H.S. Kwok, D.J. Krajnovich, A. Tramer, Y.R. Shen and Y.T. Lee, J. Chem. Phys. **77**, 47 (1982).

133. G.T. Fraser, D.D. Nelsen, Jr., A. Charo and W. Klemperer, J. Chem. Phys. **82**, 2535 (1985).

134. D.D. Nelsen, Jr., G.T. Fraser and W. Klemperer, J. Chem. Phys. **83**, 6201 (1985).

135. A.S. Pine in Structure and Dynamics of Weakly Bonded Molecular Complexes, ed. A. Weber, Reidel, Dordrecht (1987) pp. 93.

136. A.S. Pine and G.T. Fraser, J. Chem. Phys. **89**, 100 (1988).

137. A.S. Pine and G.T. Fraser, J. Chem. Phys. **89**, 6636 (1988).

138. G.T. Fraser and A.S. Pine, J. Chem. Phys. **91**, 633, 637 (1989).

139. H.D. Barth and F. Huisken, XIth Int. Symp. on Molecular Beams, Univ. Edinburgh (13–17 July, 1987).

140. H.D. Barth and F. Huisken, J. Chem. Phys. **87**, 2549 (1987); XIth Int. Symp. Mol. Beams, U. Edinburgh (1987).

141. M. Snels and G. Baldacchini, App. Phys. **B47**, 277 (1988).

142. H. Shinohara, N. Nishi and N. Washida, J. Chem. Phys. **83**, 1939 (1985); H. Shinohara and N. Nishi, Chem. Phys. Letts. **87**, 561 (1982); H. Shinohara, J. Chem. Phys. **79**, 1732 (1983).

143. R.H. Prince and G.R. Floyd, Chem. Phys. Letts. **43**, 326 (1976).

144. R.J. Speedy, J. Phys. Chem. **88**, 3364 (1984).

145. S.J. Weidenschilling and J.S. Lewis, Icarus **20**, 465 (1973).

146. D.J. Stevenson, Nature **298**, 142 (1982).

147. G.S. Orton, J.F. Appleby and J.V. Martonchik, Icarus **52**, 94 (1982).

148. G.S. Orton, Icarus **53**, 293 (1983).

149. B. Bezard, J.P. Baluteau and A. Marten, Icarus **54**, 434 (1983).

150. R.W. Randall, M.A. Walsh and B.J. Howard, Faraday Disc. Chem. Soc. **85**, 13 (1988).

151. M. Gaveau, D. Boscher and J.P. Martin, Chem. Phys. Letts. **107**, 31 (1984).

152. J.B. Anderson, in Molecular Beam and Low Density Gas Dynamics, ed. P.P. Wegner, Marcel Dekker, New York (1974), Chapter 1.

153. G.A. Pubanz, M. Maroncelli and J.W. Nibelr, Chem. Phys. Letts. **120**, 313 (1985).

154. S. Wuelfert, D. Herren and S. Leutwyler, J. Chem. Phys. **86**, 3751 (1987).

155. F. Koenig, P. Oesterlin and R.L. Byer, Chem. Phys. Letts. **88**, 477 (1982).

156. F.P. Reding and D.F. Hornig, J. Chem. Phys. **19**, 594 (1951).

157. H. Wolff, H.G. Rollar and E. Wolff, J. Chem. Phys. **55**, 1373 (1971).

158. A. Bromberg, S. Kimel and A. Ron, Chem. Phys. Letts., **46**, 262 (1977).

159. C.A. Plint, R.M.B. Small and H.L. Welsh, Can. J. Phys. **32**, 653 (1954).

160. M. Schwartz and C.H. Wang, J. Chem. Phys. **59**, 5258 (1973).

161. R. Angstl, H. Finsterhoelzl, H. Frunder, D. Illig, D. Papousek, P. Pracna, K.N. Rao, H.W. Schroetter and S. Urban, J. Mol. Spectr. **114**, 454 (1985).

162. W.S. Benedict, E.K. Plyler and E.D. Tidwell, J. Chem. Phys. **32**, 32 (1960).

163. Z. Latajka and S. Scheiner, J. Chem. Phys. **81**, 407 (1984).

164. N.C. Baird, Int. J. Quantum Chem. **1**, 49 (1974).

165. W.A. Sokalski, P.C. Hariharan and J.J. Kaufman, J. Phys. Chem. **87**, 2803 (1983).

166. N.K. Ray, M. Shibata, G. Bolis and R. Rain, Int. J. Quantum Chem. **27**, 427 (1985).

167. K. Ohta, Y. Yoshioka, K. Morokuma and K. Kitaura, Chem. Phys. Letts. **101**, 12 (1983).

168. W.C. Topp and L.C. Allen, J. Am. Chem. Soc. **99**, 1316 (1977).

169. K.C. Janda, Adv. Chem. Phys. **60**, 201 (1985).

170. W.R. Gentry, Am. Chem. Soc. Symp. Series **263**, 289 (1984).

171. R.E. Miller, J. Phys. Chem. **90**, 3301 (1986).

172. G. Fischer, R.E. Miller, P.F. Vohralik and R.O. Watts, J. Chem. Phys. **83**, 1471 (1985).

173. F. Huisken, H. Meyer, Ch. Lauenstein, R. Sroka and U. Buck, J. Chem. Phys. **84**, 1042 (1986); U. Buck, F. Huisken, Ch. Lauenstein, H. Meyer and R. Sroka, J. Chem. Phys. **87**, 6276 (1987).

174. U. Buck, F. Huisken, Ch. Lauenstein, T. Pertsch and R. Sroka, in Structure and Dynamics of Weakly Bonded Molecular Complexes, ed. A. Weber, D. Reidel Publishing Co. (1987) pp. 477.

175. A. van der Avoird, P.E.S. Wormer, P. Mulder and R.M. Berns, in Topics in Current Chemistry, **93**, 1 (1980).

2. Probing the Transition State

N. Sathyamurthy
Department of Chemistry
Indian Institute of Technology
Kanpur, India

Abstract

Not too long ago, there was a feeling that transition states (TS) for chemical reactions could not be probed directly in the laboratory as, by their nature, they won't be "stable enough" to be "observed". Things have changed in the last few years. The definition of the TS has undergone a significant change and it has become possible to study the characteristics of the "transition range species" experimentally as well as theoretically. Recent developments in the area in the last few years are summarized below.

1. INTRODUCTION

Chemists have come a long way from the days of alchemy but the dream of "bond-selective chemistry" is yet to be realised. The key to success in practising "Molecular Engineering" lies in attaining an understanding of how chemical reactions occur. From a study of reaction rates (dependence on concentration of reactants, catalysts/inhibitors, temperature etc.) the kineticist comes up with a mechanism by putting together a lot of direct and indirect evidence. But there is nothing like "seeing" or watching the reaction "live" or "watching molecules while they change" as the Nobel Laureate John C. Polanyi would put it [1].

From the days of Michael Polanyi [2], chemists have been aware of the fact that reagents go through a "transition state" before they transform into products. Characterising the transition state (TS) of a chemical reaction has been a long-cherished dream of kineticists. In the years that have gone by, the definition of the TS has undergone a significant change.

Let us consider the collision between an atom (A) and a diatomic molecule (BC) along a straight line. The possible outcomes are :

$$A + BC \rightarrow AB + C \qquad (R1)$$

$$\rightarrow A + B + C \qquad (R2)$$

$$\rightarrow (ABC) \qquad (R3)$$

While (R1) and (R2) are the familiar "exchange" and "collision-induced-dissociation" processes respectively, (R3) would constitute the less common class of association reactions. In an extreme case (beyond the scope of chemistry) the united atom could result. The different arrangement channels are represented in the configuration space in terms of bond distances in Fig. 1. From a formal point of view, in the limit $R_{AB} \to \infty$ we have the reactants, $\lim R_{BC} \to \infty$ corresponds to the exchange products, $\lim R_{AB} \to \infty$ *and* $R_{BC} \to \infty$ the dissociative products and $\lim R_{AB} \to 0$ *and* $R_{BC} \to 0$ the united atom. Somewhere in between is the "transition state"—in a global sense. If we restrict ourselves to exchange reactions only, the choice of region for the TS in the configuration space becomes restrictive.

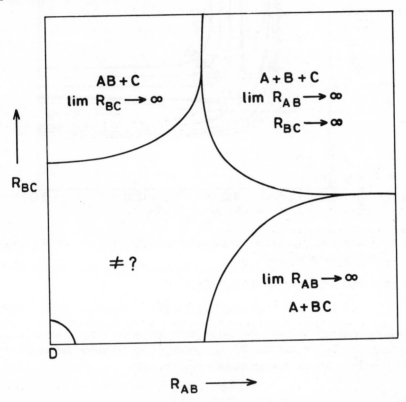

Fig. 1. Configuration space apportioned into different channels and the transition region.

Historically, the publication [3] of the potential-energy surface (PES) for the collinear exchange reaction

$$H + H_2 \to H_2 + H \tag{R4}$$

is considered the beginning of research in reaction dynamics. For this symmetric system, the $R_{AB} = R_{BC}$ line is the "logical" dividing line for separating the reactants and the exchange products. The lowest energy point along this dividing line is the saddle point which came to be identified with the TS as illustrated in Fig. 2. Such a definition was adequate under thermal conditions as the dissociation and the united atom limits were not energetically allowed. The limitation of the definition of the TS in terms of the saddle point became clear when the chemists

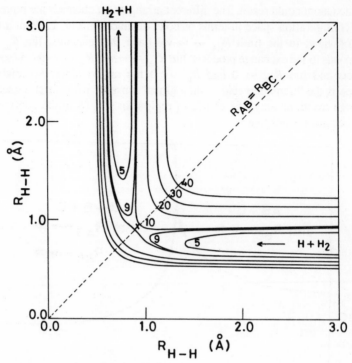

Fig. 2.   Potential-energy contours in kcal·mole^{-1} for collinear H—H—H. The saddle point is indicated by a ×.

considered "more interesting" reactions like

$$F + H_2 \rightarrow FH + H \tag{R5}$$

For this exothermic reaction, the saddle point lies in the entry channel [4] as illustrated in Fig. 3 and the TS is considered to resemble the reactants. Understandably, for the reverse, endothermic reaction

$$H + HF \rightarrow H_2 + F \tag{R6}$$

the saddle point lies in the exit channel and the TS would resemble the products. For a reaction like

$$He + H_2^+ \rightarrow HeH^+ + H \tag{R7}$$

there is no saddle point for the collinear geometry [5] and the traditional definition of the TS breaks down. To some extent, the difficulty is removed in the variational transition state theory [6] in which the dividing line is varied such that the flux across the dividing surface in the phase space (which includes the configuration and the momentum space) corresponds to an extremum. In hyperspherical coordinates [7] which are being used extensively these days, the ridge along the angular coordinate seems to be the natural choice [8, 9] of dividing line between the reagents and the exchange products as illustrated in Fig. 3 for the reaction (R7). Thus it becomes clear that there is no unique definition of the TS. Therefore,

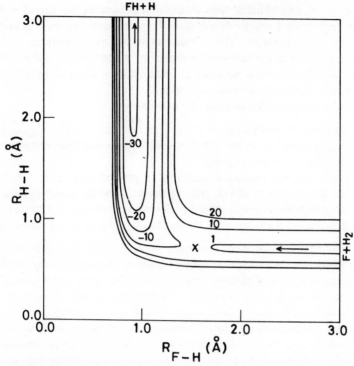

Fig. 3. Potential-energy contours in kcal·mol⁻¹ for collinear F—H—H. The saddle point is indicated by a ×.

it should not come as a surprise that, in recent years, all possible configurations in the intermediate region are collectively called the "transition state". Puritans would prefer the term "transitory state" or its equivalent(s).

With the changing definition of the TS the meaning of its "characterization" also has undergone a significant change. Until the sixties, the saddle point (or the barrier) height was taken to be approximately the same as the activation energy and the TS structure was considered to be intermediate between reactants and products. Using "chemical" sense a typical structure was chosen and the structural parameters were varied within "reasonable" limits until agreement between transition state theoretic and experimental rate constants resulted. The sixties and the seventies witnessed a dramatic change in the attitude as to what constitutes an "understanding" of what happens during a chemical reaction.

2. DIFFERENT STRATEGIES

2.1 Initial State Selection and Final State Analysis

The infrared chemiluminescence (IRCL) experiments characterised the product energy distribution, and molecular beams made possible translational energy and in some cases rotational state as well as orientation selection possible for the reactants. Chemical lasers enabled initial vibrational and rotational state selection and final state detection. The principle of microscopic reversibility as well as the concept of "pre-reaction" resulting from an IRCL experiment also contributed to the study of the role of initial state selection in influencing the rate of a chemical reaction and product energy distribution. To summarise, we were getting close to "state-to-state chemistry" [10]. Thanks to the electronic computers, elaborate classical mechanical studies were possible on several model potential energy surfaces and also on a few accurate ab initio PESs. A few benchmark quantum mechanical calculations also were completed.

A few generalizations emerged, for example:

(i) translational enhancement of the reaction rate would suggest that the saddle point lies in the entry channel while vibrational enhancement its location in the exit channel.

(ii) predominantly backward scattering of product molecules indicates that the interaction is direct and repulsive; forward scattering suggests a stripping mechanism; forward-backward symmetry in the product angular distribution is evidence for the existence of a long-lived intermediate.

Understandably, with more and more systems being studied in greater and greater detail, subtle and not so subtle variations to such generalisations were also becoming known. Kinematic (mass-dependent) effects and statistical factors were being distinguished from dynamical (potential-energy dependent) effects. The role of relative reagent orientation on reaction rate and product alignment also became a subject of dynamical investigations. From *scalar* observables, the shift is presently to *vector* observables [11]. In spite of such an increase in the sophistication, the fact remains that the dynamical studies provide only an indirect evidence to what is happening during a molecular collision. That is, knowing the "initial" and "final", we infer what happens "in-between".

2.2 Resonances

It has been pointed out [12] that characterization of dynamical resonances provides a direct route to vibrational spectroscopy of the transition state. Several quantum mechanical calculations have revealed a number of scattering resonances for a variety of collinear systems [13]. They have since been identified in terms of bound states of vibrational adiabatic potentials in hyperspherical coordinates (for example, see [14]). It is worth emphasizing that even on a repulsive surface it is possible to identify bound states and hence resonances. Approximate three dimensional quantum calculations [15] showed that the dynamical resonances for the reaction

$$F + H_2 (v = 0) \rightarrow FH(v') + H \tag{R8}$$

occurred at increasingly larger impact parameters (b) with increase in E_{tr}. Although it is not possible to control b in an experiment, it *is* possible to infer the consequences in the product angular distribution. It was expected that if the transition state [F—H—H]* had a lifetime smaller than its rotational period, the product FH would be scattered in the forward direction in contrast to FH being backward scattered in a direct collision. Highly resolved molecular beam experiments [16] indeed revealed enhanced forward scattering for $v' = 3$.

Nieh and Valentini [17] reported several oscillations in the $v' = 1$ partial cross sections as a function of E_{tr} for the reaction

$$H + p\text{-}H_2 \, (v = 0, \; j = 0, 2) \rightarrow o, p\text{-}H_2 \, (v', \; j') + H \tag{R9}$$

The maxima at 0.70, 0.93 and 0.98 eV are in agreement with the Feshbach resonances predicted on the basis of the excited vibrational states $(1, 0, 0)$, $(1, 2^0, 0)$ and $(1, 2^2, 0)$ of H_3 thus constituting the vibrational spectroscopy of the transition state. But it must be added that while individual partial waves show the oscillations, fully converged quantal calculations [18] summed over all partial waves do not show any sharp resonance suggesting that the experimental results may be due to some other factor.

For systems of the type

$$\mathbf{H + LH \rightarrow HL + H} \tag{R10}$$

where **H** and **L** represent heavy and light atoms respectively, the reaction probability oscillates dramatically as a function of E_{tr} and there are a large number of resonances superimposed on those oscillations. For example, see [19] and references therein. Metz et al [20] showed that they could probe the transition state in

$$Cl + HCl \rightarrow [ClHCl]^* \rightarrow ClH + Cl \tag{R11}$$

reaction by expanding a mixture of NF_3, HCl and Ar through a pulsed molecular beam and crossing the neutral beam with a 1 keV electron beam just outside the valve orifice. The resulting $ClHCl^-$ ions were mass-selected and irradiated by an excimer laser pulse and a small fraction of the ejected photoelectrons were energy analyzed. The conclusion that the peaks in the photodetachment spectrum were indeed due to the transition state was arrived at from the observation that: (i) the spacing of these peaks was different from HCl vibrational spacing, (ii) spacing of the peaks changed in going from $[ClHCl]^-$ to $[ClDCl]^-$ as would be expected of such states, and (iii) there was good correspondence between the peaks and energies of resonances seen in collinear reactive scattering calculations [19]. Subsequent three dimensional reactive scattering calculations coupled with a Franck-Condon model for the photoexcitation by Schatz [21] have supported the conclusion. Using the same approach, Schatz [22] was also able to explain the photodetachment spectrum for IHI^- obtained by Weaver et al [23]. Metz et al [24] have extended their study recently to the Br analog and also to mixed halide systems.

2.3 Direct Probing of the Transition State

About a decade ago, Polanyi [25] suggested that we might be in a position to probe the TS directly. We outline here what has been accomplished since. For an extensive review of the subject the reader is referred to [26].

Polanyi and coworkers [27] demonstrated that they could monitor the "wings" to the sodium-D line emission in the reaction

$$F + Na_2 \rightarrow [FNaNa]^{**} \rightarrow FNa + Na^* \tag{R12}$$
$$\downarrow \quad \text{D line}$$
$$Na$$

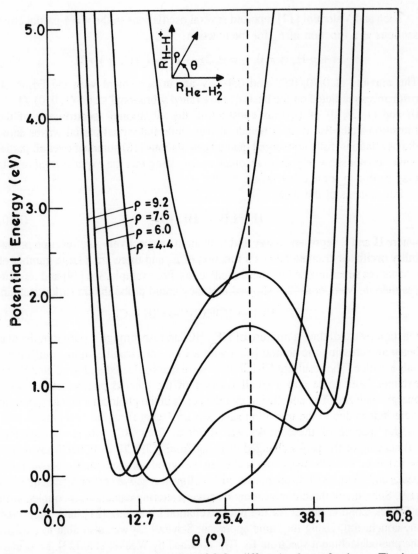

Fig. 4.   Potential energy as a function of θ for different values of ρ in au. The inset
illustrates the hyperspherical coordinates ρ and θ.

Schematically, the idea is illustrated in Fig. 4. The D line emission comes from
the isolated Na*. However, when the emission takes place while the other product
specie is still in the vicinity, it will be (blue or red) shifted indicating that the
PESs for the ground and the excited states of the triatomic species are not
parallel. Since the wings would contain information on the energy spacing between
the two states, in principle, one could infer the shape of one PES given the other
under favourable circumstances. Polanyi and Wolf [28] demonstrated the viability
of the proposition by stimulating the dynamics using model surfaces. The key to
the success of the experiment was the realisation that the wings would be six
orders of magnitude lower in intensity than the D line. The lifetime of the TS

would be around 10^{-12} s, about four orders less than that of Na* and thus a reduction in intensity by 10^4 is anticipated. If the wings are considered as 100 spectral windows, the intensity would drop by another two orders of magnitude.

Through a subsequent experiment, Polanyi and coworkers [29] showed that they could identify the TS for the reaction

$$H + D_2 \rightarrow [HDD]^* \rightarrow HD + H \tag{R13}$$

by velocity-selected time of flight mass spectrometry. In their *pump and probe* experiment, the first laser L_1 (248 nm) pumped H_2S to generate H atoms which reacted with D_2 to form $[HD_2]^*$ which in turn was probed by the second laser L_2 (193 nm) through resonantly enhanced multi-photon ionization. By varying the time delay between L_1 and L_2, they concluded that the detected $[HD_2]^+$ came from $[HD_2]^*$. Varying the wavelength of L_2 and probing the TS would literally constitute the spectroscopy of the transition state. Unfortunately, it turns out [30] that there was an error in the analysis of the experimental results and direct probing of HD_2^* remains to be established.

In a parallel development Brooks and collaborators [31] carried out a 3-beam experiment: they crossed beams of K, $HgBr_2$ and $h\nu$ and monitored fluorescence from the product HgBr*.

$$
\begin{array}{ccc}
[KHgBr_2]^{**} & \rightarrow & KBr + HgBr* \\
\uparrow & & \downarrow \\
K + HgBr_2 \rightarrow & [KHgBr_2]^* & HgBr
\end{array}
\tag{R14}
$$

They performed a similar experiment [32] with K, NaCl and $h\nu$ and monitored the D line emission from Na*:

$$
\begin{array}{ccc}
[KClNa]^{**} & \rightarrow & KCl + Na* \\
\uparrow & & \downarrow \; D\ line \\
K + NaCl \rightarrow & [KClNa]^* & Na
\end{array}
\tag{R15}
$$

The laser photon chosen to excite the TS $[KClNa]^*$ did not have enough energy to excite K or NaCl, to take the system to the excited state PES. It is worth re-iterating that the reagent photon was to the red of the D line.

Kleiber et al [33] had demonstrated that the endoergic reaction

$$Mg + H_2 \rightarrow MgH + H \tag{R16}$$

takes place in the presence of a Nd: YAG laser. Presumably the laser photon is absorbed by the TS $[MgH_2]^*$ which becomes $[MgH_2]^{**}$ and yields either excited reagents (Mg* + H_2) or products MgH + H.

A precursor-geometry-limited (PGL) approach has been developed recently to achieve a certain amount of energy, orientation and impact parameter selection in a bimolecular collision. For example, Wittig and coworkers [34] used $\lambda = 193$ nm laser to photodissociate the HBr in a CO_2-HBr van der Waals complex and monitored the OH rotational distribution arising out of the reaction

$$H + CO_2 \rightarrow HO + CO \tag{R17}$$

and concluded that the reaction proceeded through a long-lived complex with a lifetime of ~1 ps.

In a similar but "real-time" measurement Scherer et al [35] photolysed the HI bond in an I-H$\cdots$O = C = O van der Waals complex coming from a supersonic nozzle so that the reaction (R17) could be "clocked". The initiation pulse (pump laser, 239 nm) was followed by the probe pulse (308 nm) to monitor the OH product by laser-induced fluorescence. The rise time of the OH signal was found to be 5-15 ps which represents the transient decay time of the collision complex in accord with the estimates from the Wittig group.

In contrast to the above experiments which involve "full" collisions, there have been reports of "half" collisions which provide insight into the nature of the TS. Kinsey and coworkers [36] monitored the emission from photo-dissociating CH_3I and O_3 and in conjunction with Heller's semiclassical theory [37] were able to infer the nature of the excited state PES. In these experiments, at time $t = 0$, the absorption of a photon causes the initial ground state vibrational wavefunction to be prepared on the excited state PES. Its evolution in time constitutes the dynamical process of interest and the light emission from the excited state in the frequency domain contains the equivalent information in time and also maps out unique levels of the ground state PES.

In a real-time experiment involving femtosecond (fs) pulses, Dantus et al [38] followed the breaking of the I—CN bond. A (100–150) fs pulse was used to excite the bound ICN to an upper repulsive (I—C) surface and a second fs pulse probed the birth of the CN fragment as a function of time and wavelength (λ) at different I—C distances. The shape of the transient spectrum was strongly dependent on the λ of the probe pulse emphasizing the value of the spectroscopy of the transition state. A more detailed account of these half-collision experiments is given in Chapter 4. We must however add a word of caution that the gain in time resolution in these experiments is lost in terms of spectral resolution.

Much before the experimentalists could develop the additional techniques needed to go beyond state-to-state chemistry to the probing of the TS, theorists had the capability to study the details of the reaction dynamics and hence to characterise the TS. Polanyi and coworkers [28] computed classical trajectories to follow the dynamics of (R12) on the excited state surface modelled using the "old faithful" London-Eyring-Polanyi-Sato formalism, constructed the probability density by counting the number of visits made by the trajectories to each "box" in the configuration space and with the assumption of Franck-Condon transitions and constant transition moment, predicted the emission spectrum and thus the wings to the D-line.

They extended the study [39] to predict the absorption spectrum of H_3^* in (H, H_2) collisions using the accurate SLTH surface [40] for the ground state and a diatomics-in-molecules [41] surface and some model PESs for the excited state. Their study revealed the information content of the shape of the wings and showed that many of the spectral features could survive on going from collinear to non-collinear collisions. Yamashita et al [42] used a similar approach to simulate the absorption spectrum for the TS in K + NaCl collisions.

Agrawal et al [43] also used a similar approach but replaced the swarm of trajectories by a wave packet and solved the time-dependent Schrödinger equation for the (H, H_2) collision on the SLTH surface. A time-independent quantum mechanical (TIQM) study by Engel et al [44] gave qualitatively the same result as the time-dependent analog and the quasiclassical trajectory method. A simple one dimensional TIQM model [45] mimicking the features of the ground and excited state PESs could also reproduce the basic features of the wings. Bersohn and Zewail [46] proposed the use of a classical Lorentzian absorption formula in conjunction with a single trajectory in a one dimensional model for predicting the TS absorption for photodissociating systems like ICN in fs time scale.

Recently, Lee et al [47] developed a quantum theory for TS absorption/ emission along the lines developed earlier by Heller [48]. For a system prepared by a pump pulse, for example, in its electronic state $|e_1\rangle$ with a vibrational Hamiltonian h_1 it was assumed that the probe pulse linked it optically to another electronic state $|e_2\rangle$ with its vibrational Hamiltonian h_2. For the case of a δ-function probe pulse of frequency ω at time τ, the absorption (emission) cross section $\sigma(\tau, \omega)$ was related to the correlation function given by the overlap between two non-stationary wave packets, one on $|e_1\rangle$ and another on $|e_2\rangle$ both coupled by the probe pulse as follows:

$$\sigma(\tau, \omega) = (4\pi\omega/c\hbar)\,\mathrm{Re}\left(\int_0^\infty dt\,\exp\,(i\omega t - t/T_2)\right.$$

$$\left. \times\,\langle\phi_1(\tau)\,|\exp(ih_1 t/\hbar)\,\mu_{12}(Q)\,\exp\,(-ih_2 t/\hbar)\mu_{21}(Q)|\,\phi_1(\tau)\rangle\right) \quad (1)$$

where $|\phi_1(\tau)\rangle$ is the time-evolved wave packet in $|e_1\rangle$ at τ, $\mu_{12}(Q)$ and $\mu_{21}(Q)$ are electronic transition dipole moments as functions of vibrational coordinates Q and T_2 is the time constant for electronic dephasing between $|e_1\rangle$ and $|e_2\rangle$.

Assuming that the propagator in time (nearly) commutes with the transition dipole moment for short times, Lee et al [49] approximated the correlation

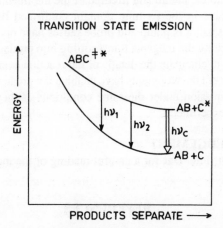

Fig. 5. Schematic diagram of emission from the TS in a typical chemical reaction. Emission from ABC* during separation of products results in "wings" to the atomic transition.

function by truncating the propagator to linear terms in t and showed that

$$\sigma_L(\tau, \omega) = (4\pi\omega/c) \int_{-\infty}^{\infty} \cdots \int_{-\infty}^{\infty} dQ \, |\mu_{12}(Q)|^2 \, |\phi_1(Q, \tau)|^2$$

$$\times \frac{\gamma}{\gamma^2 + [V_2(Q) - V_1(Q) - \hbar\omega]^2} \qquad (2)$$

where $\gamma = \hbar/T_2$ and L stands for Lorentzian. If T_2 is long compared to the width of the correlation function, $\gamma \to 0$ and

$$\sigma(\tau, \omega) = (4\pi^2 \omega/c) \int_{-\infty}^{\infty} \cdots \int_{-\infty}^{\infty} dQ \, |\mu_{12}(Q)|^2 \, |\phi_1(Q, \tau)|^2$$

$$\times \delta[V_2(Q) \quad V_1(Q) - \hbar\omega] \qquad (3)$$

They also showed that the results of Engel et al arise from the time integration of eq. (1) and that the classical and the time-dependent quantal results follow from the short-time approximation.

3. CONCLUSION

Ever since the possibility of probing the transition state by monitoring the absorption/emission of one of the products while the other is still in the vicinity was pointed out by J.C. Polanyi, substantial progress has been made. Briefly, experiments from Polanyi's laboratory established the existence of wings to the sodium D-line and thereby inferred the possible range of transition species. Raman-like emission from the photodissociating O_3 and CH_3I measured by Kinsey and coworkers could shed light on the nature of the excited species. Photoinitiated reactions within a van der Waals complex like IH ... O = C = O followed by monitoring of the rovibrational distribution by Wittig and coworkers have provided valuable insight into the nature and lifetime of the intermediate. While the time-resolved experiments in the ps time domain confirmed these findings, more recent experiments using fs pump and probe pulses have opened up the exciting possibility of watching the reagents transforming into products. Although theory had the capability to elucidate the details of the reaction events as they occur all along, the more recent developments have enabled the prediction of the transition state absorption/emission under the same conditions as they exist in the ultra-fast time domain experiments.

4. ACKNOWLEDGEMENT

I am grateful to Dr. P.K. Das for a careful reading of the manuscript.

REFERENCES

1. Globe and Mail, Toronto, Dec. 12, 1987.
2. M. Polanyi, Atomic Reactions, Williams & Norgate Ltd., London, 1932.
3. H. Eyring and M. Polanyi, Z. Phys. Chem. **B12**, 279 (1931).

4. C.F. Bender, S.V. O'Neil, P.K. Pearson and H.F. Schaefer, Science **176**, 1412 (1972).
5. D.R. Mclaughlin and D.L. Thompson, J. Chem. Phys. **70**, 2748 (1979).
6. B.C. Garrett and D.G. Truhlar, Acc. Chem. Res. **13**, 440 (1980).
7. J. Manz, Comments At. Mol. Phys. **17**, 91 (1985).
8. H. Nakamura, A. Ohsaki and M. Baer, J. Phys. Chem. **90**, 6176 (1986).
9. N. Sathyamurthy, M. Baer and T. Joseph, Chem. Phys. **114**, 73 (1987).
10. a) P.R. Brooks and E.F. Hayes, ed. State-to-State Chemistry, American Chemical Society, Washington D.C. 1977;
    b) R.D. Levine and R.B. Bernstein, Molecular Reaction Dynamics and Chemical Reactivity, Oxford University Press, New York, 1987;
    c) J.C. Polanyi, Science **236**, 680 (1987); Chemica Scripta **27**, 229 (1987);
    d) Y.T. Lee, Science **236**, 793 (1987);
    e) D.R. Herschbach, Angew. Chem. Int. Ed. Engl. **26**, 1221 (1987).
11. J.C. Whitehead, ed. Selectivity in Chemical Reactions, Kluwer, Dordrecht, 1987.
12. A. Kuppermann, in Potential Energy Surfaces and Dynamics Calculations, ed. D.G. Truhlar, Plenum, New York (1981), p. 375.
13. a) D.G. Truhlar, ed. Resonances in Electron-Molecule Scattering, van der Waals Complexes and Reactive Chemical Dynamics, ACS Symposium Series, Washington D.C. (1984);
    b) V. Aquilanti, in The Theory of Chemical Reaction Dynamics, ed. D.C. Clary, Reidel, Dordrecht (1986).
14. A. Ohsaki and H. Nakamura, Phys. Rep. **187**, 1 (1990).
15. R.E. Wyatt, J.F. McNutt and M.J. Redmon, Ber. Bunsenges. Phys. Chem. **86**, 437 (1982).
16. D.M. Neumark, A.M. Wodtke, G.N. Robinson, C.C. Hayden and Y.T. Lee, J. Chem. Phys. **82**, 3045 (1985).
17. J.-C. Nieh and J.J. Valentini, Phys. Rev. Lett. **60**, 519 (1988); J. Chem. Phys. **92**, 1083 (1990).
18. a) M. Mladenovic, M. Zhao, D.G. Truhlar, D.W. Schwenke, Y. Sun and D.J. Kouri, Chem. Phys. Lett. **146**, 358 (1988); J. Phys. Chem. **92**, 7035 (1988);
    b) J.Z.H. Zhang and W.H. Miller, Chem. Phys. Lett. **153**, 465 (1988);
    c) D.E. Manolopoulos and R.E. Wyatt, Chem. Phys. Lett. **159**, 123 (1989).
19. a) D.K. Bondi, J.N.L. Connor, J. Manz and J. Römlt, Mol. Phys. **50**, 467 (1983);
    b) J.N.L. Connor and W. Jakubetz, in Supercomputer algorithms for reactivity, dynamics and kinetics of small molecules, ed. A. Lagana, Kluwer, Dordrecht (1989).
20. R.B. Metz, T. Kitsopoulos, A. Weaver and D.M. Neumark, J. Chem. Phys. **88**, 1463 (1988).
21. G.C. Schatz, J. Chem. Phys. **90**, 3582 (1989).
22. G.C. Schatz, J. Chem. Phys. **90**, 4847 (1989).
23. A. Weaver, R.B. Metz, S.E. Bradforth and D.M. Neumark, J. Phys. Chem. **92**, 5558 (1988).
24. a) R.B. Metz, A. Weaver, S.E. Bradforth, T.N. Kitsopoulos and D.M. Neumark, J. Phys. Chem. **94**, 1377 (1990);
    b) S.E. Bradforth, A. Weaver, D.W. Arnold, R.B. Metz and D.M. Neumark, J.Chem. Phys. **92**, 7205 (1990).
25. J.C. Polanyi, Faraday Discuss. Chem. Soc. **67**, 129 (1979).
26. P.R. Brooks, Chem. Rev. **88**, 407 (1988).

27. a) P. Arrowsmith, F.E. Bartoszek, S.H.P. Bly, T. Carrington, Jr., P.E. Charters and J.C. Polanyi, J. Chem. Phys. **73**, 5895 (1980);
    b) P. Arrowsmith, S.H.P. Bly, P.E. Charters and J.C. Polanyi, J. Chem. Phys. **79**, 283 (1983).
28. J.C. Polanyi and R. Wolf, J. Chem. Phys. **75**, 5951 (1981).
29. B.A. Collings, J.C. Polanyi, M.A. Smith, A. Stolow and A.W. Tarr, Phys. Rev. Lett. **59**, 2551 (1987).
30. B.A. Collings, J.C. Polanyi, M.A. Smith, A. Stolow and A.W. Tarr, Phys. Rev. Lett. **63**, 2160 (1989).
31. P. Hering, P.R. Brooks, R.F. Curl, R.S. Judson and R.S. Lowe, Phys. Rev. Lett. **44**, 687 (1980).
32. a) T.C. Maguire, P.R. Brooks and R.F. Curl, Phys. Rev. Lett. **50**, 1918 (1983);
    b) T.C. Maguire, P.R. Brooks, R.F. Curl, J.H. Spence and S.J. Ulvick, J. Chem. Phys. **85**, 844 (1986);
    c) S. Kaesdorf, P.R. Brooks, R.F. Curl, J.H. Spence and S.J. Ulvick, Phys. Rev. **A34**, 4418, (1986).
33. a) P.D. Kleiber, A.M. Lyyra, K.M. Sando, S.P. Henegham and W.C. Stwalley, Phys. Rev. Lett. **54**, 2003 (1985);
    b) P.D. Kleiber, A.M. Lyyra, K.M. Sando, V. Zafiropulos and W.C. Stwalley, J. Chem. Phys., **85**, 5493 (1986).
34. C. Wittig, S. Sharpe and R.A. Beaudet, Acc. Chem. Res. **21**, 341 (1988).
35. N.F. Scherer, L.R. Khundkar, R.B. Bernstein and A.H. Zewail, J. Chem. Phys. **87**, 1451 (1987).
36. a) D.G. Imre, J.L. Kinsey, R.W. Field and D.H. Katayama, J. Phys. Chem. **86**, 2564 (1984);
    b) D.G. Imre, J.L. Kinsey, A. Sinha and J. Krenos, J. Phys. Chem. **88**, 3956 (1984);
    c) H.O. Hale, G.E. Galica, S.G. Glogover and J.L. Kinsey, J. Phys. Chem. **90**, 4997 (1986).
37. a) S.-Y. Lee and E.J. Heller, J. Chem. Phys. **71**, 4777 (1979);
    b) E.J. Heller, R. Sundberg and D.J. Tannor, J. Phys. Chem. **86**, 1822 (1982);
    c) D.J. Tannor and E.J. Heller, J. Chem. Phys. **77**, 202 (1982).
38. a) M. Dantus, M.J. Rosker and A.H. Zewail, J. Chem. Phys. **87**, 2395 (1987);
    b) T.S. Rose, M.J. Rosker and A.H. Zewail, J. Chem. Phys. **88**, 6672 (1988);
    c) M.J. Rosker, T.S. Rose and A.H. Zewail, Chem. Phys. Lett. **146**, 175 (1988);
    d) M.J. Rosker, M. Dantus and A.H. Zewail, Science, **241**, 1200 (1988); J. Chem. Phys. **89**, 6113 (1988);
    e) M. Dantus, M.J. Rosker and A.H. Zewail, J. Chem. Phys. **89**, 6128 (1988);
    f) A.H. Zewail and R.B. Bernstein, C & E News, Nov. 7 (1988), p. 24.
39. a) H.R. Mayne, R.A. Poirier and J.C. Polanyi, J. Chem. Phys. **80**, 4025 (1984);
    b) H.R. Mayne, J.C. Polanyi, N. Sathyamurthy and S. Raynor, J. Phys. Chem. **88**, 4064 (1984).
40. a) B. Liu, J. Chem. Phys. **58**, 1925 (1973);
    b) P. Siegbahn and B. Liu, ibid. **68**, 2457 (1978);
    c) D.G. Truhlar and C.J. Horowitz, ibid. **68**, 2466 (1978); **71**, 1514 (1979).
41. S. Raynor and D.R. Herschbach, J. Phys. Chem. **86**, 1214 (1982).
42. K. Yamashita and K. Morokuma, J. Phys. Chem. **92**, 3109 (1988).
43. P.M. Agrawal, V. Mohan and N. Sathyamurthy, Chem. Phys. Lett. **114**, 343 (1985).
44. a) V. Engel, Z. Bacic, R. Schinke and M. Shapiro, J. Chem. Phys. **82**, 4844 (1985);

b) V. Engel and R. Schinke, Chem. Phys. Lett. **122**, 103 (1985).

45. S. Sinha, N. Sathyamurthy and K. Banerjee, Proc. Indian Acad. Sci. (Chem. Sci.) **96**, 215 (1986).
46. R. Bersohn and A.H. Zewail, Ber. Bunsensges. Phys. Chem. **92**, 373 (1988).
47. S.-Y. Lee, W.T. Pollard and R.A. Mathies, Chem. Phys. Lett. **160**, 531 (1989).
48. E.J. Heller, Acc. Chem. Res. **14**, 368 (1981).
49. S.-Y. Lee, W.T. Pollard and R.A. Mathies, Chem. Phys. Lett. **163**, 11 (1989).

3. Photodissociation Dynamics : State selection and beyond

Puspendu Kumar Das

Department of Inorganic and Physical Chemistry
Indian Institute of Science
Bangalore, India

Abstract

Photodissociation dynamics has come a long way since its inception over half a century ago. Until the early 80's, scientists working in this area were mainly studying state-to-state photodissociations. A molecule is prepared in a well defined excited electronic state (with precise vibrational and rotational quantum numbers in case of a predissociation) with the help of a tunable laser and the nascent internal energies of the resulting fragments are subsequently probed. With the advent of femtosecond lasers, narrow-band tunable lasers, highly sensitive detectors, efficient pumps, etc., a few new types of 'photodissociation' experiments burst upon the field in the last decade. They include vector correlations in state-to-state photodissociations, external control in unimolecular dissociation product yields, transition state spectroscopy in time and frequency domains and photodissociation of adsorbed species on solid surfaces, among other things. In this article I have attempted to deal with these rather recent advances in photodissociation dynamics. Each technique has been outlined followed by some examples. Future directions have been speculated in the concluding part.

1. INTRODUCTION

This article attempts to describe some of the recent advances in the field of 'Photodissociation Dynamics' in the last decade or so. Parts of what is written here may be found in detail in the literature cited and the list by no means is exhaustive. For limitation of space and the author's own understanding, some important topics such as infrared multiphoton dissociation, fragmentation of van der Waals molecules and clusters, and dissociation of ions have been omitted. Mainly four topics will be discussed here. They are: i) product correlation in photodissociation, ii) mode selective dissociation, iii) emission from molecules in the process of dissociation, and iv) dissociation of adsorbed species.

Since the first observation [1] of the final state of the sodium atoms in terms of yellow emission from sodium iodide when irradiated with uv light, molecular fragmentation has been studied by a variety of techniques for many years. The photochemist is interested in generating reactive species (free radicals) through photodissociation. The astrophysicist is keen on studying photodissociation for he is interested in understanding the formation of stable molecules in the upper atmosphere or in the cooler parts of stars. But why are dynamicists interested in studying photodissociation? The reason I believe, is that at least for simple molecules the dynamics can be accurately described theoretically even under 'nonisolated' conditions, e.g. in the adsorbed state. Also the advent of femtosecond lasers, molecular beam, mass spectrometer and highly efficient pumps have made it possible to carry out simple experiments under controlled conditions and detection of weak events has become possible.

Photodissociation dynamics is a study of the distribution and conservation of energy (scalar) and angular momentum (vector). In a conventional 'pump' and 'probe' experiment, a molecule is excited to a higher electronic energy state with a 'pump' laser. In case of dissociation the initial photon energy is distributed into: a) work done to produce the fragments, b) relative translational energy of the products, and c) internal energy of the fragments. At high collision energies electronic excitation of fragments is also possible. A 'probe' laser then intercepts the fragments in the nascent state (before any relaxation) and one finds out how exactly the initial excitation energy is distributed into the fragment states. In some cases the identity of the products are determined by mass spectrometry and their translational energies analysed by the time-of-flight technique. Product internal state distribution is probed by ir fluorescence from vibrationally excited fragments, absorption via electronic transitions (dye laser excitation) and also vibrational transitions (diode laser excitation), laser induced fluorescence, multiphoton ionization, coherent anti-Stokes Raman Scattering and various other techniques. Suppose the translational and internal energies of the BC fragment are measured, then the energy distribution of the other fragment is automatically determined since the conservation of energy requires

$$E_{ABC} + h\nu = E_d + E_t + E_A + E_{BC} \tag{1}$$

where $h\nu$ is the energy of the absorbed photon, E_{ABC} is the energy of the parent molecule, E_d is the dissociation energy of the A—BC bond with ABC, A and BC all in their lowest possible states. E_t is the recoil energy of the fragments and E_A and E_{BC} their internal energies. This is scalar-scalar correlation between energies of the two fragments. The literature is rich in these types of experiments carried out for a vast number of molecules including triatomics and they won't be discussed here. Interested readers are directed to a few recent reviews [2-14] written on them.

What poses problem to our ability to relate microscopic observations on reactive scattering (including photofragmentation) to microscopic information (point) on a potential energy surface is our difficulty to understand the conservation of angular momentum. The initial orbital angular momentum is not known. If a molecule ABC is dissociated into an atom A and a diatomic BC the conservation of angular momentum may be written as:

$$\mathbf{J}_{AB} + \mathbf{J}_{h\nu} = \mathbf{J}_A + \mathbf{L}' + \mathbf{J}_{BC} \tag{2}$$

where **J**s are the respective rotational angular momenta and **L′** is the orbital angular momentum of the recoiling fragments. If the molecules are expanded in a molecular beam (which is normally done) and if we neglect the angular momentum of **A**, then **L′** and $\mathbf{J}_{BC}$ become equal in magnitude and opposite in direction to each other. Therefore, a distribution over the rotational states of BC is also a distribution over **L′**. Then we can write

$$|\mathbf{J}_{BC}| = |\mathbf{L'}| = \mu v b \qquad (3)$$

where b is the exit channel impact parameter. It turns out that there is a correlation between the velocity of the fragment and its angular momentum. This vector-vector correlation will be discussed in detail at the bottom.

2. PRODUCT CORRELATION IN PHOTODISSOCIATION

There are two types of correlations that are talked about in the context of photodissociation. By using equation (1) and measuring the energy distribution in one of the fragments we can get information regarding the other. This is a scalar-scalar correlation (correlation arising out of energy matching in order to maintain the conservation) in the products. The other type of correlation which is a vector-vector correlation arises out of the correlations between angular momenta and velocities of the fragments with the **E** vector of light that generates them. This later correlation was ignored for a long time but experiments done in four labs [15-18] simultaneously revealed that this plays an important role in understanding the dynamics of many simple molecules and will be discussed at length in this section.

Before understanding the angular momentum-recoil velocity correlation in a photodissociation process we have to know a little bit about the anisotropic distribution and various frames of reference important to describe such a distribution. If a beam of particles collides with target particles which are isotropically distributed in space, as a result of collision the beam particles and target particles will be anisotropically distributed. In the context of photodissociation the beam particles are photons and the target particles are molecules (say). Since the photon is anisotropic and the subsequent collision is such a violent act, the anisotropy of the target particles is not surprising. The frame of reference which is most readily understood is the space fixed system or the laboratory frame. A second important frame of reference is that of the parent molecule. And a final frame of reference is that of the fragments. But we can easily relate these three frames of reference. To understand the angular distribution of the photofragments in space we consider again the example of a triatomic dissociation ABC → A + BC. Initially the ABC molecules are distributed randomly in the laboratory frame. Immediately after collision with photons they will be aligned and/or oriented in a particular fashion in the laboratory frame. The classical distribution function $W(\Theta, \phi)$ which gives the probability that an axis fixed in the target particle (parent molecular frame) can be related to space fixed axes XYZ (laboratory frame) by the angles Θ, ϕ, has the value $(1/4)\pi$ for isotropically distributed particles. The necessary condition that an anisotropic distribution of the excited particles is obtained is that the transition probability for the excitation process depends on the orientation of the target with respect to the polarization of the beam if it is linearly polarized. If ABC* is formed with a probability proportional to the square of the cosine of an angle Θ between a space fixed axis and a target fixed axis, then

$$W(\Theta) = 1/4\pi \ [1 + \beta P_2 \ (\Theta)] \tag{4}$$

for a nondegenerate transition, where P_2 (Θ) is the second Legendre polynomial and β is the well-known anisotropy parameter whose value is determined by the nature of transition, the time scale of photodissociation, etc. For a degenerate transition this equation may be modified suitably [19]. This distribution is in turn related to a distribution over angular momentum states by the following

$$W(\Theta, f) = \sum_{J'} \sum_{M'} W_{J'M'} \ |J'M' \ (\Theta,\phi)|^2 \tag{5}$$

which is independent of angle if $W_{J'M'}$ is independent of M' (Unsold's theorem). If the total angular momentum J is expressed as a vector defined by its projection along the Z direction of the space fixed axis and if we expand it in terms of multipole moments, then the monopole component gives rise to isotropy and consequently we have all the magnetic sublevels equally populated. For orientation, the population of the M and $-M$ sublevels differ and is proportional to the magnetic dipole of the ensemble of molecules. The quadrupole moment gives rise to alignment of the molecules and the population may be unequal for different $|M|$ values [20]. What is an extremely important result to realise is that angular anisotropy of the fragments manifests itself as unequal populations of the different magnetic sublevels.

If we now fix another angle α as the angle between the dissociation momentum **P** (or the recoil velocity) and the transition dipole moment **μ** (defined in the parent reference frame), then a little spherical trigonometry shows that the distribution over the laboratory angle Θ is given by [21, 22]

$$W(\Theta) = 1/4\pi \ [1 + \beta P_2 \ (\Theta) \ P_2 \ (\alpha)] \tag{6}$$

The four quantities that have been related by equation (6) are: (i) the dissociation momentum **P** or the recoil velocity **v**, (ii) the angular momentum vector (s), **J** of the photofragments, (iii) the transition dipole moment, **μ** of the parent molecule, and (iv) the electric vector **E** of the dissociating light. The first two quantities are properties of the fragments, the third quantity is a property of the parent system and the fourth is defined readily in the laboratory frame. Experiments which first reported measurement of this anisotropy of fragment recoil were by photolysis mapping [23-25]. A more quantitative method later on was developed to measure the angular distribution using mass spectrometry [26-28]. These experiments mainly pointed out the correlation between the electric vector of light **E**, the recoil velocity **v**, and indirectly the transition dipole moment of the parent molecule **μ** . Measurement of polarization of fluorescence (emitted from an excited fragment) is yet another way of obtaining the orientation or alignment of the fragments [29-35]. But most recently Doppler techniques and polarization measurements have been combined to obtain more detailed information regarding the correlation between some of these vector quantities. This last technique will be illustrated with an example in the following section.

When a moving molecule absorbs light the frequency of the light absorbed is shifted by an amount depending on the relative velocity of the molecule with respect to the source of light. This is the Doppler effect (which was originally pointed out by J.C. Doppler in the context of hearing sound waves generated by a moving source, by a stationary person) and the frequency of the light absorbed is related to the relative velocity in the following manner

$$\nu_{abs} = \nu_0 [1 - (\mathbf{v} \cdot \mathbf{k}/c)] \tag{7}$$

where ν_0 is the frequency that would be absorbed in the absence of relative motion and $\mathbf{k}$ is the direction of propagation of the probe beam. Therefore, the distribution of absorption frequencies must be directly related to the distribution of relative speed. This had been suggested by Zare and Herschbach [36]. Experimental verification of this technique has been reported by Schmiedl et al [37] who measured the Doppler profile of the hydrogen atoms produced by 266 nm dissociation of HI. Two distinct hydrogen atom translational energies were obtained. These channels corresponding to the two spin orbit iodine states show different angular distributions, which indirectly points out a correlation between the magnitude and direction of the recoil velocity.

In 1978, Case et al [38] pointed out that since $\mathbf{J}$ and $\mathbf{v}$ are correlated with $\mathbf{\mu}$, they must be correlated with each other and this would have important consequences on the photodissociation dynamics. Nearly a decade later four groups [15-18] reported experimental Doppler profiles of individual rotational transitions exhibiting dramatic effects as a consequence of this correlation. CO produced in the 222 nm dissociation of OCS was probed by one photon laser induced fluorescence where Doppler profiles for individual rotational transitions were obtained [15, 39-46].

The dissociation of OCS at 222 nm yields either CO + S (^{3}P) or CO + S (^{1}D), the former having 20,000 cm^{-1} excess energy available for CO internal excitation and product translation. The second channel has only 10,000 cm^{-1} excess energy for distribution into the product modes. CO in the ground electronic and vibrational states was probed by the technique of laser induced fluorescence and it was observed that the rotational distribution was bimodal as well as inverted peaking around $J = 54$ and $J = 65$ [47]. At first it looks like these peaks are associated with two channels, the higher J is produced in coincidence with S(^{3}P) and the lower J with S(^{1}D). But this turns out not to be the case when the Doppler profiles for CO ($J = 65$) and CO ($J = 54$) were measured [45, 48]. In fact the Doppler profile for the former was narrower than the latter (the opposite of what is expected if it were true that the two peaks correspond to the two different channels). If we, on the contrary, assumed that both the peaks were due to a single channel producing CO + S(^{1}D), then it is not surprising that the Doppler profiles for CO ($J = 65$) is narrower than for that of CO ($J = 54$) for the former has more energy tied up in internal degrees of freedom and thus has less available for translation. To understand this in detail let us first consider the Doppler profiles predicted for a linear molecule whose transition dipole is along the

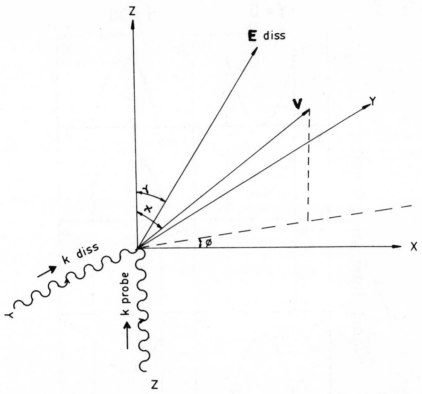

Fig. 1 The Doppler profile when the probe light (k_{probe}) is propagating along the Z axis and the dissociating light (k_{diss}) along the Y axis in the laboratory frame. The electric vector of the dissociating light lies on the XZ plane and makes an angle γ with k_{probe}. The recoil velocity v makes an angle χ with the Z axis and an angle φ with the X axis. The Doppler profile is given by equation (8) mentioned in text.

breaking bond and which is dissociated by linearly polarized light (Fig. 1). Also consider that the dissociation of the excited parent molecule is rapid compared to its rotational time scale and consequently there is no loss of alignment of the initially prepared molecule. Let us also simplify the event by considering only axial recoil of the photofragments. Commonly the fragments are probed by absorption and subsequent fluorescence (LIF) using linearly polarized light (k) propagating either parallel or perpendicular to E of the dissociating light. For the parallel case, the products will be moving towards or away from the probe light with very few moving perpendicular to the probe (i.e., parallel to μ) direction resulting in a strong absorption at the wings of the transition (in fact the absorption is distributed according to v·k) and weak at the centre giving rise to a split Doppler profile (Fig. 2(a)). For the perpendicular case, most molecules will be moving perpendicular to k (parallel to μ) and will absorb at the line centre (Fig. 2(b)). In the general case the Doppler profile is given by [1]

$$I(\chi) = [1 + \beta\, P_2(\gamma)\, P_2(\chi)] \tag{8}$$

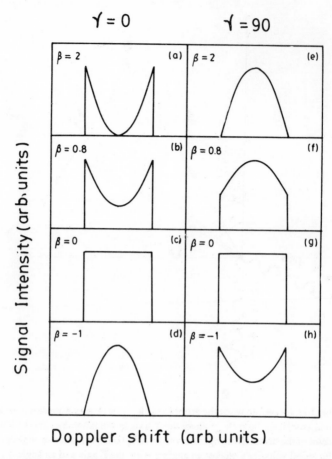

Fig. 2   Examples of Doppler profiles predicted for a photofragment with a single speed and with various degrees of anisotropy characterized by the anisotropy parameter β. Two cases with $\gamma = 0°$ and $\gamma = 90°$ correspond to $\mathbf{E}_{diss} \parallel \mathbf{k}_{probe}$ and $\mathbf{E}_{diss} \perp \mathbf{k}_{probe}$ respectively. The value of $\beta = 0$ indicates an isotropic distribution, while $\beta = 2$ represents $\mathbf{v} \parallel \mathbf{\mu}$ and $\beta = -1$ indicatess $\mathbf{v} \perp \mathbf{\mu}$. The left column (a)-(d) is for $\gamma = 0°$ and the right column (e)—(h) is for $\gamma = 90°$. Reproduced with permission from   P.L. Houston, Acc. Chem. Res., **22**, 309 (1989).

where γ is the angle between the $\mathbf{E}$ and $\mathbf{k}$, χ is the angle between $\mathbf{v}$ and $\mathbf{k}$, P_2 is the second Legendre polynomial, and β the anisotropy parameter that characterizes the spatial distribution of $\mathbf{v}$. For a nondegenerate transition with linearly polarized light where the dissociation timescale is short compared to the rotational period, β assumes a value of 2 for a 'parallel' transition ($\mathbf{\mu}$ parallel to $\mathbf{E}$) and -1 for a 'perpendicular' transition. The quantitative Doppler profiles for several combinations of all these vector quantities have been displayed in Fig. 2.

The experimental results obtained for the 222 nm photolysis of OCS are shown in Fig. 3. The Doppler profiles for the Q (58) line in horizontal ($\mathbf{E}$ parrallel $\mathbf{k}$) and vertical ($\mathbf{E}$ perpendicular $\mathbf{k}$) polarizations appear to have a value

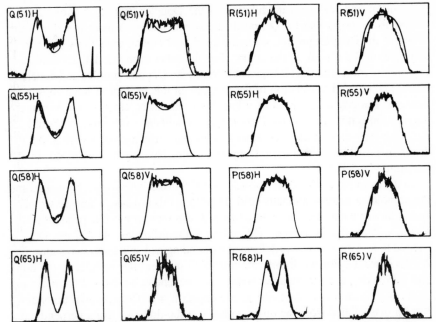

Fig 3   Doppler profiles of representative CO(J) lines taken on different transitions and with different geometrical arrangements. *P*, *Q*, and *R* represent different branches; H corresponds to horizontal geometry ($\gamma = 0°$) and *V* represents vertical geometry ($\gamma = 90°$). The smooth lines are calculated profiles based on the model described in text. The scale on the abscissa of each plot is laser detuning from $v_0 - 0.5$ to $v_0 + 0.5$ cm^{-1}. Reproduced with permission from P.L. Houston Acc. Chem. Res., **22**, 309 (1989).

of β in between 0.8 (for parallel) and 0.0 (for perpendicular). This means β, the anisotropy parameter changes its value depending on the nature of the polarization of the probe beam. But that cannot be true. This was the indication to the Cornell group that something else is happening at this point which has not been taken into account while getting the profiles of Fig. 2. Further probing of different rotational transitions of the *P*, *Q*, and *R* branches of CO clearly showed that the situation is much more complex than we expect.

Let us consider the photolysis of OCS at 222 nm. If the **v**, **J** correlations are neglected (as done in predicting the Doppler profiles of Fig. 2) and if **v** is isotropically distributed in space, one would expect a 'flat-topped' Doppler profile as predicted in Fig. 2. But this correlation cannot be neglected since **v** and **J** are constrained. If they are perpendicular to each other the Doppler profile will have a modulation. This is because the strength of absorption of the probe light by the fragment will depend on its M_J distribution. Consider the case where **v** $\perp$ **J** and along the direction of **k** (also parallel to parent **μ**). The **J** which is also $\perp$ **k** will have its projection along the z-axis (the direction of **k**) and will yield only $M_J = 0$ component in the wings of the profile. On the contrary, in the centre of the Doppler profile where **v** $\perp$ **k** and the projection of *J* along the z-axis will span values from $-J$ to $+J$. The strength of absorption will change with the M_J

distribution and we see a modulation in the Doppler profile. A more careful examination shows that for Q branch transitions ($\Delta J = 0$) there is a dip in the centre of the Doppler profile, whereas, for P or R branch transitions ($\Delta J = \mp 1$) there should be a peak at the centre. For the other case $\mathbf{v} \parallel \mathbf{J}$ the situation is completely reversed. Thus it is possible to see the Doppler profiles and conclude if there is any $\mathbf{v}$, $\mathbf{J}$ correlation in the process. In this example I have chosen an isotropic velocity distribution of $\mathbf{v}$ but this need not be always true. When the distribution is not isotropic the Doppler profile will carry information about both the anisotropy of $\mathbf{v}$ (in the laboratory frame) and correlation of $\mathbf{v}$ with $\mathbf{J}$. All the different possibilities and their Doppler profiles have been worked out in the literature [48–50].

In the example of OCS it is known that OCS dissociates from a bent state and initial molecules are rotationally cold. Therefore, this is a case where dissociation takes place in the molecular plane and $\mathbf{v} \perp \mathbf{J}$. But then why is β dependent on the rotational state that is probed? The reason is the following. At 222 nm OCS is excited to a $^1\Delta$ state which is deformed by bending and splits into two states, one A', the other A''. For the former the transition moment lies parallel to the bond that is breaking and for the latter state it lies perpendicular. Now if the molecule dissociates from the A' state one would expect $\beta = 2$ (for a parallel transition). But for dissociation from the other state A'', β should be -1 (for a perpendicular transition). In reality one finds a mixed transition (to both the states) and consequently a β value ranging between 2 and -1. In fact assuming that higher rotational levels come from A' surface and lower ones come from A'' surface an excellent agreement with experimental and calculated Doppler profiles has been achieved (Fig. 3). The $\mathbf{v} - \mathbf{J}$ correlation was also obtained by the same technique by dissociating OCS at 157 nm [43]. At this wavelength β is measured as 1.8 ± 0.2 which seems to indicate that the transition moment in OCS is parallel to the $\mathbf{E}$ of the dissociating light. But the transition at 157 nm [51] is assigned as $^1\pi \leftarrow {}^1\Sigma^+$ [51], which is a perpendicular transition. This is only possible if the excited state geometry is sufficiently bent and Renner-Teller distortion mixes it with a A'' state (which would have been a $^1\pi$ state in the linear configuration) and thus showing it as a parallel transition. But it is also reported that OCS has a $^1\Sigma^+$ state around 150 nm. A mixing of this state with the $^1\pi$ state and subsequent rapid dissociation from the $^1\pi$ state cannot be ruled out and thus the identification of the dissociating state at the 157 nm excitation is not unambiguous at this point.

In a similar fashion ClCN [52], BrCN, HCN [35], ICN [53-56], H_2O [57-58], NO_2 [59-60], CS_2 [60], NOCl [61-62], NOBr [61], HONO [13], H_2O_2 [63-64], $(CH_3)_3$ CONO [13], $(CH_3)_2$NNO [13], CH_3ONO [13], CHOCHO [65], CH_3COCH_3 [65], H_2CO [66], HCOOH [67], CH_3COOH [68], CH_3I [69], CH_3Cl [70], and HN_3 [71], molecules have been dissociated in the uv or vuv and products have been subsequently probed for $\mathbf{v}$, $\mathbf{J}$ correlation by Doppler profiles. Numerous techniques other than single photon LIF have been suggested for measurement of Doppler profiles and subsequent determination of vector correlations. R.N. Zare and his coworkers [72-73], have suggested ways to obtain population, alignment and orientation using laser induced fluorescence with unresolved emission. The use of 1 + 1 multiphoton ionization technique has also been considered [74], and applied [75], to extract information on population and alignment. Mons and Dimicoli [76], have discussed the use of REMPI detection of photofragments to measure the angular distribution of **v** as well as the **v** – **J** correlation in fragments during a polarized photolysis. Winniczek et al [77] have demonstrated how circular dichroism of photoelectron angular distributions can be utilized to obtain alignment information of a system. Possibilities of using 2 + n multiphoton ionization or LIF techniques to probe the photofragment population, alignment and orientation have also been discussed [78-79]. A number of special cases have been dealt with and results derived.

Finally, it is evident from the discussion above that the vector-vector correlation studies will reveal interesting dynamics (in the context of photodissociation) for many molecules in the near future. This may also be aided by use of high resolution narrow-band cw lasers for probing the Doppler profiles of the resulting photofragments. Currently mostly triatomics are tried but in the future tetraatomics and higher polyatomic molecules will also be attempted. An additional problem for dissociation of the type ABCD → AB + CD is that we must determine which internal states of AB fragments are generated in coincidence with given states of CD fragments. But this could be overcome by using a two dimensional imaging technique developed by D.W. Chandler et al [80-82]. In this technique one measures three dimensional spatial distribution of a photofragment in a mass specific way at a set time after photodissociation. This 3D distribution is then projected onto a suitable 2D plane to get the necessary information. The technique has been successfully used to study the 266 nm dissociation of CH_3I [82]. Another new direction in the future will be concerned with measurements of orientation using circularly polarized radiation both for dissociation and probing. This may be more (?) or equally informative as alignment measurements [56]. With continued efforts and further finer experiments correlated photodissociation will be growing very fast in the coming years.

3. MODE SELECTIVE DISSOCIATION

After gaining confidence in manipulations of laser wavelengths, pulse shapes (both temporal and spatial), polarizations, etc. a dynamicist would like to get a control over the pathways for dissociation in order to command a specific outcome. Thus mode selective chemistry has been envisaged and success has been claimed in several contexts of interaction of radiation with molecules [10, 12, 83-87]. In all the examples found so far what has been observed is that a particular set of products (channel) is favoured in spite of many possibilities in a chemical process. This has certainly proven the point that it is possible to find systems that under experimental conditions will give preference to a particular exit channel. But until now what has not been achieved is to gain an external control which can be manipulated by changing the conditions of the laser radiation used in these experiments, over the reaction/photodissociation pathways. One can only get a marginal control over the product yield by thermodynamic alterations (by changing temperature, pressure, etc. to bias the equilibrium in a favourable direction). In the late eighties two theorists M. Shapiro and P. Brumer came up with a brilliant idea (of course, in principle, barring computer experiments) of coherent radiative control of unimolecular reactions [88-101]. Their method will be discussed in the following section and the reader may try to do the experiment in order to test their theory!

Consider photodissociation of a molecule A in the initial state $| m \rangle$, where m denotes the bound state quantum numbers. The energy of the state is E_m. The system is such that at an incident photon energy $\hbar w$ a few chemically distinct product channels are accessible. We distinguish these arrangement channels by a numerical label q (q = 1, 2, etc.). In the time independent picture the molecule is excited from an initial stationary state of energy E_m to a total energy E. The resultant wavefunction has components in each arrangement channel whose magnitude determines the extent of product formation in that channel. The product yield as well as internal distribution is dictated by two factors: the nature of the excitation and the nature of the wavefunction at energy E. A wavefunction at this total energy E is written as a linear superposition of degenerate eigenstates, i.e.,

$$| \psi(t) \rangle = \exp(-iEt/\hbar) \sum_{n,q} c_{q,n} | E, n, q^- \rangle \qquad (9)$$

which has a plane wave component in the asymptotic limit in channel q given as

$$| \psi(t) \rangle \underset{\substack{R_q \to \infty}}{\longrightarrow} \exp(-iEt/\hbar) \sum_{n,q} c_{q,n} | E, n, q^0 \rangle \qquad (10)$$

where $| E, n, q^- \rangle$ displays the incoming spherical waves and $| E, n, q^0 \rangle$ an outgoing plane wave component at large R_q. n represents the internal quantum numbers (vibrational, rotational, translational, etc.) of the fragments as well as the scattering angles. In this description it is clear that the system is degenerate at energy E and actually it is infinitely degenerate since n includes all possible scattering angles. The time dependence appears in terms of an overall phase factor. By virtue of equation (10), $|c_{q,n}|^2$ provides the probability of forming the product in final state $| E, n, q^0 \rangle$. Therefore, external control of the resultant product distribution may be achieved by experimental manipulation of these coefficients in the created continuum state. In the weak field limit photodissociation theory for one photon absorption from $| m \rangle$ to $| E, n, q^- \rangle$ gives [102–105]

$$| c_{q,n} |^2 = (\pi/\hbar)^2 | E(w) \langle E, n, q^- | \hat{\mu}_e | m \rangle |^2 \qquad (11)$$

where $\hat{\mu}_e$ is the component of the dipole moment operator along the electric field vector $\mathbf{E}(w)$. The probability of forming the product in $| E, n, q^0 \rangle$ is defined by

$$P(n,q) = \frac{| c_{n,q} |^2}{\sum_{n,q} | c_{n,q} |^2}$$

According to this, the only way to manoeuvre the control over the product formation in traditional photodissociation is by varying the excitation energy and allowing nature to dictate its terms regarding the future of the photo-

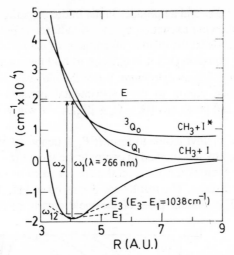

Fig. 4 Cuts through the potential energy surfaces for first few states of CH_3I. Also shown are the location of the two bound states $|E_1\rangle$ and $|E_3\rangle$ and the particular excitation energy $E = \hbar w_1 = 37593.9$ cm^{-1}. Adapted from P. Brumer and M. Shapiro, Chem. Phys. Letts., **126**, 541 (1986) with permission.

dissociation. At this juncture Brumer and Shapiro suggested the idea of phase coherent control of directly influencing the prepared wavefunction in the upper (continuum) state.

In their initial proposal on coherent control, there are two steps involved. First the system is prepared in a superposition of bound states (at least two) $|k\rangle$. Second, this superposition is concurrently excited with a set of frequencies $w_{Ek} = (E - E_k)/\hbar$. Thus E is accessed through several different routes each of which maintains system phases. Consequently the system is prepared with coefficients $c_{q,n}$ which are experimentally controllable (by controlling the phases and amplitudes). This may be illustrated with the example of CH_3I as shown by the authors [90, 91]. In Fig. 4 cuts through the potential energy surfaces for the ground and first two excited state surfaces are shown. Two product channels are accessible at energy E. Initially superposition of two states denoted by E_1 and E_2 may be created by excitation via a parity preserving transition (e.g., $J = 2$) at frequency $w_{12} = w_1 - w_2$ to excite the molecules from the ground level E_1 to the excited level E_2. Subsequently the sample is irradiated with two coherent beams at w_1 and w_2. The ratio of the product yields in the two channels (for this particular problem), after using the weak field photodissociation, adopting first order perturbation theory and rotating wave approximation may be written as [90, 91]

$$R(1:2, E) = \frac{P(q_1, E)}{P(q_2, E)} = \frac{|\mu_{1,1}^{(1)}|^2 + x^2 |\mu_{2,2}^{(1)}|^2 + 2\alpha^1}{|\mu_{1,1}^{(1)}|^2 + x^2 |\mu_{2,2}^{(2)}|^2 + 2\alpha^2} \tag{12}$$

where $\alpha^i = x \cos(\Theta_1 - \Theta_2 + \beta_{1,2}^i) |\mu_{1,2}^i|$, $i = 1, 2$.

The external control parameters are now Θ_i and x which may be altered by either changing phases and amplitudes in the initial preparation of superposition state or in the following excitation by two simultaneous pulses. The degree of yield control depends on the relative magnitudes of the $i = j$ | μ_{ij} (q) | as well as $i \neq j$ terms. From equation (12) it is difficult to find the conditions at which the yield say in channel 2 is an extremum. But if the molecule is such that | $\mu_{1,2}^{(1)}$ |^2 = | $\mu_{1,1}^{(1)}$ | | $\mu_{2,2}^{(1)}$ | then tuning to the experimental parameter amplitude ratio $x =$ | $\mu_{1,2}^{(1)}$ |/| $\mu_{2,2}^{(1)}$ | and phase $\cos(\Theta_1 - \Theta_2 + \beta_{1,2}^{(1)}) = -1$ will yield all the products in channel 2.

Dissociation of methyl iodide to form $I(^2P_{3/2})$, denoted I and $I(^2P_{1/2})$, denoted I^* has been studied by this method to compute the yield $I/(I + I^*)$, at 37594 cm^{-1} ($\lambda = 266$ nm) for excitation from several different pairwise combinations of the four lowest bound states. The results are displayed in Fig. 5. The channel I is labelled $q = 2$. The contour plots of the yield clearly demonstrate the broad

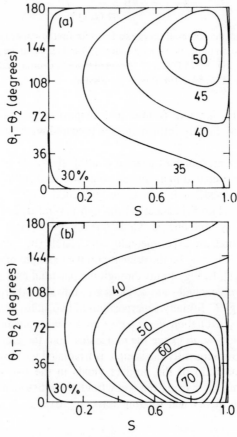

Fig. 5   Contour plot of the yield of I (% ground state iodine as product) in the photodissociation of CH$_3$I from linear superposition of (a) | E_1⟩ and | E_2⟩, (b) | E_1⟩ and | E_3⟩). The abscissa is labelled by relative amplitude parameter S and the ordinate by the relative phase parameter $\Theta_1 - \Theta_2$. Adapted from P. Brumer and M. Shapiro, Chem. Phys. Letts., **126**, 543 (1986) with permission.

range of control obtainable over the I/I^* ratio. In Fig. 5(b) corresponding to excitation from a superposition of $|E_1\rangle$ and $|E_3\rangle$ allows an increase in the yield of I from 30 to 70%. Less dramatic effects are also observed for some excitations. In general there is a strong wavelength dependence of the radiation control and consequently different control parameters are needed to obtain maximum yield at different frequencies.

Having accepted this suggestion (at least in principle) of coherent control of channels (yields) in a photodissociation experimental verification is still lacking possibly because of the difficulty in preparing three, phase matched excitation frequencies with well defined relative phases. But the authors have since suggested simplified ideas of attaining the same goal with less experimental complexities. One suggestion is to irradiate a bound state simultaneously with two frequencies, ω_1 and $\omega_2 = 3\omega_1$ to gain a control over the product yield [93]. The idea here is essentially the same as discussed above. But in principle, one reduces the complexity of the possible experimental verification tremendously. One needs only a single mode, pulsed or cw (they are essentially equivalent insofar as the average yield to the various product channels is concerned [88]) laser with a third harmonic generation (THG) crystal and cross this laser with a supersonic molecular beam. By varying the intensity of the laser the relative amplitudes of ω_1 and ω_2 can be altered. The relative phases is altered by varying thickness of a dispersive medium. However, the experiment is yet to be reported but is currently in the building stage (R. Gordon, Private Comm.).

Another suggestion is to gain active control over differential cross sections with a single laser frequency of variable elliptic polarization [92]. This approach has been applied to a model diatomic $^1\Sigma - {}^1\pi$ and $^1\Sigma - {}^1\Sigma$ photodissociation. For M selected initial states, where M is the angular momentum projection quantum number for the bound state, complete control can be achieved at a given angle, that is, a particular product channel can be totally done away with.

While experimental verification is awaited through any of the routes suggested above, a few very important points regarding control of products in unimolecular dissociations emerge from the Brumer-Shapiro formulation [94-97].

(1) The products (channels) in a unimolecular dissociation are intimately connected to how the initial state is prepared at total energy E and the dynamics is completely predetermined by this preparation. What remains to be seen is how nature takes its own course in time. This corrects some of the common misunderstanding in controlling the yields of a unimolecular reaction by a fast and shaped laser pulse and thus breaking a particular bond to guarantee a particular set of products. So long as one is exciting from a stationary state with a fixed excitation energy ($\hbar\omega$), the picture of photodissociation is time independent and no dynamics takes place in the excited state. Therefore, the nature of the excitation which prepares the system at energy E and the nature of the wavefunctions at this energy determine the product channels.

(2) Control over the channels is control over the coefficients $c_{q,n}$. Thus to force a particular product channel q', the aim is to prepare a state with $c_{q,n} = 0$ for all $q \neq q'$.

(3) Mode selective control of unimolecular reactions is certainly possible but

the same result may be obtained either with a fast shaped laser pulse or with an incoherent source operating over cw time scales. For one photon absorption the time dependence imparted by the preparation is immaterial and the idea that rapid excitation is necessary is misleading. The Brumer-Shapiro formulation clearly points out, for one photon absorption, that mode selective excitation or excitation in a strong laser field does not necessarily guarantee mode selective dissociation or reaction products and even if it is found to occur it must be more accidental than general in nature. Finally, the introduction of the coherence phenomenon in modifying the product yield in unimolecular reactions (photodissociations) and related chemical processes promises a terrific potential for application in atomic and molecular processes. This future coherence chemistry (as it is called by its inventors) opens up a vast field in atomic and molecular science where classical mechanics will no longer be adequate to describe the dynamics of the system. This will automatically force a semiclassical or a quantum mechanical description of reaction dynamics.

4. EMISSION FROM MOLECULES IN THE PROCESS OF DISSOCIATION

Photodissociation dynamics was studied in the conventional way, i.e. "after the event assessment of resulting products" for sometime until the late seventies when chemical physicists working in the field started asking questions, "what are the chances of success in probing the transition states between excitation and product formation in the photodissociation process, directly by looking at the emission from these states?" These transition states are continuously evolving intermediate states or nuclear configurations of the specie that is neither reactant nor product but the former in the process of turning into the latter. To distinguish from Eyring's conceptual "transition state", some researchers working in the field prefer to call these "transitory states". Regardless of what the nomenclature be, it does not require great insight to appreciate that we shall learn more about the process if we can directly probe those intermediate configurations during the transformation. In the conventional 'pump' and 'probe' technique only the asymptotic states of the dissociating molecule are probed and the information obtained is usually combined with theory to reconstruct what takes place during the event. This technique has no doubt proven its worth in understanding photodissociation dynamics at a microscopic level but it is still possible to get finer details about these processes by direct measurements. In the context of dissociation it reduces to detecting emission from the specie as it rolls on the upper state towards its exit. Because of the time scale involved in these processes, the technique is spectroscopic in nature. This is, therefore, also known as "transition state spectroscopy" (TSS). The concept of TSS in chemical reactions, photon assisted association reactions has also been implemented and the reader is directed to Chapter 2 of this book to read more about it.

Probing the transition states in the process of dissociation may be looked at in two different ways. Let us consider a simple process of direct dissociation with two states as shown in Fig. 6. In reality such examples are commonplace. Suppose a molecule is excited to the upper state by a photon of frequency ω_1.

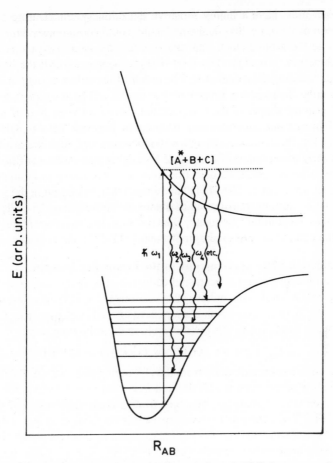

Fig. 6 Schematic representation of dissociation of ABC from a repulsive
excited state at an excitation energy $\hbar\omega_1$. The emission will be over a
range of frequencies ω_2, ω_3..., etc.

This process of absorption takes $\cong 10^{-15}$ sec. Once the molecule is prepared on
the upper state the atoms will repel each other and products will begin to separate.
This will happen because we have chosen the upper state as a repulsive state.
The fragments will then dissociate in the sense that they are no longer under the
influence of each other. A typical speed attained during dissociation might be
$\cong 10^5$ cm/sec and if the bond is extended beyond 3 Å, it is considered broken.
Thus the time of direct photodissociation is 300 fs. During this time the molecule
is travelling on the upper surface going through various transition states. In
order to probe these states in real time one would need light pulses shorter than
the time required for dissociation. This type of experiment in the "time domain"
has indeed been performed [106-108] and I shall discuss them in detail later.

Another way of looking at the transition state configurations is by monitoring
the dispersed emission from the transition state configurations into the ground
state. In this type of experiments one would not need a femtosecond light pulse.

Instead one must have a highly sensitive detection system. During the entire dissociation process, i.e. 300 fs, the molecule would continuously emit radiation and relax to the ground state. The radiative lifetime of a molecule is typically 10^{-8} s. Therefore, it is clear (based on lifetime arguments) that the intensity of the emission during dissociation will be at least four orders of magnitude lower than molecular fluorescence. Emission from the TS will be at various wavelengths depending on the shapes of the two potential energy surfaces. Now if we divide this total broadband emission into 1000 equal intervals (this is achieved by dispersing the fluorescence through a monochromator), then we are left with approximately seven orders of magnitude less signal than molecular fluorescence. Therefore, a highly sensitive detection system is necessary to monitor such a weak signal. Heller et al [109-111] have shown that this signal in the frequency domain can be Fourier transformed to obtain the desired time dependence. This type of experiment in the "frequency domain" has also been carried out success-fully in the context of dissociating molecules [112-120] and is discussed below.

4.1 Transition State Spectroscopy in the Frequency Domain

The first molecule which has been studied by monitoring the dispersed emission following excitation into a repulsive state is ozone [113, 117]. The first transition in O_3 is to the Hartley band which is a repulsive excited electronic state. Excitation of O_3 in these bands fragments the molecule in the following way:

$$O_3 + \hbar w \rightarrow [O_3]^* \rightarrow O_2^* \, (^1\Delta_g) + O^* \, (^1D) \qquad (13)$$

Weak emission has been detected from the O_3^* during dissociation. This emission is due to a transition from a well defined free state to the ground bound state. This is essentially Raman spectroscopy from a continuum resonant state. As shown in Fig. 7, at time $t = 0$ the wavepacket is transferred to the excited state (this is achieved with the help of a laser and should be done preferably with a cw laser at the appropriate wavelength). Once the system finds itself in a nonequilibrium situation, it feels forces and evolves on the excited surface as indicated by t_1, t_2, etc. The time behaviour is determined by the shape of the potential and the position of the wave packet initially. Typically short time evolution is dominated by forces $\delta V/\delta q$. Spreading of the wave packet is governed by the stiffness of the potential and thus depends on the second derivative $\delta^2 V/\delta^2 q$ and usually develops somewhat slowly. The propagation of the wave packet at long time ($t = \infty$) results in the formation of photolysis products. At short time the light emitted from the transition state is detected. This is the infomation that we really want. Two general spectral regions can be distinguished for photoemission (shown by dark and shaded areas in Fig. 7). If one of the products happens to be an atom and is capable of fast emission, wing emission will be observed (see part a of Fig. 7) to the red and or to the blue of the atomic emission line. Wing emission to the Na-D line has been reported by H. J. Foth et al [112] following uv photodissociation of NaI. This is due to emission of the excited specie (in this example Na atom) while it is still under the influence of the other fragment. If we consider that the nuclei move slowly compared to the electrons during an electronic transition, we can consider the transition vertically down and whether the emission will be blue shifted or red shifted depends on

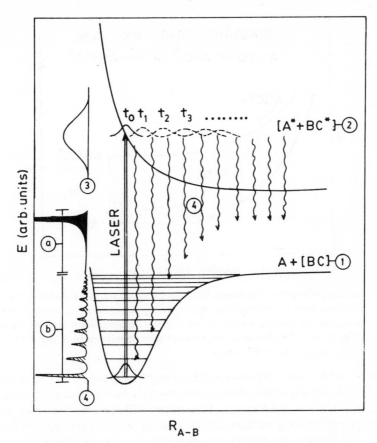

Fig. 7 A photodissociation experiment. The laser transfers the ground state wave function
to the excited state where it evolves (dashed wave packets $t_1, t_2,...$, etc.) into A* + BC.
Indicated in the figure by numbers are accessible experimental probes: (1) equilibrium
geometry and spectroscopic constants of the final BC product, (2) internal state,
angular, and translational energy distributions of the final products, (3) absorption
spectrum, (4) emission spectrum, (a) wing emission, (b) discrete emission.
Reproduced with permission from D. Imre et al., J. Phys. Chem, **88**, 3956 (1984).

the two potential energy surfaces in the vicinity of the atomic transition (shown
in Fig. 8). This is emission to the ground state continuum. This continuum is
likely to be predissociative and therefore, the broad spectrum obtained from the
wing emission may not be instructive in terms of extracting the shape of the
ground state potential energy surface at the asymptotic limits. The same spectrum
will show transitions (part b of Fig. 7) into the bound part of the same ground
state surface. The intensities for these free-bound transitions is proportional to
the square of the Franck-Condon overlap between the time-evolved wave packet
at time t and the initial wave packet. At $t = 0$ the wave packet is the initial
vibrational wave function and it has no overlap with other vibrational states. As
it starts propagating on the excited surface it develops overlaps with higher
vibrational states, especially those with significant amplitude along the direction

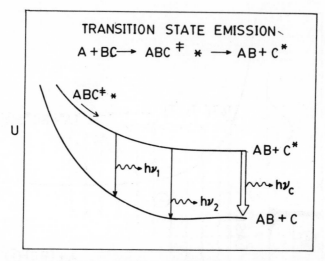

Fig. 8   Schematic diagram of emission from the transitory state in a chemical reaction. Emission from the intermediate ABC* during separation to products results in 'wings' on the atomic transition; $h\nu_1$ exemplifies a transition in the red wing, and $h\nu_2$ a transition in the blue wing. Reproduced with permission from H.J. Foth et al., J. Phys. Chem., **86**, 5027 (1982).

of motion. For a given vibrational progression the temporal development of the overlaps will follow a simple order, starting with the lowest level and continuing in a sequence of increasing energy. This spectra will contain information about both the potential energy surfaces. The frequencies and line contours of emission features will map the ground state potential. Because of large geometric changes during bond scission one can see signals due to emission into the extremely high vibrational levels of the ground state vibrational states which are otherwise difficult to access spectroscopically. Analysis of relative intensities of the various fundamentals, overtones and combinations and their dependence on the excitation wavelength reflect the dynamics of the initial wave packet as it spreads on the upper surface.

A typical experimental set-up is shown in Fig. 9. A stainless steel chamber is equipped with a molecular beam (which can be an effusive source) which is traversed perpendicularly with a laser beam a few mm downstream from the orifice. The emitted light is collected with a lens perpendicular to the molecular beam axis at the entrance slit of a monochromator. The light is dispersed and unwanted radiation is filtered out before focusing onto a photomultiplier tube. The signal from the PMT is fed into a boxcar signal averager the output of which is displayed on a stripchart recorder. I shall now discuss results obtained by frequency domain TSS experiments on some selected molecules below.

CH_3I
This is by far the only molecule for which a substantial amount of information has been obtained by probing the TS in the frequency domain. Imre et al [114]

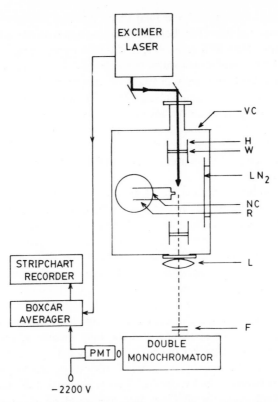

Fig. 9 Schematic of the TSS apparatus. The components shown here: VC, vacuum chamber; H, heater; W, windows; LN_2, liquid nitrogen cooled trap; NC, oven nozzle chamber; R, oven reservoir; L, lens; F, optical filters. The laser beam and the optical axis are coincident in the diagram for convenience. Reproduced from R. D. Bower et al., *J. Chem. Phys.*, **89**, 4478 (1988).

have looked into the emission spectroscopy of this molecule during dissociation at 514, 355, and 266 nm. CH_3I has a broad structureless absorption in the uv-vis region [123]. The emission spectrum at 514 nm excitation does not contain overtones. At 355 nm, two overtones are barely seen. But the emission spectrum is quite rich at 266 nm excitation. The spectrum has a long progression in the C–I stretch (q_3). Up to 29 quanta are observed, corresponding to a ground state vibrational energy equal to about 75% of the dissociation energy. Some activity in the umbrella mode (q_2) and in the C-H stretch mode is also observed. From the marked change in the spectrum with excitation wavelength it is obvious that the time resolution of the experiment can be altered by frequency tuning. To illustrate let us look at the emission amplitude which is nothing but the amplitude ξ_{if} for the Raman process that carries the molecule from the initial state i to the final state f (the ground electronic state for this molecule). That is

$$\xi_{if} = \exp(-it\Delta w) \langle \phi_f \mid \phi_0(t) \rangle \, dt \qquad (14)$$

where $\Delta w = w_i - w_f = E_i - E_f$ which is the amount of detuning and $\langle \phi_f \mid \phi_0 \rangle$ the overlap integral for the initial and final states. At $t = 0$ the wave packet is still the initial vibrational wave function. It has no overlap with any other vibrational state at that time. Now as it starts to spread on the upper surface it will develop overlap with higher vibrational states of the ground state. Any difference in the configuration of the two states will lead to an additional feature in the emission spectrum. In other words a small change in the bond length is transcribed into a change of frequency of emission. Moving off-resonance one samples dynamics on a short time scale. The time scale decreases with increasing w. In the limit of very large detuning only short time dynamics will dominate the intensity pattern. To the contrary long time dynamics can be probed by tuning the excitation wave length at resonance.

For methyl iodide excitation at 514 nm ($\Delta w = 18,500$ cm^{-1}) no overtones are observed as expected. At 355 nm ($\Delta w = 10,000$ cm^{-1}) the extent of detuning is still high and the spectrum is not very different from the previous one. A new band with two quanta in the C-I stretch is visible. This points out that within about a few femtoseconds following excitation, the wave packet has spread enough to have some overlap with $v'' = 2$. This indirectly implies that the initial motion of the wave packet is along the C-I stretch. As the excitation is brought closer to the resonance, e.g. 266 nm ($\Delta w = 1,000$ cm^{-1}) the spectrum is dominated by a long progression in the C-I stretch (q_3). Some activities in the other modes are also apparent in the spectrum. But the long intense v_3 progression is a fingerprint of the wave packet dynamics on a resonantly excited surface. The first few features are purely v_3 overtones. Further along the progression combination bands between v_3 and v_2 appear. This indicates that the initial motion is along v_3 and subsequently develops into motion along v_2. A qualitative 2D potential energy contour map was developed keeping the experimental observations in mind and typical trajectories were run to get a dynamical picture of the dissociation process.

O_3

Emission studies on photodissociating ozone molecules at 266 nm were also studied by Imre et al [113, 117]. The excitation at 266 nm is in fact at the centre of the absorption band which means that dynamics on the long time scale are probed. The three vibrations in ozone are symmetric stretch (q_1), asymmetric stretch (q_3) and bending mode (q_2). The emission spectrum is dominated by v_1 progressions. Bands up to 500 cm^{-1} below the dissociation limit have been observed. Even numbered levels in v_3, as well as combination bands of v_1 with even quanta of v_3 are also found with appreciable intensities. The analysis of the emission spectrum leads to the conclusion that the vibrational wave packet from the ground state is initially significantly displaced from the excited state minimum along the q_1 coordinate. The forces acting in this direction cause the wave packet to accelerate rapidly along q_1. At the same time the wave packet spreads along q_3. The spreading motion maintains symmetry about the C_{2v} axis, causing the overlap with states with odd vibrational quanta (which are asymmetric) to vanish. Therefore, only the even quanta in v_3 are found. There are other features in the spectrum that have not been assigned yet due to the lack of knowledge of the other excited surfaces at this energy. But several new vibrational energy levels of the ground state have been assigned tentatively. In spite of difficulties in understanding the entire emission spectrum, some useful information about potential energy surfaces and dynamics of dissociation of ozone have been obtained. Any theoretical model to treat such short time dynamics and geometry changes should have large amplitudes at least along the dissociative coordinate [117]. However, more involved calculations are needed in order to understand the ozone emission spectrum fully.

NO_2

Transition states in the process of dissociation of NO_2 in the uv have been probed by the same technique by Rohlfing et al [115]. NO_2 is known to predissociate from its $^2B_2$ state at 398 nm. Resonance Raman spectra have been recorded as a function of excitation frequency in the range 0–8,000 cm^{-1} above the predissoci-ation threshold. Each spectrum shows extensive activity in both the symmetric stretch mode (q_1) and the bending mode (q_2), and overtone and combination bands containing up to five quanta of v_1 and six quanta of v_2 are observed. Another striking feature that is observed in the spectrum is a dramatic change in the intensities of the bend to stretch fundamentals in the detuning range 50–2250 cm^{-1}. This indirectly leads to the speculation that the predissociative state lives longer than a few vibrational periods before dissociating, thereby allowing the wave packet to return to the Franck-Condon region. The experimental findings are in good agreement with the ab initio potential energy surface for $^2B_2$. The upper limits of the real or imaginary frequency of the antisymmetric stretch vibration (that is not seen in the spectra) in the $^2B_2$ state have been calculated from the observed data. These limits are $w_{13} = 2720$ cm^{-1} and $w_{13} = i1470$ cm^{-1}. The imaginary frequency implies a C_s geometry of the $^2B_2$ state with unequal N—O bond lengths.

H_2S

The emission from dissociating H_2S molecules at 193 nm (which is about the maximum of the absorption band of this molecule) was reported by Kleinermanns et al [116]. Emission was detected in the region 193–320 nm. While stretch and combination of stretch and bend progression have been detected, no sole bend vibration in the region is observed. Following excitation the activity starts in the stretching mode and the dissociation proceeds. At long S—H distances the initial geometry (with HSH angle 92°) starts opening up and the combination bands of bend and stretch modes appear. This is rather similar to the dissociation of H_2O at 157 nm.

Further experiments are necessary in order to find out the upper surface(s) at this wavelength, the timescale of dissociation and detailed dynamics on the excited potential energy surface(s).

4.2 Real Time Viewing of the Transition States

As I have mentioned earlier, the transition state configurations of molecules in the process of falling apart can be probed in real time. These experiments by

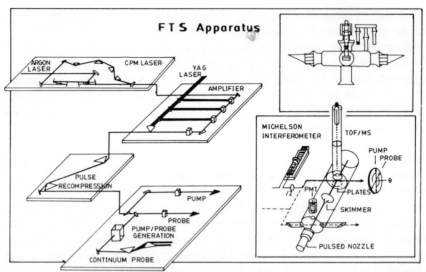

Fig. 10 Overall schematic of the femtosecond transition state spectroscopy (FTS) apparatus. The ultrafast pulses are generated in the cavity dumped mode locked (CPM) laser and are amplified in the pulsed dye amplifier. Group velocity dispersion is corrected by two prism pairs (only one pair is shown in the diagram). The pump and probe pulses are prepared through a variety of frequency conversion schemes, and are directed into the sample chamber. The chamber is either a gas cell (upper right) or a molecular beam (lower right). Reproduced from M.J. Rosker et al., J. Chem. Phys., **89**, 6113 (1988) with permission.

very nature of the short longevity of the transition states demands femtosecond lasers and have been pioneered by Prof. Zewail and his group at Cal Tech. [106-108,124-133]. Because of the stringent laser requirements these experiments are only a few years' old.

The experimental set up is shown in Fig. 10. The pump laser normally a femtosecond laser excites the molecule to an upper state which may or may not be a repulsive state. The probe laser, again another femtosecond laser, delayed from the pump laser by a variable but preset time detects a photofragment product as it is being formed. The probe laser is tuned to a wavelength corresponding to a known excitation resonance of the intercepted product. The excitation allows detection of the product (either by laser induced fluorescence or by multiphoton ionization). Then the delay between the two lasers is altered gradually while sitting at the same excitation wavelength. The entire curve of recovery (or decay depending on the time delay between the two lasers and the frequency of the probe light) is recorded. There is an induction period corresponding to the time required for complete separation of the products and generation of their identities asymptotically in their final internal states. Then the probe laser wavelength is altered by a small amount and the entire experiment described above is repeated. In a sense this is a two dimensional experiment where the probe laser frequency and time delay between the two lasers are the two variables. One normally keeps one fixed and varies the other and vice versa.

In order to change the available energy of the products one may also change the pump laser frequency and repeat the entire set of experiments. The resulting data in principle contain information from which the potential energy surface(s) involved in the dissociation can be deduced. Now I shall discuss a few examples for which the above experiment has been carried out and some intricate parts of the dissociation dynamics have been learned.

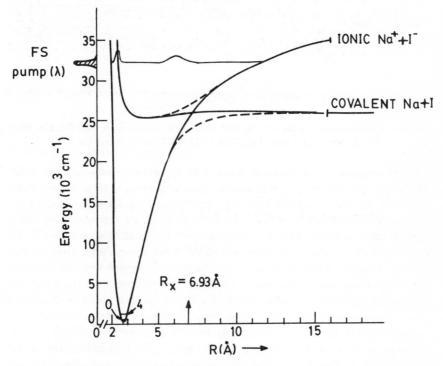

Fig. 11 Potential energy cuves of NaI involved in the FTS experiment are shown. The Na + I product states correlate with the states ($\Omega = 0^+$ and 1) of NaI and are displayed with the covalent curve. The fs pump pulse in the experiment was at 310 nm and the probe was generated from a continuum ($\lambda = 560$ nm to $\lambda = 630$ nm). Reproduced with modification from T.S. Rose et al., J. Chem. Phys., **88**, 6672 (1988) with permission.

NaI

NaI and NaBr have been studied by femtosecond real time pump and probe experiments recently [127-129]. A 50 fs pulse at 310 nm excites NaI to its first excited covalent state(s) from where it dissociates by crossing over to the ground ionic state as shown in Fig. 11. A typical spectra (in Fig. 12) when the probe laser pulse is tuned to the transition state region is observed. The number of photons detected by the LIF method shows a damped oscillatory behaviour. The frequency of these oscillations and the damping time have been related to the classical motion in the upper state well and to the Landau-Zener probability of escaping out of the well. The bound state involved in the process arises from the

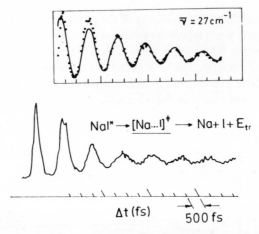

Fig. 12 Experimental results for the NaI FTS. Reproduced with modification from T.S. Rose et al., J. Chem. Phys., **88**, 6672 (1988) with permission.

avoided crossing of the covalent states with the ionic ground state. In other words these oscillations are due to a bound-bound transition. Quantum calculations [127,135] on model systems have been performed in order to understand the dynamics of dissociation of NaI. The main features are reproduced by these calculations reasonably well. Calculations show that actual pulse shapes of the probe laser do not change the outcome of the dissociation. Particularly for this system a Raman experiment described in the previous section was attempted but the interpretation was complicated [119]. But for a femtosecond pump and probe experiment this was a suitable sample for the experiment could be done at a lower temperature (600°C) and the structure be seen at this concentration and concentration of the dimer is extremely low. The measurements made by this technique seem insensitive to temperature change. The dissociation rate is not high enough to destroy the structure through broadening and, therefore, the structure observed by this technique can be used to study the properties of the upper state. The results obtained for NaBr are very similar to that of NaI. In fact these diatomics are suitable for such studies because the upper states avoid crossing the ionic ground state thereby allowing those highly informative oscillations to take place. In other molecules it is observed that the transition state is extremely shortlived (direct dissociation from a repulsive upper state), the results are less informative and more difficult to interpret.

ICN

This molecule has continued to get attention from the dynamicists for a long time. Recently this molecule has been dissociated with a 60 fs pulse at 306 nm [124,125,130]. The resulting transition state is probed around 388.5 nm (band head position for the free CN absorption). The clocking of the pump and probe pulses shows that the time taken for dissociation (when both the products are out of the influence of each other) is 205 ± 30 fs and the transition state lasts for only ~ 50 fs. A simple classical model for the dissociation of this molecule from the repulsive upper state has been developed [126]. This classical model explains some of the interesting features of the dissociating state. But the experiment was done with a pump laser operating at 306 nm which leaves an available energy of 7000 cm^{-1} into the translational mode of the products. This recoil energy takes the molecule away through the transition state very quickly and therefore, one only finds the long range behaviour of the upper potential surface. In order to probe the short range part of the potential, one must choose the energy of the dissociation laser such that the products do not have much energy to zap through the transition state even for a case like this which is directly dissociating.

I$_2$

This is yet another diatomic molecule which has been very interesting to dynamicists as well as spectroscopists of this century. The excited state potential energy surface of this molecule has been revisited several times and recently Zewail and his coworkers [131] have looked into the transition state spectroscopy of this molecule. In this experiment I$_2$ molecule is prepared in the B state which is bound. Subsequently the motion of the molecule in this state is probed by a second pulse and the oscillations in this state is imprinted in the spectrum. The vibrational period corresponds to 273 fs at the excitation wavelength of 620 nm. Keeping the probe wavelength fixed and varying the pump wavelength within the B state, i.e., starting at different points in the vibrational manifold they have observed different periods for the wave packet evolution. Choosing the pump wave length properly the experimenters have also probed the dynamics in the repulsive regions above and below the B state. At a shorter excitation wavelength less structured oscillating behaviour of the wave packet is observed than at a longer wavelength where more oscillations are visible. This is somewhat expected as one goes away from resonance one is likely to probe the short time dynamics of the system and as a result one would expect to see less structure in the spectrum. Though in principle it should be possible to 'invert' these oscillations into the potential energy surfaces of the upper state(s), in practice more theortical understanding and modelling are necessary to achieve this goal.

What is apparent from the above discussion is that in the last five years TSS experiments whether performed in the time domain or in the frequency domain have definitely made a headway. But what is lacking currently is a good theoretical understanding of these processes in order to make excellent use of the experimental data available for some simple molecules. For example diatomic molecules like NaI [119] and KI [120] give rise to resonance Raman spectra while excited at 222 nm which may seem like a free-bound spectra. Only after careful studies it is established that the spectra originated from a bound-bound transition. Though, in principle, it is possible to extract the RKR potentials from the experimental results, in practice it is far from straightforward [136]. For example, the variation of transition dipole moment as a function of internuclear distance is not known in many cases and the functional form of this variation is unknown. What one normally does to overcome this problem is that the transition dipole is assumed to be constant for the calculation purpose. This may not always be a reasonable assumption. Also detailed analysis of an emission spectrum has not been possible though partial analysis has been successful [117, 127, 133, 135]. Lately there are some theoretical attempts [121, 122, 137] to overcome some of the existing difficulties. In a sense the future of extracting more detailed information from these experiments lies in our ability to develop competent theoretical formulations to treat the data. Only then we will gain more insight into the photodissociation dynamics of simple molecules studied by the method of TSS than the usual 'pump' and 'probe' technique.

5. DISSOCIATION OF ADSORBED SPECIES

Laser induced processes on surfaces have gained attention in recent years mainly for the possibility of observing catalyzed reactions of shortlived radicals on metal, semiconductor, and insulator surfaces. Chuang et al [138-140] have observed that molecular species desorb from metal surfaces with a Boltzmann distribution over translational energy at a desorption temperature $T_d < T_s$. They have also pointed out that infrared absorption by molecules adsorbed on the surface channels enough energy to the surface to induce desorption of adsorbates. In this case the dynamics resembles that of thermal desorption. The desorption yield is also dependent on the polarization of the infrared laser when excitation is at resonance with the vibrational frequency of the adsorbate but is independent of the polarization at off-reasonant excitation [138]. Nishi et al [141] have examined the dynamics of photodissociation and photodetachment from ices of NH_3 and H_2O in one and two photon processes. The product molecules which were either NH_3 or H_2O were detected by a mass spectrometer. The "electronic exchange repulsion between an excited molecule and a ground state molecule" was proposed as the mechanism for dissociation. Detachment of ions at higher laser fluences were also observed by them. Multiphoton dissociation of adsorbed molecules on rough metal surfaces have been reported by G.M. Goncher et al [142,143] in the literature. Through photodissociation of a series of organic molecules in the uv they were able to produce graphitic carbon on the roughened silver surface. They were mainly concerned with the photochemistry of those molecules in the presence of a surface. The first truely dynamical study of photodissociation of an adsorbate from a sub monolayer phase has been claimed by E. B. D. Bourdon et al [144] in 1984. In this pioneering experiment CH_3Br was adsorbed on a clean single crystal of LiF (001) surface maintained under ultrahigh vacuum conditions (base pressure ~10^{-11} Torr). An unpolarized uv laser at 222 nm was incident on the surface of the crystal at a glancing angle. The combination of the CH_3Br pressure inside the chamber, the time interval between two consecutive laser pulses (0.1 s) and the temperatue of the crystal (typically 115 K) was such that the coverage on the surface was approximately 0.01 Langmuir under the experimental conditions. CH_3Br absorbs strongly at 222 nm and in the gas phase it is known to undergo rupture of the C—Br bond in the following manner

$$CH_3Br \rightarrow CH_3 + Br \ (^2P_J) \tag{15}$$

where $J = 1/2, 3/2$. In the surface photodissociation experiment CH_3 fragments were detected inside a quadrupole mass spectrometer at a distance of 15.8 cm from the crystal [149]. A typical time-of-flight spectrum is shown in Fig. 13.

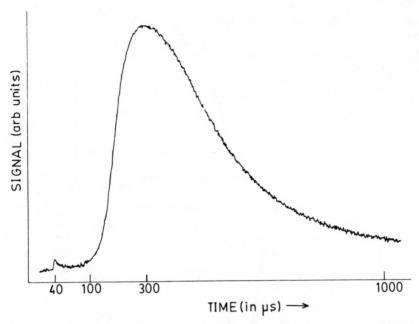

Fig. 13 A typical time-of-flight spectrum of CH_3 radicals resulting from the 222 nm irradiation of adsorbed CH_3Br. The flight path is ca. 23.6 cm.

The first hump in the spectrum results from the dissociation of adsorbed CH_3Br at 222 nm. The second and much bigger hump is a consequence of photon induced surface heating and subsequent desorption of molecules. The second process fortunately happens in a longer time scale and thus can be separated from the first event, i.e. photodissociation. Photodesorption (which is the second process) is beyond the scope of this article and I shall eschew a discussion on this. The first hump is magnified and displayed in Fig. 14. The signal maximum corresponds to 1.7 eV of translational energy which turns out to be 65% of the total available energy. Fig. 15 compares the results of surface photodissociation with that observed in the gas phase. Though the two channels producing Br in the $^2P_{1/2}$ and $^2P_{3/2}$ states are not resolved in the gas-surface experiment, comparison with the gas phase results of van Veen et al [146] points out that bromine atoms are produced in higher yield in the excited spin orbit state ($^2P_{1/2}$) on the surface. Since then a few photodissociations on the surface (i.e., LiF (100)) have been studied by J.C. Polanyi et al [147-156] and others [157-160]. At this point one would like to ask the following pertinent questions with regard to surface photodissociation of adsorbed molecules:

(1) Is the photodissociation really nonthermal?
(2) Are the molecules in the adsorbed state when the bond rupture is taking place?
(3) Is the adsorption leading to preferred geometries and at preferred sites?
(4) Is the dissociation taking place at a submonolayer coverage and not from an 'ice' (multilayer) state?

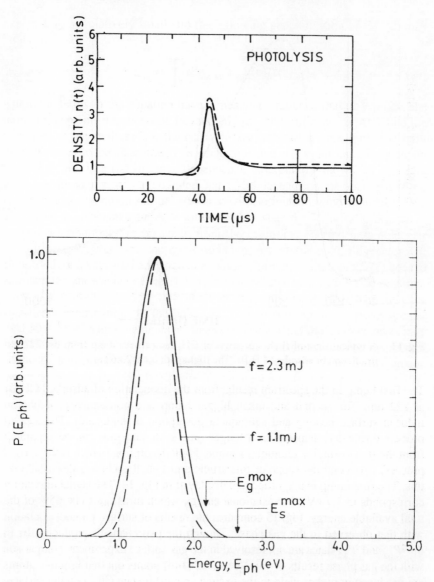

Fig. 14   (a) Time-of-flight spectrum of CH_3 photofragments at high and low laser powers. E_g^{max} gives the time-of-flight of molecules having the maximum allowable energy in the gas, and E_s^{max} the same for the surface. (b) The energy distribution of CH_3 photofragments normalized to a common peak height, showing invariance of $P(E_{ph})$ with laser power. Adapted with permission from E. B. D. Bourdon et al, J. Phys. Chem., **88**, 6100 (1984).

The answer to the first question is simple. It is evident from Fig. 13 that a large amount of energy is released in a nonBoltzamann distribution peaking at a high energy (1.7 eV). If it was simple laser heating of the surface inducing desorption one would expect a distribution more or less following

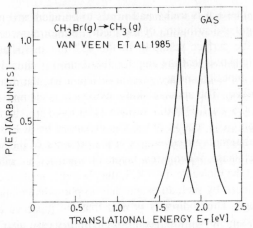

Fig. 15 Translational energy distributions of the methyl fragments from 222 nm photodissociation of CH_3Br. The gas phase result has been derived from G.N.A. van Veen et al., Chem. Phys., **92**, 59 (1985). Reproduced from E.B. D. Bourdon et al., Farad. Disc. Chem. Soc., **82**, 343 (1986).

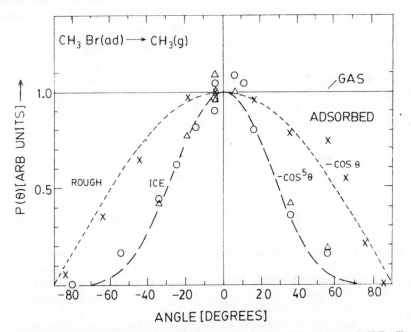

Fig. 16 Angular distribution of methyl fragments from 222 nm dissociation of CH_3Br. The solid line would result for gas phase photolysis, neglecting polarization of the uv on reflection at the crystal surface. The long dashes are for CH_3Br 'ice' and short dashes are for CH_3Br on an unannealed LiF (001) substrate. Reproduced from E.B.D. Bourdon et al., Farad. Disc. Chem. Soc., **82**, 343 (1986).

Boltzmann pattern and the released energy will be small for the crystal will act as a heat sink.

The second question is tricky and needs to be addressed carefully. Fig. 16 displays the angular distribution of the methyl photofragments with respect to the normal to the surface resulting in the 222 nm dissociation of adsorbed CH_3Br. It clearly shows that the angular distribution is altered by the nature of the surface. An annealed surface gives a different angular distribution from an unannealed surface. The most striking evidence is demonstrated in the uv photolysis of OCS on LiF (001) surface [150,154-156]. In this example the photodissociation cross section of OCS is enhanced by at least three orders of magnitude at submonolayer coverages in the presence of the surface compared to that in the gas phase. When a few layers of water-ice are interposed between the substrate and the molecule, i.e. OCS, the photodissociation cross section was dramatically reduced by such an extent that no photodissociation was observed at .04 L coverage. This indirectly proved that the presence of the surface is absolutely necessary to see any such effect. In this case also the translational energy distributions of the fragments differed drastically from the gas phase results.

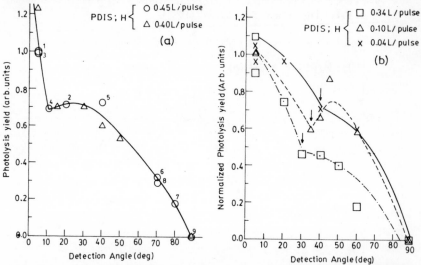

Fig. 17   (a) High coverage angular distribution of the H photofragment yield (normalized to the laser power) from the 222 nm dissociation of H_2S adsorbed on LiF (001). The circled data were taken at a dosing of 0.45 L/ laser pulse and a laser power of 8.2 ± 0.3 mJ/pulse. The triangle data were taken three months later on a separate LiF crystal at a dosing of 0.4 L/laser pulse and a laser power of 4.1 ± 0.2 mJ/pulse. The sequence of data taking is indicated for the circles. The solid curve was drawn to emphasize the bimodal nature of the angular distribution. (b) Angular distribution of H photofragments from the 222 nm dissociation of H_2S at several coverages on a LiF (001) substrate. Each data set was normalized with respect to laser power, and unit yield was set at $\Theta = 5°$. The curves are not fits but simply aids to the eye; the arrows give best estimates of the location of the points of inflection. Adapted from I. Harrison et al., J. Chem., Phys., **89**, 1498 (1988) with permission.

The third question may be answered by taking the above example and stating that annealed and unannealed LiF surfaces produce different angular distributions for CH_3 fragments. This means differently ordered crystals align the C-Br bond differently. Another example of preferential geometries on adsorption is found in the photodissociation of H_2S. Fig. 17 displays the bimodal angular distribution of H-atoms resulting from 222 nm photodissociation of H_2S (ads). The bimodal nature of the distribution shows that there are two preferred orientations of H_2S (ads), one leading to photoproduct H moving normal to the surface and another producing H moving at mean angle $\Theta \cong 40°$ to the surface normal. The distribution also changes as a function of surface coverage at low coverages [149]. In fact, the H atoms ejected in the direction of the surface normal are likely to be originated by the fragments formed initially with velocities along the direction of the surface normal. For the second peak the initially formed H atom may have undergone a collision with the nearest neighbour before being detected in the mass spectrometer. From this it seems that the H_2S molecules are adsorbed at preferred sites at preferred geometries and not all geometries are allowed (for this situation we shall expect a cos Θ distribution around the surface normal).

The answer to the fourth question is not very straightforward. The complication lies in estimating the coverage on the surface accurately. Ideally speaking one would like to cover the surface with a monolayer (or a fraction of that) of molecules. Once the laser fires all the molecules adsorbed on the surface should leave the surface in order to prepare it for the next coverage-desorption event. In other words the surface must go back to the starting point before the consecutive laser pulse arrives and the burst of fresh molecules arrive (from either a pulsed molecular beam source or from a doser). If D is the dosing in Langmuirs (1 $L = 10^{-6}$ Torr sec) per laser shot and S is the sticking coefficient, then the steady state coverage $\sigma = S \times D/E$, where E is the desorption efficiency [149]. As these experiments are normally carried out at low temperatures the sticking coefficient is taken to be unity. Therefore, the coverage becomes inversely proportional to the desorption efficiency. The sticking coefficient may also be measured experimentally from the slope of the line obtained by plotting the integrated thermal desorption spectra as a function of exposure. If the molecules are bound to the surface the adsorption energy (E_{ad}) determined from the TDS spectra assuming first order kinetics must vary with the coverage. On the contrary, the adsorption energy will be invariant as a function of surface coverage if the molecules are bound to themselves (i.e. "ice" or "cluster" formation takes place on the surface). In fact, photodissociation of CH_3Br at 193 nm from multilayer of CH_3Br formed at 30 K on LiF (100) surface has been reported by F.L. Tabares et al [157]. Under their experimental conditions they failed to detect photodissociation of CH_3Br in its first uv band at a submonolayer coverage. In this case, E.B.D. Bourdon et al succeeded mainly because they worked at a higher temperature. These two experiments in reality are complementary to each other, both establishing two unrelated phenomena at the surface. Photodissociation of small molecules from a multilayer on semiconductor surfaces has been reported by H. Sato et al [158, 159]. They have measured the translational energy distribution of the resulting chlorine atoms produced by uv photolysis of Cl_2 on

Si wafers. But their experiment was complicated by reaction of the resulting atoms with the photoelectrons or photoablated metal ions from the surface of metal substrates. The photoinduced reaction between O_2 and CO has been studied recently by W.D. Mieher et al [160] by coadsorbing the two gases on Pt (111) surface. Oxygen molecule was dissociated at the adsorbed state by irradiation with a Xe lamp and the yield of CO_2 resulting from the reaction O + CO, as a function of irradiation time was monitored. The reaction was carried out at submonolayer coverage of the reactants. Though this is not a dynamical study in a sense, the phenomenon of photodissociation at the surface was exploited in order to see the desired reaction products.

Classical trajectory calculations [145, 148] have been carried out to study the dynamics of the displacement reaction H + BrH′ (ad) = HBr(g) + H′ initiated by a photon on a LiF (001) surface. Cross section function and product distribution were found markedly different from the gas phase studies for two idealized geometries (collinear and bent) on the surface. This reaction on the adsorbed state has, indeed, been observed for both HCl and HBr as reactants on the LiF (001) surface [151,153]. In the theoretical calculations, angular distributions in both geometries were narrower than in the gas phase results. The product rotational distribution was also substantially narrower than for the gas phase reaction. Similar studies for the photoreaction of H produced by photolysis of H_2S (ad) with an undissociated H_2S on LiF (001) surface were made. The product H_2 translational energy is markedly bimodal with a high as well as a low energy component. The fast component is thought to be due to a direct pick-up reaction with the fast moving H atoms colliding with H_2S within the range of reactive impact parameters. The indirect mechanism could possibly originate from H moving parallel to the surface, thereby giving rise to secondary encounters which substantially thermalise the resulting H_2 product. This photon initiated reaction has been seen experimentally. The product H_2, indeed showed a bimodal translational energy distribution and the agreement with classical trajectory predictions is spectacular considering that the surface is merely a spectator in these calculations and its only influence on the reaction is in terms of restricting the geometry of approach of the reactants. Though it is too early to expect a lot out of these trajectory calculations at this stage, if proven in general, alignment of molecules in the presence of a surface will vastly restrict the orientation as well as impact parameters for a reaction, hence rendering product attributes more informative.

So far I have discussed dissociations occuring at an insulator surface. But this by no means puts a restriction on using other surfaces as well. Recently photodissociation dynamics of HCl adsorbed on Ag (111) surface has been studied at 248 nm [152]. The measured cross section for dissociation is 6×10^{-19} cm^2 which is about 200 times greater than that for gas phase photolysis of HCl at the same wave length. The mechanism of dissociation is supposed to be through an electron detachment from the metal surface which is taken by the adsorbed HCl molecule to form a negative ion on the surface which eventually releases a hydrogen atom. This conjecture is supported by the fact that the cross section for dissociation diminishes as the work function of the substrate (through chlorination) is increased. This type of photoinduced charge transfer dissociation is also thought to play a role in the photodissociation of adsorbed CH_3Cl, CH_3Br and CCl_4 on a Ni (111) surface [161,162]. Direct photofragmentation competes with electron transfer mediated dissociation in these systems.

Finally from what I have discussed above it seems that the photodissociation dynamics of adsorbed molecules promise a great deal of different chemistry and physics than we are used to from similar studies in the gas phase. Currently there are only a few groups pursuing this kind of research (which is also very expensive in terms of initial investment) and our understanding of the dissociation of even small molecules at the surface is largely limited by the systems they can study within a limited period of time, but this is definitely the beginning. The next few years will be very crucial for the growth in this field and for our efforts to use solid surfaces to our advantage.

6. CONCLUSION

In this review I have attempted to discuss some of the directions in which photodissociation dynamics is expanding currently. As we are determined to do finer experiments, the dynamics revealed by them seems more detailed and our understanding regarding the dynamics is continuously evolving. However, there are a few points worth noting. While one can measure high resolution Doppler profiles today with narrow band lasers, one must also prepare parent molecular state very selectively. In other words, high resolution Doppler profiles will only be meaningful if matched by highly selective parent state preparation. In studying weak emissions from dissociating molecules whether in real time or in the frequency domain one must be careful about formulating the theory especially when one is close to the asymptotic region (long time behaviour of the system). Mode selectivity after Brumer and Shapiro's formulation needs a qualitatively different approach and may be achieved externally by preparing the dissociating state(s) through coherent excitation. Coadsorbing molecules on a surface and subsequent dissociation of the desired molecule to generate reactive species with a restricted range of impact parameters may be one way of achieving product-selective-reactions in the future [163].

Theoretical understanding of dynamics also needs concerted attention. Potential energy surfaces whether ab initio or semiempirical are still not developed for most molecules. Accuracy of ab initio calculations for crucial quantities like activation energy, correlation energy, etc. has not been quite satisfactory yet. This sometimes leads to difficulties in interpretation of experimental results. However, with modern computers with ever so much crunching power, things are slowly improving in this area [164].

Stereochemistry (whether inherent or forced) will play an important role in our understanding of photodissociation of polyatomic molecules in the coming years [165]. Dynamical stereochemistry as discussed in the vector-vector correlation above is already an important factor in understanding the angular distribution of photofragments or Doppler broadening of rotational lines. There may be more complicated types of such correlations (stereochemistry) to be obtained as yet. For example nothing is known about orbital alignment, or spin alignment in a photodissociation, or vector correlations of product $v–Js$ in a many body dissociation, etc. Needless to mention that photodissociation of adsorbed molecules are only qualitatively understood and it will take a long time before we develop the confidence of doing finer experiments like the ones done in the gas phase, with adsorbed molecules. Therefore, the final chapter on photodissociation dynamics remains to be written and with concerted efforts by scientists all over the world, this field will continue to grow.

7. ACKNOWLEDGEMENT

I am grateful to Professors P. Brumer, P.L. Houston, A.H. Zewail and J.C. Polanyi for sending me some of their reprints before publication. In addition P. Brumer, P.L. Houston, A.H. Zewail and N. Sathyamurthy critically read part of this manuscript and sent their suggestions promptly. H.N. Sathyanarayana provided crucial assistance for drafting the figures.

REFERENCES

1. A. Terenin, Z. Phys., **37**, 98 (1926).
2. W.M. Jackson and H. Okabe, Adv. Photochem., **13**, 95 (1986).
3. R. Bersohn, in *Molecular Photodissociation Dynamics*, edited by M.N.R. Ashfold and J.E. Baggott (Roy. Soc. of Chem., London, 1987) and all the references therein.
4. E. Hirota and K. Kawaguchi, Ann. Rev. Phys. Chem., **36**, 53 (1985) and all the references therein.
5. A.E. deVries, Comm. At. Mol. Phys., **11**, 157 (1982).
6. R.N. Zare and P.J. Dagdigian, Science, **185**, 739 (1974).
7. S.R. Leone, Adv. Chem. Phys., **50**, 255 (1982).
8. J.L. Kinsey, Ann. Rev. Phys. Chem., **28**, 354 (1977).
9. J.J. Valentini, in *Spectrometric Techniques*, Vol. 4, 2, (Acad. Press, New York 1985).
10. L.J. Butler, E.J. Hintsa, S.F. Shane, and Y.T. Lee, J. Chem. Phys., **86**, 2051 (1987).
11. J.A. O'Neill, T.G. Kreutz, and G.W. Flynn, J. Chem. Phys., **87**, 4598 (1987).
12. F.F. Crim, Ann. Rev. Phys. Chem., **35**, 657 (1985).
13. H. Reisler, M. Noble and C. Wittig, in *Molecular Photodissociation Dynamics*, edited by M.N.R. Ashfold and J.E. Baggott (Roy. Soc. Chem., London 1987) and all the references therein.
14. P. Andresen, Comments, At. Mol. Phys., **18**, 1 (1986).
15. G.E. Hall, N. Sivakumar, P.L. Houston, and I. Burak, Phys. Rev. Letts., **56**, 1671 (1986).
16. M. Dubs, U. Bruhlman, and J.R. Huber, Chem. Phys., **84**, 3106 (1986).
17. M.P. Docker, A. Hodgson, and J.P. Simons, Chem. Phys. Letts., **128**, 264 (1986).
18. K.–H. Gericke, S. Klee, F.J. Comes, and R.N. Dixon, J. Chem. Phys., **85**, 4463 (1986).
19. R. Bersohn and S.H. Lin, Adv. Chem. Phys., **16**, 67 (1967).
20. C.H. Greene and R.N. Zare, Ann. Rev. Phys. Chem., **33**, 119 (1982); R.N. Zare, Mol. Photochem., **4**, 1 (1972).
21. R. Bersohn, Isr. J. Chem., **11**, 675 (1973).

22. S.C. Yang and R. Bersohn, J. Chem. Phys., **61**, 4400 (1974).
23. J. Solomon, J. Chem. Phys., **47**, 889 (1967).
24. C. Jonah, P. Chandra, and R. Bersohn, J. Chem. Phys., **55**, 1903 (1971).
25. J. Solomon, C. Jonah, P. Chandra, and R. Bersohn, J. Chem. Phys., **55**, 1908 (1971).
26. G.E. Busch, J.F. Cornelius, R.T. Mahoney, R.I. Morse, D.W. Schlosser, and K.R. Wilson, Rev, Sci. Instr., **41**, 1066 (1971).
27. M.J. Dzvonik and S.C. Yang, Rev. Sci. Instr., **45**, 750 (1974).
28. S.J. Riley and K.R. Wilson, Disc. Farad. Soc., **53**, 132 (1972).
29. R.J. Van Brunt and R.N. Zare, J. Chem. Phys., **48**, 4304 (1968).
30. M.T. Macpherson, J.P. Simons, and R.N. Zare, Mol. Phys., **38**, 2049 (1979).
31. C.H. Greene and R.N. Zare, J. Chem. Phys. **78**, 6741 (1983).
32. U. Fano and J.H. Macek, Rev. Mod. Phys., **45**, 553 (1973).
33. R. Altkorn and R.N. Zare, Ann. Rev. Phys. Chem., **35**, 265 (1984).
34. T. Nagata, T. Kondow, K. Kuchitsu, G.W. Loge, and R.N. Zare, Mol. Phys., **50**, 49 (1983).
35. G.A. Chamberlain and J.P. Simons, Chem. Phys., Letts., **32**, 355 (1975).
36. R.N. Zare and D. Herschbach, Proc. IEEE, **51**, 173 (1963).
37. R. Schmiedl, H. Dugan, W. Meier, and K.H. Welge, Z. Phys. A **304**, 137 (1982).
38. D.A. Case, G.M. McClelland, and D.R. Herschbach, Mol. Phys., **35**, 541 (1978).
39. P.L. Houston, Acc. Chem. Res., **22**, 309 (1989).
40. G.E. Hall and P.L. Houston, Ann. Rev. Phys. Chem., **40**, 375 (1989).
41. P.L. Houston, J. Phys. Chem., **91**, 5388 (1987).
42. G.E. Hall, R.O. Loo, H.-P. Haerri, N. Sivakumar, D. Chawla, P.L. Houston, D.W. Chandler, J.W. Hepburn, and I. Burak, Ber. Bunsenges. Phys. Chem., **92**, 281 (1988).
43. C.E. Strauss, G.C. McBane, P.L. Houston, I. Burak, and J.W. Hepburn, J. Chem. Phys., **90**, 5364 (1989).
44. G.E. Hall, N. Sivakumar, R. Ogorzalek, D. Chawla, H.-P. Haerri, P.L. Houston, I. Burak and J.W. Hepburn, Farad. Disc. Chem. Soc., **82**, 13 (1986).
45. N. Sivakumar, G.E. Hall, P.L. Houston, I. Burak, and J.W. Hepburn, J. Chem. Phys., **88**, 3692 (1988).
46. G.E. Hall, N. Sivakumar, D. Chawla, P.L. Houston, I. Burak, I.M. Waller, H.F. Davis, and J.W. Hepburn, Chem. Phys. Res. Report (Univ. of Waterloo, Canada, 1986).
47. N. Sivakumar, I. Burak, W.-Y. Cheung, P.L. Houston, and J.W. Hepburn, J. Phys. Chem., **89**, 3609 (1985).
48. G.E. Hall, N. Sivakumar, D. Chawla, P.L. Houston, and I. Burak, J. Chem. Phys., **88**, 3682 (1988).
49. R.N. Dixon, J. Chem. Phys., **85**, 1866 (1986).
50. Z. Xu, B. Koplitz, and C. Wittig, J. Chem. Phys., **90**, 2692 (1989).
51. M.I. McCarthy and V. Vaida, J. Phys. Chem., **92**, 5879 (1988).
52. J.A. Guest, M.A. O'Halloran, and R.N. Zare, Chem. Phys. Letts., **103**, 261 (1984).
53. I. Nadler, D. Mahgerefteh, H. Reisler, and C. Wittig, J. Chem. Phys., **82**, 3885 (1984).
54. G.E. Hall, N. Sivakumar, and P.L. Houston, J. Chem. Phys., **84**, 2120 (1985).
55. M.A. O'Halloran, H. Joswig, R.N. Zare, and M.S. Child, J. Chem. Phys., **87**, 303 (1987).
56. J.F. Black, J.R. Waldeck and R.N. Zare, J. Chem. Soc. Farad. Trans., in press (1989); Chem. Phys., **126**, 191 (1989).

57. D. Hausler, P. Andresen, and R. Schinke, J. Chem. Phys., **83**, 4522 (1987) and all the references therein.

58. A. Hodgson, J.P. Simons, M.N.R. Ashfold, J.M. Bayley, and R. N. Dixon., Mol. Phys., **54**, 351 (1985) and all the references therein.

59. M. Mons and I. Dimicoli, Chem. Phys., **130**, 307 (1988).

60. M. Kawasaki, H. Sato, T. Kikuchi, A. Fukuroda, S. Kobayashi, and S. Arikawa, J. Chem. Phys., **86**, 4425 (1987).

61. A. Ticktin. A.E. Bruno, U. Bruhlmann, and J.R. Huber, Chem. Phys., **125**, 403 (1988).

62. C.X.W. Qian, A. Ogai, L. Iwata, and H. Reisler, J. Chem. Phys., **89**, 6547 (1988).

63. K.–H. Gericke, A. Grunewald, and F.J. Comes, J. Chem. Phys., **88**, 6255 (1988) and all the references therein.

64. U. Gerlach-Meyer, E. Linnebach, K. Kleinermanns, and J. Wolfrum, Chem. Phys. Letts., **133**, 113 (1987).

65. I. Burak, J.W. Hepburn, N. Sivakumar, G.E. Hall, G. Chawla, and P.L. Houston, J. Chem. Phys., **86**, 1258 (1987), K.A. Trentelman, S.H. Cable, D.M. Moss, and P.L. Houston, ibid, **91**, 7498 (1989).

66. T.J. Butenhoff, K.L. Carleton, M.C. Chuang, and C.B. Moore, J. Chem. Soc. Farad. Trans., to be published and all the references therein.

67. T. Ebata, T. Amano, and M. Ito, J. Chem. Phys., **90**, 112 (1989) and references therein.

68. S.S. Hunnicutt, L.D. Waits, and J.A. Guest, to be published.

69. J. Black, and I. Powis, J. Phys. Chem., **93**, 2461 (1989) and all the references therein.

70. Y. Matsumi, P.K. Das, and M. Kawasaki, J. Chem. Phys., **92**, 1696 (1990).

71. K.–H. Gericke, R. Theinl, and F.J. Comes, Chem. Phys., Lett., **164**, 605 (1989).

72. A.C. Kummel, G.O. Sitz, and R.N. Zare, J. Chem. Phys., **88**, 7357 (1988).

73. J.A. Waldeck, A.C. Kummel, G.O. Sitz, and R.N. Zare, J. Chem. Phys., **90**, 4112 (1989).

74. D.C. Jacobs, and R.N. Zare, J. Chem. Phys., **85**, 5457 (1986).

75. D.C. Jacobs, R.J. Madix, and R.N. Zare, J. Chem. Phys., **85**, 5469 (1986).

76. M. Mons and I. Dimicoli, J. Chem. Phys., **90**, 4037 (1989).

77. J.W. Winniczek, R.L. Dubs, J.R. Appling, V. Mckoy, and M.G. White, J. Chem. Phys., **90**, 949 (1989).

78. A.C. Kummel, G.O. Sitz, and R.N. Zare, J. Chem. Phys., **88**, 6707 (1988).

79. M.P. Docker, Chem. Phys., **125**, 185 (1988).

80. D.W. Chandler and P.L. Houston, J. Chem. Phys., **87**, 1445 (1987).

81. D.H. Parker, Z.W. Wang, M.H.M. Janssen, and D.W. Chandler, J. Chem. Phys., **90**, 60 (1989).

82. D.W. Chandler, J.W. Thoman Jr., M.H.M. Janssen, and D.H. Parker, Chem. Phys. Letts., **156**, 151 (1989).

83. N. Bloembergen, and A.H. Zewail, J. Phys. Chem., 88, 5459 (1984) and the references therein.

84. R. Kosloff, S.A. Rice, P. Gaspard, S. Tersigni, and D.J. Tannor, Chem. Phys., 139, 201 (1989) and references therein.

85. T.F. George, I.H. Zimmerman, J.-M. Yuan, J.R. Lang, and P. L. De Vries, Acc. Chem. Res., **10**, 449 (1977).

86. D.W. Lupo and M. Quack, Chem. Rev., **87**, 181 (1987) and references therein.

87. S. Shi, A. Woody, and H. Rabitz, J. Chem. Phys., **88**, 6870 (1988).

88. M. Shapiro and P. Brumer, J. Chem. Phys., **84**, 540 (1986).

89. M. Shapiro and P. Brumer, J. Chem. Phys., **84**, 4103 (1986).
90. P. Brumer, and M. Shapiro, Farad. Disc. Chem. Soc., **82**, 177 (1986).
91. P. Brumer, and M. Shapiro. Chem. Phys. Letts., **126**, 541 (1986).
92. C. Asaro, P. Brumer, and M. Shapiro, Phys. Rev. Letts., **60**, 1634 (1988).
93. M. Shapiro, J.W. Hepburn, and P. Brumer, Chem. Phys. Letts., **149**, 451 (1988).
94. G. Kurizki, M. Shapiro, and P. Brumer, Phys. Rev. B **39**, 3435 (1989).
95. T. Seideman, M. Shapiro, and P. Brumer, J. Chem. Phys., **90**, 7132 (1989).
96. M. Shapiro and P. Brumer, J. Chem. Phys., **90**, 6179 (1989).
97. P. Brumer and M. Shapiro, J. Phys. Chem. (to be published).
98. P. Brumer and M. Shapiro, Chem. Phys., **139**, 221 (1989).
99. P. Brumer and M. Shapiro, Acc. Chem. Res., **22**, 407 (1989).
100. J. Krause, M. Shapiro, and P. Brumer, J. Chem. Phys., in press.
101. X.P. Jiang, P. Brumer, and M. Shapiro, to be published.
102. M. Shapiro and R. Bersohn, Ann. Rev. Phys. Chem., **33**, 403 (1982).
103. P. Brumer and M. Shapiro, Adv. Chem. Phys., **60**, 371 (1985).
104. G.G. Balint-kurti and M. Shapiro, in *Photodissociation and Photoionization*, edited by K.P. Lawley (John Wiley & Sons, New York, 1985).
105. R. Schinke, Ann. Rev. Phys. Chem., **39**, 39 (1988).
106. A.H. Zewail, and R.B. Bernstein, C & E News, **66**, 24 (1988).
107. M.J. Rosker, M. Dantus, and A.H. Zewail, Science, **241**, 200 (1988); A.H. Zewail, Science, **242**, 1645 (1988).
108. J.L. Knee, and A.H. Zewail, Spectroscopy, **3**, 44 (1988).
109. E.J. Heller, Acc. Chem. Res., **14**, 368 (1981).
110. E.J. Heller, R.L. Sundberg, and D. Tannor, J. Phys. Chem., **86**, 1822 (1982).
111. S.Y. Lee and E.J. Heller, J. Chem. Phys., **71**, 4777 (1979).
112. H.J. Foth, J.C. Polanyi, and H.H. Telle, J. Phys. Chem., **86**, 5027 (1982); H.J. Foth, H.R. Mayne, R.A. Poirier, J.C. Polanyi, and H.H. Telle, Laser Chem., **2**, 229 (1983).
113. D.G. Imre, J.L. Kinsey, R.W. Field, and D.H. Katayama, J. Phys. Chem., **86**, 2564 (1982).
114. D.G. Imre, J.L. Kinsey, A. Sinha, and J. Krenos, J. Phys. Chem. **88**, 3956 (1984).
115. E.A. Rohlfing, and J.J. Velentini, J. Chem. Phys., **83**, 521 (1985).
116. K. Kleinermanns, E. Linnebach, and Suntz, J. Phys. Chem., **91**, 5543 (1987).
117. B.R. Johnson, and J.L. Kinsey, J. Chem. Phys., **87**, 1525 (1987).
118. P.R. Brooks, Chem. Rev., **88**, 407 (1988).
119. R.D. Bower, P. Chevrier, P. Das, H.J. Foth, J.C. Polanyi, M.G. Prisant, and J.P. Visticot, J. Chem. Phys., **89**, 4478 (1988).
120. P. Chevrier, B. Collings, P. Das, J.C. Polanyi, M.G. Prisant, and J.P. Visticot, Chem. Phys., **133**, 1 (1989).
121. S. Ling, D.G. Imre, and E.J. Heller, J. Phys. Chem., **93**, 7107 (1989).
122. M. Jacon, O. Atabek, and C. Leforestier, J. Chem. Phys., **91**, 1585 (1989).
123. A. Gedanken and M.D. Rowe, Chem. Phys. Letts., **34**, 39 (1979).
124. M. Dantus, M.J. Rosker, and A.H. Zewail, J. Chem. Phys., **87**, 2395 (1987); ibid **89**, 6128 (1988).
125. M.J. Rosker, M. Dantus, and A.H. Zewail, J. Chem. Phys., **89**, 6113 (1988).
126. R. Bersohn, and A.H. Zewail, Bunsenges. Phys. Chem., **92**, 373 (1988).
127. V. Engel, H. Metiu, R. Almeida, R.A. Marcus, and A.H. Zewail, Chem. Phys. Letts., **152**, 1 (1988).
128. T.S. Rose, M.J. Rosker, and A.H. Zewail, J. Chem. Phys., **88**, 6672 (1988); ibid, **91**, 7415 (1989).

129. M.J. Rosker, T.S. Rose, and A.H. Zewail, Chem. Phys. Letts., **146**, 175 (1988).
130. M. Dantus, R.M. Bowman, J.S. Baskin, and A.H. Zewail, Chem. Phys. Letts., **159**, 496 (1989).
131. R.M. Bowman, M. Dantus, and A.H. Zewail, Chem. Phys. Letts., **161**, 297 (1989).
132. A.H. Zewail, J. Chem. Soc. Farad. Trans. II, **85**, 1221 (1989).
133. R.B. Bernstein and A.H. Zewail, J. Chem. Phys., **90**, 829 (1989).
134. M. Dantus, R.M. Bowman, J.S. Baskin, and A.H. Zewail, Chem. Phys. Letts., **159**, 406 (1989).
135. V. Engel and H. Metiu, J. Chem. Phys., **90**, 6116 (1989), **91**, 1596 (1989).
136. J. Tellinghuisen, in *Photodissociation and Photoionization*, edited by K.P. Lawley, Adv. Chem. Phys., **60**, 299 (1985).
137. S.Y. Lee, W.T. Pollard, and R.A. Mathies, Chem. Phys. Letts, **160**, 531 (1989), ibid, **163**, 11 (1989).
138. T.J. Chuang and H. Seki, Phys. Rev. Letts., **49**, 382 (1982).
139. T.J. Chuang, J. Chem. Phys., **76**, 3828 (1982).
140. T.J. Chuang and I. Hassia, Phys. Rev. Letts., **52**, 2045 (1984).
141. N. Nishi, H. Shinohara, and T. Okuyama, J. Chem. Phys., **80**, 3898 (1984).
142. G.M. Goncher and C.B. Harris, J. Chem. Phys., **77**, 3767 (1982).
143. G.M. Goncher, C.A. Parsons, and C.B. Harris, J. Phys. Chem., **88**, 4200 (1984).
144. E.B.D. Bourdon, J.P. Cowin, I. Harrison, J.C. Polanyi, J. Segner, C.D. Stanners, and P.A. Young, J. Phys. Chem., **88**, 6100 (1984).
145. E.B.D. Bourdon, P. Das, I. Harrison, J.C. Polanyi, J. Segner, C.D. Stanners, R.J. Williams, and P.A. Young, Farad. Disc. Chem. Soc., **82**, 343 (1986).
146. G.N.A. Vanveen, T. Baller, and A.E. De Vries, Chem. Phys., **92**, 59 (1985).
147. J.C. Polanyi, Farad. Disc. Chem. Soc., **84**, 1 (1987).
148. J.C. Polanyi and R.J. Williams, J. Chem. Phys., **88**, 3363 (1988).
149. I. Harrison, J.C. Polanyi, and P.A. Young, J. Chem. Phys., **89**, 1475 (1988); **89**, 1498 (1988).
150. S.J. Dixon-Warren, I. Harrison, K. Leggett, M.S. Matyjaszczyk, J.C. Polanyi, and P.A. Young, J. Chem. Phys., **88**, 4092 (1988).
151. C.C. Cho, J.C. Polanyi, and C.D. Stanners, J. Chem. Phys., **90**, 598 (1989).
152. C.C. Cho, B.A. Collings, R.E. Hammer, J.C. Polanyi C.D. Stanners, J.H. Wang and G.-Q. Xu, J. Phys. Chem., **93**, 7761 (1989).
153. E.B.D. Bourdon, C.C. Cho, P. Das, J.C. Polanyi, and C.D. Stanners, to be published.
154. S.J. Dixon-Warren, K. Leggett, M.S. Matyjaszczyk, J.C. Polanyi and P.A. Young, submitted for publication.
155. J.C. Polanyi and P.A. Young, submitted for publication.
156. K. Leggett, J.C. Polanyi, and P.A. Young, submitted for publication.
157. F.L. Tabares, E.P. Marsh, G.A. Bach, and J.P. Cowin, J. Chem. Phys., **86**, 738 (1987).
158. M. Kawasaki, H. Sato, and N. Nishi, J. Appl. Phys., **65**, 792 (1989).
159. H. Sato and M. Kawasaki, to be published.
160. W.D. Mieher and W. Ho, J. Chem. Phys., **91**, 2755 (1989).
161. E.P. Marsh, T.L. Gilton, W. Meier, M.R. Schnider, and J.P. Cowin, Phys. Rev. Letts., **61**, 2725 (1988).
162. T.L. Gilton, C. Dehnbostel, and J.P. Cowin, J. Chem. Phys., **91**, 1937 (1989).
163. J.W. Gadzuk, Chem. Phys. Letts., **136**, 402 (1987).
164. D.R. Herschbach, Farad, Disc. Chem. Soc., **84**, 465 (1987).
165. J. Phys. Chem., **91**, all the articles in the 21st issue (1987).

4. Chaos in Chemical Dynamics

Ramakrishna Ramaswamy*
Division of Theoretical Studies
Institute for Molecular Science
Myodaiji, Okazaki, Japan

Abstract

The importance of nonlinear phenomena in a chemical context is discussed in this chapter. The methods of nonlinear dynamics are briefly reviewed, and the relevance of regular and chaotic motions in molecular systems is described. The implications of these in both classical and quantum mechanics, vis-a-vis static and dynamic properties are discussed for isolated molecule or scattering systems. Also described in this chapter are aspects of chaos in dissipative systems. These are of importance in chemical kinetics, where complex spatial and temporal behaviour can obtain from the nonlinearity of the mass-action law.

1. INTRODUCTION

Chaos in dynamical systems is a much studied phenomenon [1-3]. In chemical systems, the relevance and importance of chaotic motion has long been recognized, for example, in the context of intramolecular relaxation problems [4–7], but also more recently in a variety of other situations, including complex kinetics [8] and scattering [9,10].

In trying to describe fundamental molecular processes, it is quite common to use classical mechanics. Many features of typical polyatomic molecules are often adequately and accurately described in classical or semiclassical, rather than quantum terms. Classical trajectories are widely used in studying bimolecular collisions or intramolecular processes. Refinements such as the classical S-matrix theory, or other semiclassical methods [11] can give excellent agreement with the results of quantum mechanics. Further, classical mechanics is typically more tractable for large molecular systems than exact quantal methods, owing to the very large number of quantum states involved in any process of chemical interest.

In the past few decades, the traditional view of classical dynamics has undergone a significant modification [12–15]. In particular, the importance of nonlinearity, in the way in which this can completely change dynamics, is more

(*On leave from School of Physical Sciences, Jawaharlal Nehru University, New Delhi, India)

widely recognized. Since most molecular systems are nonlinear, the pertinence of these effects in a chemical context is also necessary to gauge. In this chapter I will first describe some of the fundamental notions of classical chaos in Hamiltonian systems. Its relevance and applications in chemical contexts, involving both bound and scattering systems, is discussed. A major and related area of current research interest is in the quantum manifestations of classical chaos, the so called problem of quantum chaos. Some aspects of this subject are also elaborated. Finally, aspects of chaos in dissipative systems are described, with special relevance to chemical kinetics. The exposition here is of necessity brief, since many of these topics have been reviewed recently in the literature. In addition, several textbooks (both at the graduate and undergraduate level) that deal with some of these topics in detail have become available.

2. CLASSICAL CHAOS

In the Hamiltonian formulation, a classical mechanical system of N degrees of freedom is described by a set of coordinates q and conjugate momenta p, which evolve according to

$$\dot{p}_i = \frac{-\partial H(\mathbf{p}, \mathbf{q})}{\partial q_i}; \qquad \dot{q}_i = \frac{-\partial H(\mathbf{p}, \mathbf{q})}{\partial p_i} \qquad i = 1, 2,...,N \qquad (1)$$

where $H(\mathbf{p}, \mathbf{q})$ is the Hamiltonian function. The state of the system at given time t is completely specified by the values $(\mathbf{q}(t), \mathbf{p}(t))$ and the overdot signifies d/dt. It is convenient to describe the dynamics in the 2N-dimensional phase space $(\mathbf{q}, \mathbf{p})$ where, given the values of the coordinates and momenta at time $t = 0$, the subsequent evolution according to Eq. (1) defines an orbit or trajectory.

Given an arbitrary dynamical system, one would like to know the nature of the classical trajectories, both at a qualitative and at a quantitative level, since any other question regarding the system can then be completely answered. "Solving" the dynamics exactly, in this sense, is sometimes possible when the system is of a special type, termed integrable [16]. In an integrable N degree of freedom system, there are N constants of motion, $F_1(\mathbf{p}, \mathbf{q})...F_N(\mathbf{p}, \mathbf{q})$ (including the Hamiltonian itself) in involution, i.e. the Poisson bracket

$$\{F_i, F_j\} = \sum_k \left[\frac{\partial F_i}{\partial q_k} \frac{\partial F_j}{\partial p_k} - \frac{\partial F_i}{\partial p_k} \frac{\partial F_j}{\partial q_k} \right] \qquad (2)$$

between any pair of these vanishes. Then the equations of motion can be reduced to quadratures, and integrated in terms of known special functions. This is equivalent to finding the appropriate canonical transformation from the variables $(\mathbf{p}, \mathbf{q})$ to the so-called action angle variables $(\mathbf{I}, \boldsymbol{\theta})$, such that the Hamiltonian is expressible as a function of the action variables alone, since

$$(\mathbf{p}, \mathbf{q}) \rightarrow (\mathbf{I}, \boldsymbol{\theta}); H(\mathbf{p}, \mathbf{q}) \rightarrow H(\mathbf{I})$$

$$\dot{I}_i = -\partial H/\partial \theta_i = 0 \qquad \dot{\theta}_i = \partial H/\partial I_i \qquad i = 1,...,N \qquad (3)$$

All systems with 1 degree of freedom are therefore integrable; a multidimensional integrable system composed of N uncoupled 1-degree of freedom systems is termed separable. In integrable systems, the motion is constrained to lie on the surface of N dimensional tori in the $2N$ dimensional phase space. Further, if the energy is conserved, this places an additional constraint, so that the energy shell is actually $2N - 1$ dimensional. Thus if $N \geq 1$, orbits in the system *cannot* explore the entire available state space. An example of an integrable system is the "Toda lattice", a 1-dimensional chain of N particles interacting via an exponential interaction. For 3 particles, the Hamiltonian is

$$H = \frac{1}{2}\left(p_1^2 + p_2^2\right) + \frac{1}{24}\left[e^{2q_1 + 2\sqrt{3}\,q_2}\,e^{2q_1 - 2\sqrt{3}\,q_2} + e^{-4q_1}\right] - \frac{1}{8} \qquad (4)$$

The system is not separable in any set of obvious coordinates, but possesses two independent constants of motion [12].

However, since integrable systems are so special, they are also rare in the sense that the slightest perturbation can make the system non-integrable. Typically then there exist no constants of the motion other than the total energy (here we consider autonomous systems). It is then natural to ask what the nature of the dynamics in such systems is.

The major theoretical result regarding nonintegrable systems lies in the Kolmogorov-Arnol'd-Moser (or KAM) theorem [16] which states that in nonintegrable systems that are perturbations of integrable ones, for sufficiently small perturbations, in sufficiently nonlinear systems, most of the motion remains on N-dimensional tori. That is to say, one can construct local (rather than global) constants of motion in a perturbative manner in most regions of phase space. There are also, however, regions where this cannot be done, and here the motion is no longer confined to N-dimensional tori, but is instead wandering over the entire $2N - 1$ dimensional energy shell. The latter type of motion, although resulting from purely deterministic equations of motion, has features of randomness or stochasticity, and is termed chaotic. Examples of orbits in integrable and nonintegrable systems are shown in Fig. 1. The KAM theorem also provides a method for constructing the tori when they exist.

The KAM theorem provides an understanding of the complex dynamical behaviour observed in generic or typical hamiltonian systems. It provides an

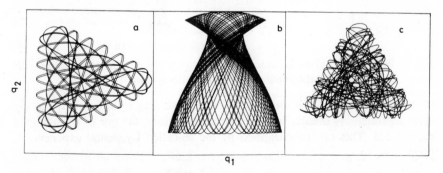

Fig. 1 Coordinate space projections of trajectories in 2 degree-of-freedom Hamiltonian systems: (a) Orbit in the (integrable) Toda system, Eq. (4), (b) Toroidal orbit in the Hénon-Heiles system and (c) Chaotic orbit in the Hénon-Heiles system.

explanation for why tori exist even in strongly nonlinear systems, as well as why even the smallest nonlinearity can lead to some measure of chaotic motions. Thus, at a qualitative level, the expectation is that when the extent of perturbation is small, most of the motion will be on tori. When the perturbation is large, the dynamics is expected to be mainly chaotic. (This is an obviously naive simplification of the rather complicated and intricate KAM theory.) In systems of the sort typically encountered in intramolecular dynamics, one usually has toroidal motion in the low energy regime, and chaotic motion at higher energies. For scattering problems, the opposite is true. There can, however, be significant differences from system to system.

In principle, trajectories in integrable systems can be obtained in closed form since the equations of motion can be integrated, while those in nonintegrable systems must be obtained by numerically solving the appropriate Hamilton's equations with specified initial conditions. There are several striking differences between orbits confined to tori and those that are not. The former are periodic or quasiperiodic in time, whereas the latter are aperiodic; this distinction shows up, for example, in the power spectrum of any dynamical variable, F,

$$I(w) = \frac{1}{2\pi} \lim_{T\to\infty} \frac{1}{T} \left| \int_{-T}^{T} dt\, e^{iwt}\, F(t) \right|^2 \tag{5}$$

(see Fig. 2). A quantitative distinction can be made by examining the behaviour

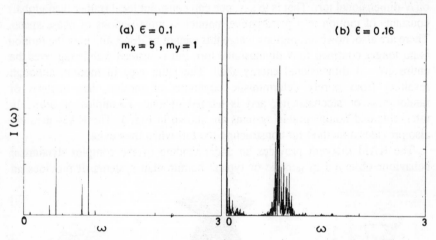

Fig. 2 Power spectra of the dynamical variable $F(t) = q_1(t) + q_2(t)$, for (a) a quasiperiodic orbit and (b) a chaotic orbit in the Hénon-Heiles system.

of nearby trajectories. On tori, two trajectories starting infinitesimally closely apart separate only linearly in time. In chaotic regions, the rate of separation is exponential. This can be quantified by the so-called Lyapunov exponent, σ, defined as

$$\sigma = \lim_{\substack{t\to\infty \\ \varepsilon\to\infty}} \frac{1}{t} \ln\left[\frac{d(t)}{\varepsilon}\right] \tag{6}$$

where ε is the initial separation, and $d(t)$ the separation at time t. For chaotic motion, σ is positive. Such a sensitive dependence on initial conditions is a hallmark of all chaotic motion.

Furthermore, since there is a physical restriction on orbits on tori, it is clear that for $N \geq 1$, these cannot be ergodic. The ergodic hypothesis, that phase space average of dynamical variables are equal to their time average,

$$\lim_{T \to \infty} \frac{1}{T} \int_{-T}^{T} dt F(\mathbf{p}(t), \mathbf{q}(t)) = \int d\mathbf{p} \int d\mathbf{q} \, \delta \, (E - H(\mathbf{p}, \mathbf{q})) F(\mathbf{p}, \mathbf{q}) \qquad (7)$$

must break down when the motion is largely quasiperiodic. Even for chaotic motions, ergodicity may or may not hold, depending on the extent to which a chaotic orbit explores the available phase space.

Linear systems are integrable, and thus can show no chaos. The introduction of nonlinearity in any dynamical model therefore has profound qualitative and quantitative consequences.

The above is an elementary and qualitative outline of the phenomenology of classical chaos; for details the reader is referred to the excellent articles by Berry [12], and by Henon [17], and the texts by Tabor [13] and Ozorio de Almeida [14] and Sagdeev et al [15]. A good introduction to modern classical dynamics can be found in the text by Percival and Richards [18].

3. IRREGULAR SPECTRA AND QUANTUM CHAOS

Although classical methods can be employed to learn a great deal about molecular systems, eventual contact with quantum mechanics is necessary, especially for small systems. A major and continuing motivation in several studies has been to explore the parallels and correspondence between the classical and quantum mechanics. One convenient path to explore such correspondence is through semiclassical mechanics. (The discussion below is confined to bound state phenomena, though with little alteration it applies to scattering situations as well. See the section on irregular scattering).

Semiclassical methods have been employed since the time of the old quantum theory as a means of quantizing classically separable systems (the Bohr-Sommerfeld quantization). The recent revival of interest in such methods stems from the fact that when the number of states or number of degrees of freedom is large, then quantum methods become intractable. For integrable, but nonseparable systems, where the motion is confined to N-dimensional tori, the appropriate semiclassical technique [4, 12–14, 19] is the Einstein-Brillouin-Keller (EBK) method, wherein the correspondence is made between the classical action variables and quantum numbers. On the N-tori, the action integrals are defined as

$$I_j = \oint_{C_j} \mathbf{p} \cdot d\mathbf{q} \qquad j = 1, 2, ..., N \qquad (8)$$

where the C_js are the topologically distinct paths on which the (in general quasiperiodic) motion takes place. The quantization conditions are

$$I_j = \left(n_j + \frac{\alpha_j}{4} \right) h \qquad j = 1, 2, ..., N \qquad (9)$$

where α_j is the Maslov index which counts the number of turning points, h is the Planck constant, and n_j is an integer quantum number. Requiring that all N conditions be satisfied simultaneously suffices in (uniquely) identifying the energy eigenvalue at which such a torus can be found.

Since the EBK method requires only that tori exist, in principle it can be applied to nonintegrable systems as well, in the KAM regime of low perturbation when most tori in the system have not been destroyed. Accordingly, several applications to such systems, most notably the Hénon-Heiles Hamiltonian,

$$H(\mathbf{p}, \mathbf{q}) = \frac{1}{2}\left(p_1^2 + p_2^2\right) + \frac{1}{2}\left(\omega_1^2 q_1^2 + \omega_2^2 q_2^2\right) + \lambda q_1\left(q_2^2 - q_1^2/3\right) \quad (10)$$

have been made. (This Hamiltonian may be considered appropriate to model a simple collinearly vibrating triatomic molecule, with ω_1 and ω_2 denoting the frequencies of the symmetric and asymmetric stretch normal modes). A variety of semiclassical techniques, ranging from 'exact' to perturbative have been devised. These include methods that go beyond the primitive WKB theory, those that can be applied to arbitrary (rather than EBK) tori [20, 21], and techniques that employ perturbation and adiabatic methods. See [4, 5] for reviews.

A quantum analysis of such systems proceeds by first constructing the Hamiltonian operator corresponding to the classical Hamiltonian (by a standard procedure such as the Weyl rule) and then diagonalizing it in a basis to obtain eigenvalues and eigenfunctions. It is important to know how (or if) the underlying classical dynamics affects the quantum bound state properties. The semiclassical EBK methods are inapplicable when the perturbation is large enough that tori are destroyed, since then the action integrals are no longer properly defined. When semiclassical methods fail, quantum states can still, of course, exist. It is of interest to explore whether there is any significant difference between the two types of quantum states: those that have a semiclassical parallel, and those that do not.

The first conjectures relating to this distinction were made by Percival [22], who termed these regular (R) and irregular (I) states, based on an identification between classical orbits and quantum wavefunctions in the $h \to 0$ limit. Several qualitative predictions were made in order to distinguish between such states. R states have well defined quantum numbers, I states do not. R states are insensitive to small perturbations in the parameter, I states are extremely sensitive. R states are strongly coupled to a few neighbouring states (strong selection rules), whereas I states are coupled to a band of similar states (weak, if any, selection rules). Other distinctions can also be made. Some of these conjectures have been substantiated, mainly in numerical experiments.

When the eigenvalues of a Hamiltonian such as Eq. (10) are plotted versus a parameter in the system, such as λ there, it is well known that levels of the same symmetry type must avoid crossing each other. When several of these avoided crossings occur in a small range of energy and parameter space, then the levels become mixed, and display many of the properties of I states [23, 24]. At a qualitative level, the quantum irregular states are those involved in multiple overlapping avoided crossings (e.g. Fig. 3). The parallel between classical

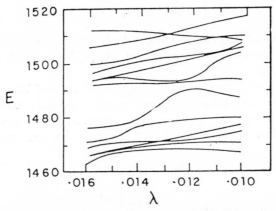

Fig. 3 Typical variation of quantum eigenvalues in a (classically) nonintegrable system. Note the single and multiple avoided crossings as a single parameter is varied. (Degeneracies can occur only if two or more parameters are varied).

resonances and quantum degeneracies suggests that quantum overlapping avoided crossings be identified with regions of classical overlapping resonances, which is one method of identifying the occurrence of classical chaos [13].

However, more quantitative measures are required. Such analysis was applied [25] to the eigenlevels of complex (atomic and nuclear) systems, where it is seen that there are distinct (and few) universality classes depending on the symmetry properties of the Hamiltonian. The same analysis has been remarkably successful in application to the eigenvalues of classically chaotic systems, which appear to fall in the same universality classes as the complex systems studied earlier [26, 27].

The statistical analysis proceeds as follows. The cumulative level number $N(\varepsilon)$ for a sequence of levels ε_i is (Θ is the Heaviside function),

$$N(\varepsilon) = \Sigma_i \Theta \, (\varepsilon - \varepsilon_i). \tag{11}$$

Determining a smooth function $\overline{N(\varepsilon)}$ which approximates $N(\varepsilon)$, one obtains the average level density $\rho(\varepsilon) = d\overline{N}/d\varepsilon$. The "unfolded" sequence of levels E_i is constructed from the original levels ε_i by the mapping $E_i = \overline{N(\varepsilon_i)}$; this new sequence has constant level density (= 1), and defines $N(E)$.

The usual quantities that are computed are: the nearest neighbour spacing distribution (NNSD)

$P(S) \, dS$ = Probability that there are levels E_i and E_{i+1} such that

$$(E_{i+1} - E_i) \in [S, S + dS] \tag{12}$$

the Δ statistic, which gives the average least square deviation of the integrated density of states of the unfolded levels from the best straight line fitting it,

$$\Delta(L) = \langle \frac{1}{L} \min A, B \int_{-L/2}^{L/2} (N(E) - AE - B)^2 \, dE \rangle, \tag{13}$$

and the average number variance,

$$\Sigma^2(L) = \langle (n - L)^2 \rangle \qquad (14)$$

where n is the number of levels lying in the interval L. Δ and Σ^2 are measures of long range correlations in the eigenvalue spectra, whereas $P(S)$ indicates short range correlations.

When the underlying system is integrable, Berry and Tabor showed [28], using semiclassical arguments, that the nearest neighbour spacings distribution should be Poisson, corresponding to a completely unstructured sequence of eigenlevels. Thus, for classically integrable systems, the quantum spectra should have

$$P(S) = e^{-s}$$

$$\Delta(L) = L/15 \qquad (15)$$

$$\Sigma^2(L) = L$$

For chaotic systems, there is now considerable evidence that the eigenvalue spectra have the same statistical properties as the eigenvalues of ensembles of random matrices, although a firm theoretical foundation as to why random matrix theory should apply to chaotic systems is lacking (there are several plausible arguments). The basic feature of these energy levels is repulsion. Degeneracies are forbidden due to avoided crossings, and as a result, the spectra have structure and long range correlations. (It may seem paradoxical that regular classical systems have structureless quantum spectra, and irregular classical systems have a structured or *rigid* spectrum!). For ensembles of random hermitian matrices appropriate in describing complex systems (the Gaussian Orthogonal, Unitary or Symplectic Ensembles, GOE, GUE or GSE), all these measures are well known. For symmetric matrices (and this applies to Hamiltonians such as the Hénon-Heiles, and more generally for isolated molecular systems), the quantum spectra should have

$$P(S) \approx \frac{\pi}{2} S e^{-\pi S^2/4}$$

$$\Delta(L) \approx \frac{1}{\pi^2} \log L + \dots \qquad (16)$$

$$\Sigma^2(L) \approx \frac{2}{\pi^2} \log 2\pi L + \dots$$

The expected values for the NNSD is shown in Fig. 4 for the Poisson and GOE cases. The differences in $P(S)$ are apparent for small S: in the chaotic case, degeneracies are less probable, while in the integrable case, degeneracies dominate the eigenvalue spectrum. The Δ and Σ^2 statistics are also very different for the two cases. (It should also be mentioned that the universal behaviour for the long range correlations usually breaks down for large L, and this can be traced [29], using semiclassical arguments to the nature of the periodic orbits in the classical system).

The Poisson and GOE limits are valid for extreme cases of integrable or completely chaotic systems. For systems which are not at these extremes, i.e. systems where some of the dynamics is on tori and some is chaotic, different

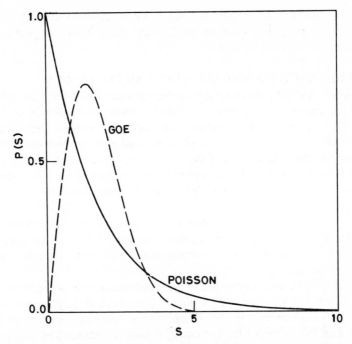

Fig. 4   The nearest neighbour spacing distribution, NNSD for the Poisson and GOE cases, corresponding to the integrable and chaotic limits.

distributions that interpolate between these limits must be used. (One such distribution has been suggested by Berry and Robnik [30], which superposes Poisson and GOE distributions in proportions corresponding to the proportions of phase space occupied by toroidal and chaotic motions). In the analysis of typical experimental data where several symmetry species are likely to be mixed, particular care requires to be taken to deduce the proper behaviour [31].

This type of analysis is termed quantum chaology [26]: the *study of the semiclassical but nonclassical behaviour characteristic of systems whose classical motion exhibits chaos.*

Quantum chaological analysis has been applied [32] to the energy levels of atomic and molecular systems, to verify if the expectations of high energy chaos are well justified. Excited state spectroscopy for small molecular systems is currently sufficiently accurate to be able to identify individual vibrational levels to high precision. Although not entirely unequivocal, it does seem that the statistics of the excited vibrational levels in molecules such as acetylene are well described by random-matrix theory. For atomic systems, such as the electronic levels of uranium, the evidence is more compelling. Some molecular systems are also integrable, and recently, experimental verification of the Poisson distribution for level spacings in such cases has also been made [33].

Many of the ideas pertaining to quantum irregularity are still in a formative stage. There is considerable debate over the use of the term *quantum chaos* itself, and indeed, as to what precisely constitutes the quantum analogue to classical irregular motion. In contrast, classical chaos is defined in a more satisfactory manner. Nevertheless, since much of the behaviour of molecular systems is determined by quantum mechanical effects, these are fundamentally interesting questions to explore.

4. RELEVANCE TO INTRAMOLECULAR PROCESSES

The role of chaos in promoting intramolecular energy transfer is an intuitively easy one to appreciate. In theories of unimolecular decomposition [6, 7, 34] such as the RRK or RRKM, the assumption is made that energy initially delivered into a molecule by collisional or photo excitation is randomized within the molecule rapidly. This follows if the behaviour is statistical. Classically, if the motion is ergodic, then it is guaranteed that every part of the phase space, i.e. every possible configuration will be accessible under the dynamics from the initial excitation.

This assumption, from the earlier discussion of classical chaos, is not automatically guaranteed for any nonlinear system; it depends on whether the motion is mainly chaotic or mainly quasiperiodic, and on the quantum analogues of these properties.

For many molecular systems where the intramolecular vibrational Hamiltonian is of the form H = kinetic energy + potential energy, and the potential energy is essentially of the normal modes + anharmonic coupling terms, a number of empirical studies show that the low energy regime is dominated by quasiperiodic, toroidal motion, while the high energy range is mainly chaotic.

It should also be noted that chaotic motion is not essential to intramolecular energy transfer. In the classical harmonic theory due to Slater, energy can be transferred from one bond to another in a purely quasiperiodic manner [4].

The quantum analogue to quasiperiodic motion seems well defined [35]. The eigenstates are localized around the semiclassical tori, and the levels form a regular spectrum. The quantum analogue of chaos is in comparison poorly defined. The association of chaos to overlapping quantum resonances is appealing [23], and seems compatible with experiments such as multiphoton absorption. However, in recent studies it has been observed [36] that even in extremely (classically) chaotic systems, the wave functions have structure; there is an enhanced probability density around unstable periodic orbits. This phenomenon, termed scarring, indicates that even in the chaotic regime, a completely statistical theory may be fundamentally inadequate. Brumer and Shapiro [7] discuss a variety of hybrid theories wherein the simplicity of the statistical approach can be combined with the minimum required dynamical information to give an accurate description of a variety of intramolecular processes.

Clearly the experimental relevance of quasiperiodicity or chaos depends to a large extent on the experimental configuration. How the system is initially prepared, whether in a pure state or in some mixture, presumably determines the subsequent dynamics and behaviour to a greater extent than the precise nature of the classical dynamics [23].

5. IRREGULAR SCATTERING (IS)

Chaotic motion, as observed in bounded dynamical systems (discussed in the preceding sections) can also be observed in scattering systems where one of the degrees of freedom asymptotically becomes unbounded. Such scattering processes are termed irregular [9], and the most dramatic way in which chaos manifests itself is that scattering functions become singular. Indeed, they are fractal [37] curves.

It is simplest to discuss the phenomenology of irregular scattering through a prototypical example. We consider collinear nonreactive scattering, the hamiltonian being

$$H = \frac{P_R^2}{2\mu} + \frac{1}{2}(p^2 + q^2) + D[V_0 \, e^{-\alpha(R - q)} - 1]^2 \qquad (17)$$

which describes, in reduced coordinates, an atom-harmonic oscillator collision. R and q denote the scattering and oscillator coordinates respectively, and P_R and p are the corresponding conjugate momenta. Such systems were studied by Gottdiener [38] (see also [39, 40]) in the context of complex scattering.

In computing the inelastic transition probability $P_{n_i \to n}$ from initial state n_i to final state n by quasiclassical or classical S-matrix methods [11], it is natural to consider the transformation of the initial classical manifold corresponding to the quantum state n_i due to the scattering process. This is usually done [41] by evolving a family of classical trajectories with initial conditions, in the example above, $p_i(0) = -(2n_i + 1)^{1/2} \sin(\phi_i)$, $q_i(0) = (2n_i + 1)^{1/2} \cos(\phi_i)$, $\phi_i \in [0, 2\pi]$. When the collision is over, i.e. as $t \to \infty$, the final action or final quantum number n_f can be evaluated, and a plot of n_f vs. ϕ_i yields information about the classical scattering process. When the scattering is irregular, then this curve is fractal, and a typical example of this is shown in Fig. 5b, to be contrasted with regular scattering from the same potential, shown in Fig. 5a.

The fractality of this curve for IS has several implications for the scattering process [10, 42]. First, there are an infinite number of trajectories with asymptotically zero kinetic energy. These are trapped and quantum mechanically can be considered to correspond to Feshbach resonances. Secondly, the transition probability $P_{n_i \to n}$ or S-matrix element $S_{n_i;n}$ is constructed [11,42] from trajectories which are located as the zeroes of the curves $n_f(\phi_i) - n$. The formal expression for the S-matrix elements is [11]

$$S_{n_i;n} = \Sigma_{traj} \left(\frac{1}{2\pi}\right)^{1/2} \left[\frac{\partial I_f}{\partial \phi_i}\right]^{-1/2} \exp[i\Phi/\hbar - i\pi\alpha/2] \qquad (18)$$

where Φ is the classical action, α the Maslov index, and the sum extends over all trajectories that satisfy the boundary condition $n_f = n$. When $n_f(\phi_i)$ is fractal, then the zeroes can be infinite (depending on the particular n) and spaced infinitesimally close. All classical and semiclassical theories break down and are clearly inapplicable.

What are the hallmarks of irregular scattering? Although the phenomenon is not completely explored, it seems that IS is sensitive to nonlinearity in the interaction potential. In the present example in Eq. (17), the interaction potential is of the Morse type, although it should be pointed out that the presence of a well in the interaction potential is neither necessary nor sufficient for IS to occur.

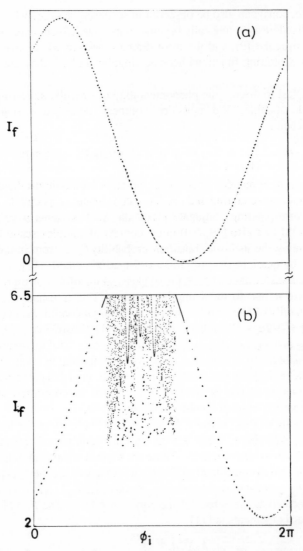

Fig. 5 Final action I_f versus initial angle ϕ_i for the case of inelastic atom-molecule collision showing: (a) regular scattering and (b) irregular scattering. Energies are (a) 5 and (b) 1 in units of the oscillator quantum respectively.

Furthermore, there is a sensitive dependence both on the initial internal state and on the kinetic energy. In some cases, a sharp onset is observed. As the energy is lowered below a threshold, the scattering becomes irregular, suggesting that this transition might occur via bifurcations [43].

Since nonlinear interaction potentials are ubiquitous in chemical systems, it is of importance to study the quantum manifestations of IS. These are, in principle, accessible to currently feasible laboratory experiments. In the case of nuclear scattering processes, it has long been observed that the cross-sections fluctuate as a function of energy. These were interpreted as arising from many overlapping nuclear resonances (with the resonance width larger than the mean spacing). Random-matrix models were also successfully applied.

Note the similarity with the bound-state situation, wherein overlapping resonances are also presumed to underlie classical or quantal irregularity. In fact, the success of random-matrix theory in the analysis of the eigenvalue spectra of bound chaotic systems suggests a similar application in the scattering situation. Blümel and Smilansky [42] argue that the eigenvalues of the S-matrix (which are distributed on the unit circle since S is unitary) in IS should fall in the same universality class. Further, the dependence of the S-matrix on the channel indices at fixed kinetic energy is erratic, as is the dependence of a given S-matrix element on the energy. Numerical studies of model systems with a few degrees of freedom seem to confirm this.

In going from the S-matrix to scattering cross-sections or other experimental observables, considerable averaging can be involved [44]. It is a moot question whether it will be possible to experimentally detect these fluctuations.

6. CHAOS IN NON-CONSERVATIVE SYSTEMS

The preceding discussion has been restricted, to conservative systems, where the total energy is held constant, and phase space volumes are preserved under the dynamics. These concepts are relevant for isolated molecules, since for such microscopic systems there are no additional effects like friction or other interactions to take into account. Several chemical systems of interest do not, however, have this feature.

One example is given by molecules in the presence of a field, when the dynamics is governed by a nonautonomous Hamiltonian. The features of energy transfer or dynamics in this situation are somewhat modified from the conservative case since the invariant surfaces in the system are no longer tori. However, it is usually possible to transform a nonautonomous Hamiltonian system to an autonomous one by augmenting the phase space appropriately. KAM-type theorems are known [16] for such systems, which are in some sense not very different from conservative Hamiltonian systems; for an application in the context of multiphoton absorption, see [45].

The case of dissipative systems is considerably more interesting, since here phase space volumes are not conserved in time. Simple examples of dissipative dynamical systems are afforded by chemical kinetic systems arising, for example, from coupled reactions with feedback. It is therefore important to describe the phenomenology of chaos in such situations [46].

Dissipative systems were first investigated with a view to understanding fluid dynamics and turbulence and in particular to understanding how, as a function of a parameter, the dynamics changes from being periodic to aperiodic.

In the simplest system with a frictional term in the equation of motion,

$$\ddot{q} + q + \gamma\dot{q} = 0, \tag{19}$$

a damped harmonic oscillator, for example, it is well known that for all initial conditions, asymptotically the trajectory reaches the point $q = \dot{q} = 0$. In other cases, the final state may not be as structureless as a single point, as in the van der Pol oscillator. The equation of motion is [13]

$$\ddot{q} - \lambda(1 - q^2)\,\dot{q} + w^2 q = 0 \qquad (20)$$

and the dynamics asymptotically reaches a limit cycle. Both these examples above are of simple attractors, since for any initial condition, the final state is the same. In more complicated dynamical systems, the nature of attractors can be rather different. Consider a system with parameter μ

$$\frac{d\mathbf{X}}{dt} = F(\mathbf{X}, \mu) \qquad (21)$$

As this parameter is varied, the nature (stability) of the steady state solutions, i.e. those points $\mathbf{X}^*$ such that

$$\frac{d\mathbf{X}}{dt}\Big|_{x=x^*} = 0 \qquad (22)$$

can change. The parameter value when this occurs is termed a bifurcation point; the occurrence of bifurcations can be deduced from a study of the eigenvalues of the linearized equations of motion around the steady states. In the Hopf bifurcation, as the parameter is varied, a stable limit point (as in equation (19) above) becomes unstable, while a limit cycle becomes stable. A well-known example [48] in a chemical kinetics setting derives from the following reaction scheme,

$$\begin{aligned}
A &\rightarrow X \\
B + X &\rightarrow D + Y \\
Y + 2X &\rightarrow 3X \\
X &\rightarrow E
\end{aligned} \qquad (23)$$

where A and B are reactant species, C and D are products, with intermediates X and Y. The kinetic equations can be written in appropriately scaled coordinates for the concentrations of X and Y as

$$\begin{aligned}
dX/dt &= A + X^2 Y - BX - X \\
dY/dt &= BX - X^2 Y
\end{aligned} \qquad (24)$$

with A and B now denoting the fixed concentrations of the reactants. It is easy to show from linear stability analysis that the steady state $X_0 = A$, $Y_0 = B/A$ is attracting for $B/A < 2$. A Hopf bifurcation occurs for $B/A = 2$, and for higher values of B/A, a limit cycle solution is attracting (Fig. 6). Although the above reaction sequence is not very realistic, the resulting dynamical system, known as the Brusselator, has helped in understanding several features of complexity in simple nonlinear dynamical systems.

As the number of components in the reaction scheme, and the number of intermediates increase, the dynamical equations are of necessity higher dimensional. In addition, a given system can have several bifurcations as parameters are varied. A sequence of Hopf bifurcations, for instance takes the motion from a limit point to a limit cycle to a limit 2-torus to a limit 3-torus and so on. (At each bifurcation, there is the creation of a new independent frequency). One scenario for the onset of chaos [13, 46, 47] in dissipative systems initially

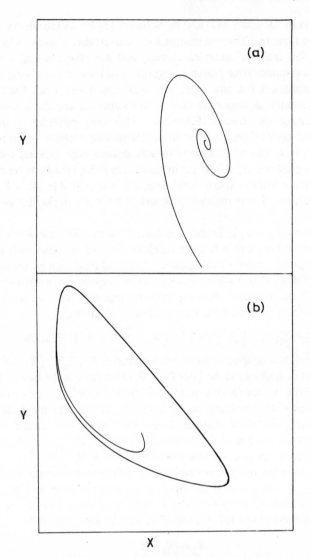

Fig. 6   Examples of (a) limit point and (b) limit cycle in a dissipative dynamical system, the Brusselator, Eq. (24). The values of the constants are: (a) $A = 1$, $B = 1$ and (b) $A = 1$, $B = 3$.

involves the above sequence of Hopf bifurcations. After the third bifurcation, however, the motion is (generically) trapped on manifolds that are not tori, but have an extremely complicated topology. Ruelle and Takens [46] call these strange attractors (SA), and show that the motion on SAs is chaotic, in the sense of having extreme sensitivity to initial conditions (a positive Lyapunov exponent).

There are other "routes to chaos", distinct from the strange attractor picture sketched above, depending on the nature of the bifurcations. When the bifurcations are of the pitchfork type, one has a period doubling and an infinite number of period-doublings precedes aperiodicity in this so called Feigenbaum scenario.

(See the texts by Devaney [47] and by Schuster [3] for an introduction to chaos in dissipative systems.) These scenarios form universality classes. A large variety of systems fall into the same categories, and are characterised by identical qualitative and quantitative features, regardless of their physical origin.

Chaotic attractors (of any type) are often low-dimensional fractal objects [37]. Consequently, an important method of identifying and characterizing them is in estimating the fractal dimension. This also provides a method of distinguishing aperiodicity arising from deterministic chaos or from random (noisy) processes. The latter case is infinite dimensional. Several methods for deducing the presence of SA's in the dynamics, as indeed methods for computing fractal dimensions from experimental data, are now available [46, 49]. Some of the best examples of experimentally observed SA's are in oscillatory chemical kinetics.

A well-known example is the Belousov-Zhabotinskii reaction wherein an easily brominated organic substance (such as citric or malonic acid) undergoes metal ion (such as cerium or manganese) catalysed oxidation by bromate ion in aqueous media of pH 0–1. When carried out in a continuous stirred tank reactor (CSTR) with the reactants flowing into the reaction cell, we have an open dynamical system with the following evolution equations,

$$\dot{X_j} = F_j(X_1...X_n) + \mu(X_j^0 - X_j) \qquad j = 1, 2, ..., n \qquad (25)$$

where the n chemical species have concentrations X_1, X_2 ..., X_n and X_j^0 is the concentration of species j in the inlet flow. $F_j(X)$ represent the kinetic equations that follow from the appropriate reaction sequence specific to this case. For the Belousov-Zhabotinsky reaction itself a variety of reaction mechanisms have been suggested, the most realistic being the Oregonator model [48]. μ is proportional to the inverse of the residence time in the reactor, and is the control parameter. The dynamics, i.e. the concentrations $X_j(t)$, $j = 1, ..., n$, can be studied as a function of the parameter μ. A typical experimental result [50] is shown in Fig. 7a where $X(t)$ is the bromide ion concentration. In Fig. 7b, $X(t)$ is plotted versus $X(t + \tau)$, which provides a visual reconstruction of the SA. Similar SA's can be found in several systems. The Rössler equations [51],

$$\dot{X_1} = (X_2 + X_3)$$
$$\dot{X_2} = X_1 + X_2/5 \qquad (26)$$
$$\dot{X_3} = X_1X_3 - 5.7X_3 + 2/5$$

also derive from a chemical reaction sequence, and the SA supported by this set of equations is shown in Fig. 8. A number of chemical and biochemical reactions are known to show periodic as well as aperiodic oscillations [8, 48], and several of these have been studied in the context of dissipative dynamical systems.

7. CONCLUDING REMARKS

Nonlinear effects are extremely important in a variety of contexts. Most nonlinear systems have a rich and complicated dynamics. In addition to regular or chaotic motion, the possibility of bifurcations vastly increases the possible dynamical

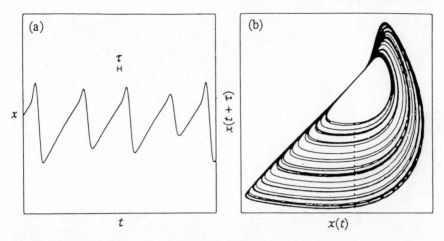

Fig. 7 Experimentally measured strange attractor in the Belousov-Zhabotinsky reaction (from [50]). The bromide ion concentration is plotted as a function of time in (a), and the reconstructed attractor is shown in (b).

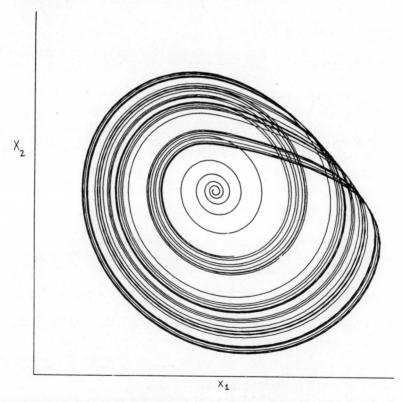

Fig. 8 Projection of the Rössler attractor on to the x-y plane; the initial condition for the flow is $(0, 0, 0)$, and it can be seen that after an initial transient period, the trajectory is confined to an annular region in the configuration space.

behaviours. Although some features are system specific and must be addressed individually, it is significant that much of the bevaviour falls into universality classes wherein the details of the individual system become unimportant.

Molecular systems have provided a good testing ground for many of the concepts of classical, semiclassical, and quantum mechanics, and in particular, the interrelations between these. Indeed, this has also provided the impetus for the development of several ideas in the present context—for example the question of quantum irregularity, and the development of semiclassical quantization methods. The importance of chaos as a means of promoting statistical behaviour in molecules is easy to appreciate; this has therefore prompted the exploration of a variety of measures of quantum chaotic behaviour.

The application of dynamical systems theory to chemical kinetic systems has also opened up interesting avenues of research. Apart from providing an easily realizable and practical demonstration of deterministic chaos in nature, this has also shown how nonlinearity (in the kinetic mass action law) can lead to aperiodic behaviour. Taken in a biochemical context, for instance, this can have significant implications for the destruction of periodicity at higher levels of organization. Chaos at the molecular level can cause perceptible changes at the cellular level.

Nonlinearity is ubiquitous in nature. As a consequence, chaotic phenomena are quite common, and occur in a wide variety of systems. Some areas where the existence and effect of dynamical chaos in chemical systems is significant have been outlined in this chapter.

8.   ACKNOWLEDGEMENTS

I thank C. Orr and K. Takatsuka for help in preparing this manuscript, and the Institute of Molecular Science for hospitality. I also thank the Computer Centre of IMS, Okazaki National Research Institute for the use of the Hitac M-680H and S-820/30 computers.

REFERENCES

1. P. Cvitanovic, *Universality in Chaos*, Adam Hilger, Bristol, 1984.
2. P. Berge, Y. Pomeau and C. Vidal, *Order within Chaos*, Hermann, Paris 1984.
3. H.G. Schuster, *Deterministic Chaos*, Physik Verlag, Weinheim, 1988.
4. D.W. Noid, M.L. Koszykowski and R.A. Marcus, Annu. Rev. Phys. Chem. **32** (1981) 267.
5. G.S. Ezra, C.C. Martens and L.E. Fried, J. Phys. Chem. **89** (1987) 3721.
6. D. Wardlaw and R.A. Marcus, Adv. Chem. Phys. **70** (1988) 231.
7. P. Brumer and M. Shapiro, Adv. Chem. Phys. **70** (1988) 365.
8. C. Vidal and A. Pacault, *Non-Equilibrium Dynamics in Chemical Systems*, Springer-Verlag, Berlin 1984.
9. B. Eckhardt, Physica **D 33** (1988) 89.
10. P. Gaspard and S.A. Rice, J. Chem. Phys. **90** (1989) 2225, 2242 and 2255.
11. W.H. Miller, Adv. Chem. Phys. **25** (1974) 69, 30 (1975) 77; Science, **233** (1986) 171.
12. M.V. Berry in *Topics in Nonlinear Dynamics*, AIP Conference Proceedings No. 46, AIP, New York, 1978.

13. M. Tabor, *Chaos and Integrability in Nonlinear Dynamics*, Wiley Interscience, New York 1989.
14. A. Ozorio de Almeida, *Hamiltonian Systems: Chaos and Quantization*, Cambridge University Press, 1989.
15. R.Z. Sagdeev, D.A. Usikov and G.M. Zaslavsky, *Nonlinear Physics*, Harwood Academic, Chur 1988.
16. V.I. Arnol'd, *Mathematical Methods of Classical Mechanics*, Springer-Verlag, New York 1978.
17. M. Hénon in *Chaotic Behaviour in Deterministic Systems*, G. Iooss, R.H.G. Helleman and R. Stora, eds, North Holland, Amsterdam (1983).
18. I. Percival and D. Richards, *Introduction to Dynamics*, Cambridge (1982).
19. M.V. Berry in *Chaotic Behaviour in Deterministic Systems*, G. Iooss, R.H.G. Helleman and R Stora, eds, North Holland, Amsterdam.
20. R. Ramaswamy, J. Chem. Phys. **82** (1985) 747.
21. S. Sinha and R. Ramaswamy, Mol. Phys. **67** (1989) 335.
22. I. Percival, J. Phys. **B6** (1974) L229; Adv. Chem. Phys. **36** (1977) 1.
23. R.A. Marcus in, *Horizons in Quantum Chemistry*, K. Fukui and B. Pullman, eds, Reidel, Dordrecht (1980); Ann. NY Acad. Sci. **357** (1980) 159.
24. R. Ramaswamy and R.A. Marcus, J. Chem. Phys. **74** (1981) 1379, 1385; R. Ramaswamy, Chem. Phys. **76** (1983) 15.
25. M.L. Mehta, *Random Matrices and the Statistical Theory of Energy Levels*, Academic, New York 1967; T.A. Brody, J. Flores, J.B. French, P.A. Mello, A. Pandey and S.S.M. Wong, Rev. Mod. Phys. **53** (1981) 385.
26. M.V. Berry, Proc. Roy. Soc. **A413** (1987) 183.
27. B. Eckhardt, Phys. Rep. **163** (1988) 205.
28. M.V. Berry and M. Tabor, Proc. Roy. Soc. **A356** (1977) 375.
29. M.V. Berry, Proc. Roy. Soc. **A400** (1985) 229.
30. M.V. Berry and M. Robnik, J. Phys. **A 17** (1984) 2413.
31. S. Sinha and R. Ramaswamy, J. Phys. **B22** (1989) 2985.
32. E. Abramson, R.W. Field, D. Imre, K.K. Innes and J.L. Kinsey, J. Chem. Phys. **83** (1985) 458; J. Chem. Phys. **80** (1984) 2298.
33. G.R. Welch, M.M. Kash, C. Iu, L. Hsu and D. Kleppner, Phys. Rev. Lett. **62** (1989) 893.
34. R.A. Marcus, Faraday Discuss. Chem. Soc. **75** (1983) 103.
35. R. Ramaswamy, J. Chem. Phys. **80** (1984) 6194.
36. E.J. Heller, Phys. Rev. Lett. **53** (1984) 1515; E Bogomolny, Physica **D 31** (1988) 169; M.V. Berry, Proc. Roy. Soc. Lond. **A 423** (1989) 219.
37. B.B. Mondelbrot, *The Fractal Geometry of Nature*, Freeman, San Francisco 1983.
38. L. Gottdiener, Mol. Phys. **29** (1975) 1309.
39. C.C. Rankin and W.H. Miller, J. Chem. Phys. **55** (1971) 3150.
40. D.W. Noid, S.K. Gray and S.A. Rice, J. Chem. Phys. **85** (1986) 2649.
41. R. Ramaswamy and A.E. DePristo, Chem. Phys. Lett. **77** (1981) 190; R. Ramaswamy, Pramana 16 (1981) 139.
42. R. Blümel and U. Smilansky, Phys. Rev. Lett. **60** (1988) 477; Physica **D36** (1989) 111; Phys. Rev. Lett. **64** (1990) 241.
43. S. Bleher, E. Ott and C. Grebogi, Phys. Rev. Lett. **63** (1989) 919.
44. R.D. Levine and R. B. Bernstein, *Molecular Reaction Dynamics and Chemical Reactivity*, Oxford University Press (1987).
45. R. B. Ramaswamy, P. Siders and R.A. Marcus, J. Chem. Phys. **74** (1981) 4418.

46. D. Ruelle, *Chaotic Evolution and Strange Attractors*, Cambridge University Press, 1989.

47. R.L. Devaney, *An Introduction to Chaotic Dynamical Systems*, Addison Wesley, Reading, 1989.

48. R.J. Field in *Theoretical Chemistry*, Vol. 4, ed. H. Eyring and D. Henderson, Academic, New York, 1978; R.J. Field and R.M. Noyes, J. Chem. Phys. **60** (1974) 1877; B.F. Gray in *Reaction Kinetics*, Vol 1, The Chemical Society, London (1975).

49. G. Mayer-Kress, ed. *Dimensions and Entropies in Chaotic Systems*, Springer-Verlag, Berlin (1986).

50. J.C. Roux and H.L. Swinney in [8].

51. N. Packard, J. Crutchfield, J.D. Farmer and R. Shaw, Phys. Rev. Lett. **45** (1980) 712.

5. Dynamics of Barrierless Chemical Reactions in Solution

Biman Bagchi

Solid State and Structural Chemistry Unit
Indian Institute of Science
Bangalore, India

Abstract

Recent advances in picosecond and subpicosecond laser spectroscopy have made it possible to study ultra-fast chemical reactions directly in the time domain with a time resolution hitherto impossible. Many important chemical reactions have been studied in recent years and many interesting discoveries have been made. In this article, we present results of our study on barrierless chemical reactions in solution, with applications to isomerization dynamics and electron transfer reactions.

1. INTRODUCTION

Many important chemical reactions occur in the absence of a significant barrier to the reactive motion. Such reactions are usually very fast, with time constants often in the picosecond and even in the subpicosecond domain. Detailed study of these reactions required the development of ultra-fast laser spectroscopy. Many important photochemical reactions in organic dye molecules are found to occur on a barrierless potential-energy surface. Barrierless reactions are also common in photochemical electron transfer reactions and in many biochemical reactions of great interest. Several detailed theoretical and experimental studies of barrierless reactions have been carried out in the recent years [1–3].

The dynamics of a barrierless reaction can differ considerably from those in the presence of a high activation barrier. In the absence of a high barrier separating the reactant from the product, there is no clear separation of time scales between the motion in the reactive region and in the rest of the potential surface. In such a situation, the usual approach to the description of a chemical reaction in terms of a time-dependent rate constant may no longer be valid. In fact, a steady state may not at all be reached within the life-time of the reactant. Theoretically, this implies that the lowest non-zero eigenvalue of the kinetic equation for the dynamics of the reaction may not alone be sufficient to describe the dynamics because the eigenvalue spectrum may be dense. In such a situation, a more detailed description of the dynamics is obviously required. An important feature of a barrierless chemical reaction is that the decay of the reactant population on the excited state surface may depend critically on the initial conditions.

In a well-known study on barrierless dynamics, Förster and Hoffmann [4] investigated the survival probability of an initially prepared excited state by modelling the reactive motion as the motion of a Brownian particle on a harmonic surface. The non-radiative decay is assumed to occur from a position dependent sink located at the origin of the excited state potential surface. However, there are several assumptions in the Förster-Hoffmann theory that are dfifficult to justify. They assume that the rate of non-radiative decay from the sink is a quadratic function of its position. If the sink is located at the minimum of the excited state surface (as is usually the case), then this assumption implies that the rate of decay from the sink increases even when the energy gap between the excited and the ground state surfaces increases. This is clearly unrealistic. The second major problem is that this theory neglects the diffusive spreading of an initially localized state on the excited state surface. In the model of Förster and Hoffmann, the system follows only an average pathway instead of following a distribution of paths which would be present in an experimental situation. The theory of Förster and Hoffmann makes several predictions some of which are in disagreement with experimental results.

Recently a detailed theory of barrierless reactions in solution has been developed by Bagchi et al [5, 6]. It makes detailed predictions on the time dependence of the excited state population density and of the dependence of the dynamics on various solvent parameters. It has been tested against experiments [1, 7, 8] and a certain degree of agreement between the theoretical predictions and experimental results has been found. Recently this theory has been generalized and extended in several directions. Barrierless reaction on a two dimensional potential energy surface has been considered [9, 10]. The theory has been used to describe polar solvent dynamic effects on barrierless electron transfer reactions [11] also.

In this article we shall discuss the essential features of the dynamics of a chemical reaction on a barrierless potential energy surface. This is presented in section 2. In section 3, we discuss the results for a barrierless electron transfer reaction and in section 4 for a photoisomerization reaction. Section 5 concludes with a brief discussion on the future problems.

2. THEORETICAL DESCRIPTION

The theoretical description proposed by Bagchi et al [5, 6] is based on the following equation of motion for the excited state probability distribution function $P(x, t)$:

$$\frac{\partial P(x, t)}{\partial t} = \mathscr{L} P(x, t) - k_0 S(x) P(x, t) - k_r P(x, t) \tag{1}$$

with the notation—x is the one dimensional reaction coordinate; t the time; $S(x)$ the position dependent sink function; k_0 a measure of the nonradiative decay rate from the sink; and k_r the position independent radiative decay rate. For over-damped motion on a harmonic surface, the operator $\mathscr{L}$ is the usual Smoluchowski operator

$$\mathscr{L}_s = A\frac{\partial^2}{\partial x^2} + B\frac{\partial}{\partial x} x \tag{2}$$

where $A = k_B T/\zeta$, $B = \mu\omega^2/\zeta$, ζ is the relevant friction coefficient, ω the frequency of the assumed harmonic surface, μ the effective mass, k_B the Boltzmann constant and T the temperature. For under-damped motion, $\mathscr{L}$ is a Fokker-Planck operator given by the following equation

$$\mathscr{L}_{FP} = -v\frac{\partial}{\partial x} + \omega^2 x\frac{\partial}{\partial v} + \frac{\zeta}{\mu}\frac{\partial}{\partial v}\left[v + \frac{k_B T}{\mu}\frac{\partial}{\partial v}\right] \tag{3}$$

where v is the instantaneous velocity of the Brownian particle.

Equation 1 embodies the competition between the rate of population relaxation on the excited state potential surface and the rate of population loss from the sink region. It is, therefore, not surprising that the relaxation depends critically on the form of the sink function, $S(x)$. We shall see that a simple description like Eq. 1 can lead to rather rich dynamical behaviour.

A similar theoretical description has been employed by Agmon and Hopfield [12] to describe the kinetics of rebinding of CO and O_2 to the iron in heme in myoglobin. Sumi and Marcus [13] and Nadler and Marcus [14] have used essentially the same equation to study solvent effects on nonadiabatic electron transfer reactions. Schulten et al [15] have earlier used a similar description, in a somewhat limited form, to describe the transfer of excitation between two groups in a large macromolecule. Because of its applicability to a wide range of problems a detailed analytical and numerical study of Eq. 1 has recently been carried out [2, 3]. In the next sections, we shall solve Eq. 1 for several forms of the sink function $S(x)$. The quantity of physical interest is the total survival probability, $P_e(t)$, defined as

$$P_e(t) = \int_{-\infty}^{\infty} dx\ P(x, t) \tag{4}$$

The time dependence of $P_e(t)$ can be measured experimentally.

As mentioned in the Introduction, for the case of barrierless reactions in solution, the usual definition of the rate constant in terms of a steady flux across the reactive region may not be applicable. An eigenvalue analysis of Eq. 1 can still be carried out and the lowest eigenvalue can be obtained, but the identification of the lowest eigenvalue with the rate constant may not be meaningful. This is because the eigenvalue spectrum may be dense such that a single exponential decay may not be achieved within the lifetime of the excited state. It is therefore useful to introduce two different rate constants. The first one is the time averaged rate constant, k_I, defined through

$$k_I^{-1} = \int_0^{\infty} dt\ P_e(t) \tag{5}$$

where $P_e(t)$, defined by Eq. 4, is the total population remaining on the excited state surface at a time t after excitation. The second is the long time rate constant, k_L, defined through the long time limit of $P_e(t)$,

$$k_L = -\lim_{t \to \infty} \frac{\partial}{\partial t} \ln P_e(t) \qquad (6)$$

There may be situations where these two rate constants differ significantly from each other. It is important to realize that these two rate constants will contain somewhat different information. The influence of the initial conditions (such as the excitation wavelength, and the frequency of the ground state potential surface) on the subsequent relaxation will be contained in k_I, but not in k_L. We shall see later that k_I and k_L may also have different viscosity dependence.

Note that in barrierless photochemical reactions, although, of course, the fluorescence yield may be measured, the usual definition of fluorescence quantum yield in terms of a radiative rate constant, k_r, and a nonradiative rate constant, k_{nr}, is no longer valid. In fact, if the decay of the fluorescing state is nonexponential over most of the lifetime of the excited state, then no unique definition of quantum-yield in terms of rate constants is possible. An approximate working definition may be provided by the following expression

$$\varphi_f \simeq \frac{k_r}{k_I + k_r}$$

For chemical reactions in the absence of a barrier the fluorescence quantum yield may depend rather strongly on the excitation wavelength and also on the viscosity of the solvent. It is important to note that for barrierless reactions the fluorescence quantum yield may not provide any direct information about the nonradiative decay rate.

2.1 Pinhole Sink and Staircase Model

The pinhole sink was introduced in [5] to model the situation where the radiationless relaxation occurs only from the neighbourhood of the origin of the excited state potential surface and where the rate of decay from the sink is much faster than that of the natural motion on the surface. Thus, the system decays with unit probability when it arrives at the origin. The attractive features of this model are that it can be solved exactly for the Smoluchowski operator and that it provides a simple, analytic expression for the survival probability, $P_e(t)$. Subsequently, two other instantaneous death models have been solved for the survival probability. The first one is a generalization [16] of the Oster-Nishijima model and the second one is new, called the staircase model [16]. Both the models consider reactive motion to occur on a "flat" surface. In the Oster-Nishijima model the diffusion is limited by two sinks (or absorbing barriers) on the two sides that give rise to the decay of the population. In the staircase model, the diffusion is limited by an elastic (reflecting) barrier on one side and an absorbing barrier on the other. Note that the staircase model is somewhat intermediate between the pinhole sink and the Oster-Nishijima models. The staircase model may describe a situation in which the relevant reactive motion is on a "flat" surface which is formed from overlap of two zero-order surfaces and the sink is located near the crossing of the two surfaces.

The instantaneous death models obviously represent drastic simplifications.

However, they may be relevant to the situation where there is a "funnel" in some region of the potential surface. This funnel may arise because of the close proximity of the ground and the excited state surfaces at some specific geometry or conformation of the molecule, as illustrated in Fig. 1. Such a funnel can be formed by a "weak" avoided crossing of two zero order surfaces.

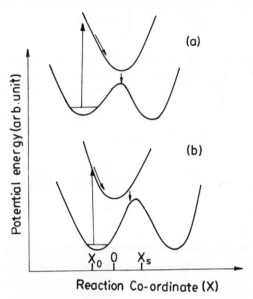

Fig. 1 Schematic illustration of potential energy surfaces in which the nonradiative relaxation occurs from: (a) symmetric sink with zero barrier and (b) a displaced (asymmetric) sink with a small internal barrier. X is the reaction coordinate which can either be a larger amplitude rotational motion in photoisomerization or the solvation energy for the electron transfer reaction.

In the following, we briefly summarize the major predictions of the instantaneous death models.

2.1.1 *Pinhole Sink*
In this case we need to solve Eq. 1 (with $\mathscr{L}$ given by Eq. 2) for the following initial-boundary values:

$$P(x, t = 0) = P_0(x) \tag{7a}$$

$$P(x = \pm \infty, t) = 0 \tag{7b}$$

$$P(x = 0, t) = 0 \tag{7c}$$

It is straightforward to solve this problem by the method of images [5]. The total population remaining on the excited state after time t, $P_e(t)$, is given by [6]

$$P_e(t) = \exp(-k_r t) \int_0^\infty dx'[P_0(x') + P_0(-x')] \, \mathrm{erf} \, F(x', t) \tag{8}$$

where

$$F(x, t) = \left[\frac{B}{2A(1 - e^{-2Bt})} \right]^{1/2} \times e^{-Bt} \tag{9a}$$

The error function, erf a, is defined by [17]

$$\text{erf } a = \frac{2}{\sqrt{\pi}} \int_0^a dy \, e^{-y^2} \tag{9b}$$

The predictions of this model will be discussed later in this section. Here we note that a simple expression can be obtained for $P_e(t)$ when $P_0(x)$ is given by the equilibrium probability distribution on the excited state surface. In that case $P_e(t)$ is given by [3, 15]

$$P_e(t) = \frac{2}{\pi} \sin^{-1}(e^{-Bt}) \tag{10}$$

This expression was first obtained by Schulten, Schulten and Szabo [15]. However, note that Eq. 10 is valid only when $P_0(x)$ is a Boltzmann distribution. Equation 8 is the general solution.

2.1.2 Staircase Model

In this case, the reactive motion occurs on a flat surface and $\mathcal{L}_s$ is given by Eq. 2 with $B = 0$. We choose the coordinate system such that the reflecting barrier is at the origin and the absorbing barrier is at $x = a$. The initial-boundary values are given by

$$P(x, t = 0) = P_0(x) \tag{11a}$$

$$\frac{\partial P}{\partial x} (x, t) \bigg|_{x=0} = 0 \tag{11b}$$

$$P(x = a, t) = 0 \tag{11c}$$

This problem can be solved by the method of repeated reflections [16] and is given by

$$P(x,t) = \int dx' P_0(x') \, (x, t | x') \tag{12a}$$

$$P(x, t \mid x') = \exp(-k_r t) \, (4\pi A t)^{-1/2}$$

$$\sum_{n=-\infty}^{\infty} (-1)^n \left\{ \exp\left[- \frac{(x - x' + 2na)^2}{4At} \right] + \exp\left[- \frac{(x + x' + 2na)^2}{4At} \right] \right\} \tag{12b}$$

The total population on the excited state surface after time t, $P_e(t)$, is obtained by integrating $P(x, t)$ which leads to a sum of four error functions [17]. However, it is convenient to simplify Eq. 12b by using Poisson summation [17]. The resulting expression for $P_e(t)$ is now given by

$$P_e(t) = \frac{4}{\pi} \exp(-k_r t) \sum_{n=0}^{\infty} (-1)^n \frac{1}{2n + 1}$$

$$\times \exp\left[-\frac{(2n + 1)^2\pi^2}{4a^2} At\right] \int_0^a dx' \cos \frac{(2n + 1)\pi x'}{2a} P_0(x') \tag{13}$$

2.2 The Gaussian sink model

The general Gaussian sink is represented by a Gaussian function centred at a position x_s, measured from the origin of the excited state potential surface and is given by

$$S(x) = \frac{1}{\sigma_s\sqrt{\pi}} \exp[-(x - x_s)^2/\sigma_s^2], \tag{14}$$

where σ_s is the usual measure of the width of the Gaussian function. The general Gaussian sink may be a realistic description of the position dependence of the nonradiative decay rate from the excited state surface. This is because the energy difference between two harmonic surfaces is a quadratic function of x (reaction coordinate) and so an exponential gap law predicts a shifted Gaussian distribution for the transition probability between the two surfaces. The Gaussian sink also has useful limiting properties. In the limit $\sigma_s \to 0$, we recover the delta-function sink introduced earlier. If one takes the limit $k_0 \to \infty$ in the delta-function sink, then we obtain the pinhole sink. As we shall see later, this last limit proves to be rather useful in our analysis.

If the excited state potential surface is not flat, then the position of the sink function, x_s, plays a very important role in the dynamics, especially for a narrow sink. If the sink is centred at the origin ($x_s = 0$), then we shall refer to it as a symmetric sink, while with $x_s \neq 0$ will be referred to as a displaced (or asymmetric) sink (see Fig. 1).

We now discuss some general aspects of the finite decay models. Note that Eq. 1, with $\mathscr{L}$ given by Eq. 2, contains three time constants, A, B, and k_0 (with ς as the rotational friction). The last two, B and k_0, depend on the potential surface, B through ω and k_0 through the energy gap between the two participating surfaces. At low friction these three time constants may be of the same order of magnitude as for many systems. At very small values of ς, the rate may even be limited by k_0. At intermediate to large values of the friction, the dynamics at long times will be largely controlled by B. It is convenient to transform Eq. 1 to the following form

$$\frac{\partial P}{\partial t_1} = \tilde{A}\frac{\partial^2 P}{\partial x^2} + \frac{\partial}{\partial x}(xP) - \tilde{k}_0 S(x)P - \tilde{k}_r P \tag{15}$$

where

$$t_1 = Bt, \ \tilde{A} = A/B, \ \tilde{k}_0 = k_0/B, \ \tilde{k}_r = \dot{k}_r/B \tag{15a}$$

Equation 15 is in a dimensionless form suitable for studying general relaxation properties. If a long time rate k_L exists, then dimensional analysis gives (for $k_r = 0$)

$$k_L \simeq Bf(\tilde{A}, \tilde{k}_0), \tag{16}$$

where the function f depends on friction only through, $\tilde{k}_0 \ (= k_0/B)$, $\tilde{A}$ is independent of friction. In the limit $\tilde{k}_0 \gg 1$, we recover the pinhole sink and f approaches unity, so $k_L = B$, i.e., inverse friction dependence. In the other limit where $\tilde{k}_0 \ll 1$, the rate is controlled by k_0/B and $f \doteq \tilde{k}_0$, so that $k_L \doteq k_0$, and the rate is independent of friction. These two limiting cases have also been confirmed numerically [16]. Thus, k_L will show fractional friction dependence for intermediate values of $\tilde{k}_0$. The behaviour of k_t is more complicated and will be discussed later.

The main point of the preceding discussion is that the dynamics of relaxation and also the friction dependence of the rate is controlled by the ratio k_0/B. It follows that the fractional friction dependence predicted here arises from a competition between the rate of the temporal evolution of the population distribution towards its equilibrium form and the rate of removal of population from the sink region. This latter process prevents the distribution from attaining its equilibrium form on the excited state potential surface.

For a realistic choice of the sink function, Eq. 1 must be solved numerically. Several methods of solving this equation have been proposed. It is interesting to note that all the numerical methods face difficulty as k_0 becomes very large. It is thus fortunate that we know exactly, for a narrow sink, the result when $k_0 \to \infty$. In this limit, we get back the pinhole sink.

3. BARRIERLESS ELECTRON TRANSFER REACTIONS

We shall now consider an outersphere barrierless electron transfer reaction and discuss the role of collective solvent dynamics on such a reaction. Examples of barrierless electron transfer reactions are the photo-induced electron transfer reactions in many conjugated aromatic molecules. These reactions are very fast, with lifetimes of the order of few picoseconds. Experiments indicate that these reactions may also be coupled strongly to the polarization relaxation of the solvent. Initial experiments of Kossower and Huppert [18] suggested that the time constants of such barrierless reactions may be directly proportional to the longitudinal relaxation time τ_L of the solvent [19]. More detailed experiments carried out later by Barbara and coworkers [20] and by Su and Simon [21] have shown that the dependence of the rate of electron transfer on τ_L may not be so simple. However, in all these later experiments a strong correlation was found between the rate of electron transfer and the rate of solvation.

The theoretical description of barrierless electron transfer reactions has been developed in several different ways. Sumi, Nadler and Marcus [13, 14] used a modified Smoluchowski equation to describe the motion of the reactant (electron + solvent in the initial state) on a harmonic surface with a position dependent sink which accounts for the decay resulting from the electron transfer to the product state. This model is similar to the one used by Bagchi, Fleming and Oxtoby [5] to describe barrierless photoisomerization reaction. Alternatively, one can use the stochastic Liouville equation, as used by Rips and Jortner [22]. In this section we discuss a recently developed microscopic theory which is based on the former approach [11].

For a microscopic calculation of the dynamic solvent effects on barrierless reactions, we consider the following simple model of an intramolecular electron transfer reaction

$$A - B \xrightarrow{\;h\nu\;} [A^{\delta+} - B^{\delta-}]^* \xrightarrow{\;ET\;} A^+ - B^-, \qquad (17)$$

where A and B are the two segments of the molecule and electron transfer takes place from one segment to the other. The intermediate step is the formation of a locally excited state which may have a small dipole moment, although the ground state may be totally neutral. The reaction coordinate is defined by the usual expression [23].

$$X(t) = -\int d\mathbf{r} \, \Delta D(\mathbf{r}) \cdot P(\mathbf{r}, t). \qquad (18)$$

The motion in the reactant well (here the locally excited state) is described by the following Smoluchowski equation for the time evolution of the probability distribution function, $P_{LE}(X, t)$, of the reaction coordinate

$$\frac{\partial}{\partial t} P_{LE}(X, t) = \frac{k_B T}{\zeta_x} \frac{\partial}{\partial X} \left[\frac{\partial}{\partial X} + \frac{\partial}{\partial X} \beta F \right] P_{LE}(X, t), \qquad (19)$$

where ζ_x is the effective friction on motion along the reaction coordinate, $\beta = (k_B T)^{-1}$ and F is the free energy of the locally excited state. It is assumed that the reactant surface is harmonic and that the free energy is given by $F = 1/2 \, \omega_x X^2$, ω_x being the frequency of the harmonic surface. Now the reaction near $X = X_c$ is described by a sink term. So, the modified Smoluchowski equation for the equation of motion of the reaction coordinate is given by Eq. 1. k_0 is now the rate of electron transfer from the origin (where the rate is maximum for a symmetric sink) and $S(X)$ is the sink function that gives the position dependence of the rate. Sumi and Marcus [13] pointed out that $k_0 S(X)$ is determined by the nature of the coupling between the two diabatic electronic surfaces. If the coupling is strong (the adiabatic limit), then $k_0 S(X)$ may be approximated by an absorbing barrier at $X = X_c$. On the other hand, for a weak coupling (the non-adiabatic limit), $k_0 S(X)$ is a finite sink [16] located at $X = X_c$.

The methods of solution of the modified Smoluchowski equation with various choices of the sink term have already been discussed. The important difference in the present problem is that the friction on the reaction coordinate arises from the electron coupling with the polarization modes of the dipolar solvent. This is no longer given by the macroscopic friction as may be the case for a large amplitude isomerization reaction. We now briefly discuss a microscopic method used recently to calculate the friction parameter, ζ_x and the frequency ω_x from first principles. They can be calculated from a knowledge of the time dependence of the reaction coordinate correlation function [11]. Now we discuss both adiabatic and non-adiabatic cases, separately.

3.1 Adiabatic Limit

It was pointed out by Sumi and Marcus [13] that in the case of a barrierless adiabatic electron transfer, the two surfaces interact strongly to create an "avoided crossing" near $X = X_c$ so that the electron transfer occurs with unit probability when the critical value $X = X_c$ is reached. Thus, this situation corresponds to the presence of an absorbing barrier at $X = X_c$. If $X_c = 0$ (that is, zero barrier limit), then one recovers the symmetric pinhole sink model of Bagchi et al [5]. For this case Eq. 4 can be solved exactly and the total population remaining in the reactant well after time t, $P_{LE}(t)$, is given by Eq. 8. If $P_0(X)$ is given by the equilibrium, Boltzmann, probability distribution on the LE surface, then $P_{LE}(t)$ can be given by the following, simpler, expression

$$P_{LE}(t) = \frac{2}{\pi} \sin^{-1} [\exp(-\omega_X^2 t/\zeta_X)] \tag{20}$$

The decay of reactant population is, in general, non-exponential. However, it can be easily seen that the long time decay is a single exponential. So, one can define a long time rate, k^L_{et}, of electron transfer which is given by $k^L_{et} = \omega^2_X/\zeta_X$. It has been shown that k_{et} is exactly the *average* rate of solvation of the newly formed charge transfer state if the solvent distortion by the reaction system is neglected [11]. We shall come to this point in the later part of this section. The effects of the short range correlations and of the translational modes of the solvent are contained in both ζ_X and ω_X. The rate of electron transfer becomes faster as the translational diffusion of the solvent molecules is increased. The rate also depends on the relative sizes of the reacting and the solvent molecules. The effects of translational modes on polarization relaxation become more important as the size of the reacting molecule is decreased. This is because the intermediate wavevector processes become more important as the size of the reacting molecule is decreased.

If the avoided crossing occurs at a position such that X_c is greater than zero so that a very small activation barrier exists for electron transfer, then it has not been possible to obtain an analytical solution for the reactant well population. One can, however, solve for the average rate. Numerical calculations have shown that in this case also the collective solvent dynamics play an important role in the electron transfer. Especially, the strong dependence of the translational diffusion remains unaltered.

3.2 Non-adiabatic limit

In this case, the zero order surfaces interact weakly so that both the two surfaces participate in the reaction and there is only a finite probability of electron transfer as the system arrives at the critical configuration. In this case, the form of the sink function, $S(X)$, and the magnitude of the intrinsic decay rate, k_0, play an important role in the electron transfer. One can envisage two limiting forms of $S(X)$: a narrow sink at X_c or a broad sink centered at X_c. As pointed out by Sumi and Marcus, the form of $S(X)$ will largely be determined by the non-reacting modes of the solute, especially the vibrational modes which will usually lead to a broadening of the sink. These authors suggested that a Gaussian form can be a sensible approximation for $S(X)$:

$$S(X) = \frac{1}{\sigma_c \sqrt{\pi}} \exp [- (X - X_c)^2/\sigma_c^2] \tag{21}$$

Note that if one takes the simultaneous limits $k_0 \to \infty$ and $\sigma_c \to 0$, then the recovers the pinhole sink discussed earlier. This suggests the possibility of a continuous transition from a non-adiabatic-like to an adiabatic-like electron transfer, mediated by the system parameters k_0 and σ_c.

Analytic solution of Eq. 1 with the sink function given by Eq. 21 has not been possible. Fortunately, extensive numerical solution of this problem has already been carried out, both with $X_c = 0$ and with a small X_c. The scaling analysis of Eq. 1 discussed in section 2 suggests that the dynamics in this case will be controlled largely by the dimensionless parameter $\tilde{k}_0$, given by $k_0 \zeta_X / \omega_X^2$.

In the following, we summarize the main results for the present situation:

If the sink is narrow (what Sumi and Marcus termed 'narrow window'), then an exponential decay is always obtained at sufficiently long times. The long time rate is proportional to ω_X^2 / ζ_X for large $\tilde{k}_0$ ($\tilde{k}_0 > 5$). The rate is independent of ω_X^2 / ζ_X at small $\tilde{k}_0$, so that there is a region of non-linear dependence of the electron transfer rate on ω_X^2 / ζ_X. We refer to a recent review [1, 20] for a detailed discussion on this point. The non-linear dependence of the rate of electron transfer on ω_X^2 / ζ_X also implies a non-linear and a non-trivial dependence of rate on the long wavelength longitudinal relaxation time, τ_L.

It is clear that both the dynamics of solvation and the dynamics of electron transfer are critically dependent on the collective orientational relaxation of the dipolar solvent. Now we discuss how far the two dynamics are different. We define the average solvation time by the following expression

$$\tau_s = \int_0^\infty dt\, C_s(t), \tag{22}$$

where $C_s(t)$ is the normalized time dependent solvation energy. It may be shown [11] that in a linear theory the following relationship holds between the average solvation time and the long time rate of electron transfer

$$\tau_s^{-1} = k_{et}^L = \frac{\omega_X^2}{\zeta_X}. \tag{23}$$

This is an important relation. It shows that the long time rate of electron transfer is equal to the average rate of solvation. This theoretical prediction supports the recent experimental observations of Barbara et al and of Su and Simon. However, the details of the dynamics of these two processes can still be very different from each other. In Fig. 2, we have plotted $C_s(t)$ and $P_{LE}(t)$ for two different values of the translational parameter p' ($= D_T / 2D_R \sigma^2$) for an adiabatic reaction. It can be seen that these two can be rather different from each other.

We now summarize the main points of this section. We have discussed a molecular theory of the effects of collective solvent dynamics on barrierless (and very low barrier) electron transfer reactions in dipolar solvents. The rate of electron transfer is critically dependent on solvent motions. Especially, the translational modes of the solvent can significantly enhance the rate of electron transfer. For a barrierless reaction, the long time rate of electron transfer is exactly the *average* rate of solvation of the newly formed charge transfer state within the one dimensional, linear, theory described here.

4. BARRIERLESS PHOTOISOMERIZATION REACTIONS

The dynamic solvent effects on barrierless photoisomerization reactions have been reviewed recently in detail [3] and we shall limit our discussion here to

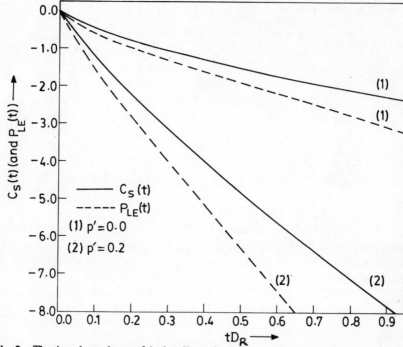

Fig. 2 The time dependence of the locally excited state population. $P_{LE}(t)$ for a barrierless adiabatic reaction is compared with the time dependence of the solvation time correlation function, $C_s(t)$ for two different values of the translation diffusion parameter $p' = D_T/2D_R\sigma^2$, where D_T and D_R are the translational and rotational diffusion coefficients of the dipolar solvent and σ is the diameter of the solvent molecules. The static dielectric constant of the solvent is 18. See [11] and [19] for more details.

some results obtained more recently. The classic example of a barrierless photo-isomerization reaction is the electronic relaxation of the TPM dye molecules such as crystal violet, ethyl violet and malachite green. In these systems, recent quantum chemical calculations [1, 24] have shown that the S_1 electronic surface has a strong dependence on the angular coordinates {θ} which are the dihedral angles between the phenyl groups at the central carbon atom. The fast non-radiative decay from S_1 surface occurs from a geometry which is different from that in the ground state. So, subsequent to the initial excitation, the phenyl groups undergo rotational motion and when the critical configuration for the non-radiative relaxation is reached, a fast decay occurs. Thus, the reactive motion is a rotational diffusion on a potential surface and Eq. 1 can again be used for a simple description of the dynamic solvent effects on such reactions. We have already discussed the main results in section II and they need not be repeated here. In the following some newer aspects are discussed.

Several recent studies have pointed out the necessity of a two dimensional description of the reaction potential surface [7–9], for the following reasons. First, the vibrational modes of the reactant can be coupled to the reactive mode.

So, the energy relaxation *on* the excited state surface may have a multidimensional character. Secondly, the Franck-Condon activity (FCA) may be localized on a small portion of S_1 surface. This position of FCA can be quite away from the sink. So, the dynamics of fluorescence decay from S_1 can be rather different from the dynamics of population decay from the sink. The original calculations of BFO [5] describe only the latter process. It can, however be easily generalized to treat the former dynamics. If $k_r(x)$ is the fluorescence window then fluorescence intensity is given by [25].

$$I_f(t) \propto \int dx \, k_r(x) \, P(x, t). \tag{24}$$

Obviously, this can be rather different from $P_e(t)$, as defined by Eq. 4. Thus, the dynamics contained in $I_f(t)$ can be rather different from the dynamics contained in the ground state recovery or in the excited state absorption experiments [7, 8].

5. CONCLUSION

Barrierless chemical reactions defy the traditional picture of a chemical reaction as a passage over a high activation barrier. The advent of laser spectroscopy has made it possible to demonstrate conclusively that many chemical reactions of great chemical and biological interest are indeed barrierless.

The theoretical models studied so far have been rather simple and unsophisticated. In most experimental situations, the dynamics can be more complicated. In barrierless reactions, the details of the potential surface may be rather important. The reaction surface may not be harmonic. The multidimensionality of the potential surface can be important. The different experimental techniques may measure different aspects of the dynamics. Thus, a simple analytical theory of the type developed by Bagchi et al may be inadequate. On the positive side, significant progress has been made in the last decade in our understanding of barrierless reactions which has been possible because of the interface between theory and experiment. Judging from the intense activity in this field, we can look forward to a better understanding of the remaining problems in this area in the near future.

6. ACKNOWLEDGEMENT

The author thanks A. Chandra, G.R. Fleming and C.S. Poornimadevi for collaboration and discussions. The work was supported in part by a grant from the Indian National Science Academy. B. Bagchi is currently a Homi Bhabha Fellow (1989-91).

7. NOTE ADDED IN THE PROOF

After this work was completed, an interesting fluorescence upconversion study of cis-stilbene isomerization was reported by Todd et al [26]. The reaction was found to be barrierless with sub-picosecond time constants in solution. The results were discussed in terms of the theory of Bagchi et al [3, 5]. I would also like to draw the reader's attention to the interesting review on chemical dynamics in solution by Fleming and Wolynes [27], which can also serve as an excellent introduction to the subject.

REFERENCES

1. E. Lippert, W. Rettig, V. Bonacic-Koutecky, V. Heisel and J. Miehe, Adv. Chem. Phys. **57**, 1 (1987).
2. B. Bagchi, Int. Rev. Phys. Chem. **6**, 1 (1987).
3. B. Bagchi and G.R. Fleming, J. Phys. Chem. **94**, 9 (1990).
4. T.H. Förster and G. Hoffmann, Z. Phys. Chem. NF75, 63 (1971).
5. B. Bagchi, G.R. Fleming and D.W. Oxtoby, J. Chem. Phys. **78**, 7375 (1983); B. Bagchi, S. Singer and D.W. Oxtoby, Chem. Phys. Lett. **99**, 225 (1983).
6. B. Bagchi, J. Chem. Phys. **87**, 5393 (1987).
7. D. Ben-Amotz and C.B. Harris, J. Chem. Phys. **86**, 4856, 5433 (1987); D. Ben-Amotz, R. Jeanloz and C.B. Harris, J. Chem. Phys. **86**, 6119 (1987).
8. V. Sundström and T. Gillbro, J. Chem. Phys. **81**, 3463 (1984); E. Akesson, H. Bergström, V. Sundström and T. Gillbro, Chem. Phys. Lett. **125**, 385 (1986).
9. B. Bagchi, U. Åberg and V. Sundström, Chem. Phys. Lett. **162**, 227 (1989).
10. C.S. Poornimadevi and B. Bagchi, Chem. Phys. Lett., **168**, 276 (1990).
11. B. Bagchi, A. Chandra and G.R. Fleming, J. Chem. Phys. in press.
12. N. Agmon and J. Hoppfield, J. Chem. Phys. **78**, 6947 (1983).
13. H. Sumi and R. Marcus, J. Chem. Phys. **84**, 4894 (1986).
14. W. Nadler and R. Marcus, J. Chem. Phys. **86**, 3906 (1987).
15. K. Schulten, Z. Schulten and A. Szabo, Physica **A100**, 599 (1980).
16. B. Bagchi, J. Chem. Phys. **87**, 5393 (1987).
17. M. Abramowitz and I.A. Stegun, Handbook of Mathematical Functions (Dover, NY 1972).
18. E.M. Kosower and D. Hupert, Ann. Rev. Phys. Chem. **37**, 127 (1986).
19. B. Bagchi, Ann. Rev. Phys. Chem. **40**, 115 (1989).
20. M.A. Kahlow, T.J. Kang and P.F. Barbara, J. Phys. Chem. **91**, 6452 (1987); P.F. Barbara and W. Jarzeba, Acc. Chem. Res. **21**, 195 (1988).
21. J.D. Simon and S.-G. Su, J. Chem. Phys. **87**, 7016 (1987); J.D. Simon, Acc. Chem. Res. **21**, 128 (1988).
22. I. Rips and J. Jortner, J. Chem. Phys. **88**, 818 (1988).
23. D.F. Calef and P.G. Wolynes, J. Phys. Chem. **87**, 3387 (1983).
24. W. Rettig (Preprint) and personal communication.
25. B. Bagchi and G.R. Fleming (Unpublished work).
26. D.C. Todd, J.M. Jean, S.J. Rosenthal, A.J. Ruggiero, D.Yang and G.R. Fleming, J. Chem. Phys., in press.
27. G.R. Fleming and P.G. Wolynes, Phys. Today, **43** (5), 24 (1990).

6. Activated Thermal Electron Transfer in Polar Liquids

Bhalachandra L. Tembe
Department of Chemistry
Indian Institute of Technology
Powai, Bombay, India

Abstract

A model that has successfully accounted for the aqueous ferrous-ferric electron exchange reaction is described. The model predicts the thermodynamic, structural and kinetic data for this reaction fairly well over the range of experimental measurements. The generalisations of the model to understand related activation controlled reactions in molecular liquids are discussed. Methods to estimate the structural and the dynamic effects of the medium on the electron transfer between reactants are also described.

1. INTRODUCTION

The rates of electron exchange and electron transfer reactions in condensed media span about twenty orders of magnitude. A study of electron transfer reactions has attracted the attention of experimental and theoretical chemists for a long time [1–6]. A fully microscopic theoretical description has become available only in the very recent times. Of particular interest is the dependence of the rates of electron transfer reactions on the separation between the reactants, and this is also being accurately elucidated. On the theoretical front, classical, semiclassical and quantum mechanical theories have been presented for a few systems. One of the simplest electron transfer reactions in a condensed medium such as water is the outer sphere electron exchange reaction in transition metal complexes. In this article, a method that has successfully described such a reaction is presented and the extensions of this approach to more complex reactions are outlined.

When an electron is transferred from a site A to a site B, the factors that need to be taken into account are: (i) the work done to bring the reactants A and B to a given separation r, (ii) the electronic factors that are involved as the initial or the reactant state A, B goes over to the final or the product state A^+, B^-, (iii) the changes in the nuclear configurations of A, B as they go over to the products, and (iv) the changes occurring in the surrounding medium as the reaction is proceeding. These factors are not unrelated, but using such a separation, the factors such as (i) and (iv) can be calculated fairly accurately using the methods of classical statistical mechanics. General treatments to calculate these factors are available [5, 7–9], and the above scheme is well suited for numerical computations.

An expression for the rate constant k_{AB} for a bimolecular reaction in the activated complex theory is:

$$k_{AB} = \kappa \, (k_B T/h) \, e^{-\Delta E_0^{\neq}/RT} \tag{1}$$

where k_B is the Boltzmann constant, T the absolute temperature, h the Planck's constant, $R = Lk_B$, L the Avogadro number, and $\Delta E_0^{\neq}$ is the energy of activation for the reaction. The transmission coefficient κ is generally taken to be 1 as it is difficult to estimate it in any meaningful manner. In the approach taken in the present article, the factors (i) to (iv) mentioned above are taken into account by combining them into the equation shown below [9]:

$$k_{AB} = \int \hat{k}_{AB}(r) \, g_{AB}(r) \, d^3r \tag{2}$$

Here $\hat{k}_{AB}(r)$ is the rate constant for the reaction between A and B when the reactants are separated by a distance r, $g_{AB}(r)$ is the pair distribution function for the reactants A and B in the medium of the reaction [10, 11] and the integration is over all space. The work done to bring the reactants together is determined by $g_{AB}(r)$. This is the first factor mentioned earlier. The remaining three factors, i.e., the changes in the electronic and nuclear configurations as well as the response of the medium to the primary electron transfer event are included in $\hat{k}_{AB}(r)$. These changes contribute to the energy of activation for the electron transfer. The integrands in Eq. (2) for two different models (Model 1 and Model 2 to be described in a later section) for the aqueous ferrous-ferric electron exchange reaction are shown in Fig. 1. It is noticed that the rate process is a compromise between the two factors in the integrand and occurs over a limited range of distance separating the reactants. The decay of the integrand to the left of the peak is due to the very small probability of bringing the reactants to very small separations. This is a consequence of steep interparticle repulsions. The fall to the right is due to the rapid fall in the electronic and nuclear factors at large separations of the reactants.

In section 2, the formalism used in the calculation of the rates of electron transfer between reactants separated by a distance r is described. In section 3, the means for calculating the work terms in molecular fluids and the models used for interparticle potentials are discussed. Section 4 presents some of the techniques for estimating the response of the medium to the primary electron transfer event. These are followed by the conclusion in section 5.

2. ELECTRON EXCHANGE RATES IN THE GAS PHASE

The general framework for the computation of rate constants in the gas phase is rather well developed now [12]. It has become possible to calculate the potential energy surfaces (PESs) and hence state-to-state rate constants fairly accurately at least for a few elementary systems. For systems where the reactants and products are complex polyatomic species, the above approach is computationally very

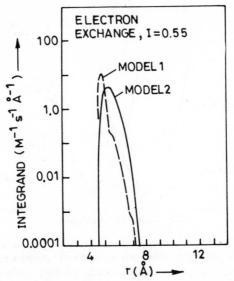

Fig. 1. The integrand of equation (2) as a function of the separation of the ferrous and ferric ions at an ionic strength of $I = 0.55$ M. The potentials used in MODEL 1 and MODEL 2 are described in section 3.

demanding. In the case of electron exchange reactions, the symmetry of the reactant and the product valleys in the PES simplifies the problem considerably and the approximation of a two state model is commonly used. One of the advantages of this model is that the effect of the environment on the rates can be readily incorporated in the formalism. Several good treatments of the two state model are available [13–15] and we shall outline the main results that are useful in calculating the rate constants.

The state of the reactants A and B (collectively referred to as R) at a separation r from each other (the distance r is to be treated as a constant in this section) may be represented by the vibronic wave function $\Psi_{R,vR} = \Phi_R(q_{el}, r) \cdot X_{vR}$ and the state of the products A^+, B^- (collectively referred to as P) by $\Psi_{P,wP} = \Phi_P(q_{el}, r) \cdot X_{wP}$. Here, Φ_R and Φ_P are the electronic wave functions of the reactants and the products respectively, q_{el} refers to the electron coordinates, X_{vR} and X_{wP} are the vibrational wave functions of the reactants and the products in the Born-Oppenheimer approximation, and v and w are the vibrational quantum numbers. Only the ground electronic states of the reactants and the products are considered in the two state model. The reactant state wavefunction is dependent on the interparticle separations between all the reactants. A section through the multidimensional potential energy surface for a reaction where R refers to the ferrous-ferric combination and P to the ferric-ferrous is shown in Fig. 2.

For an electron exchange reaction wherein the reactants and the products are identical (but for the isotopic substitution which is used in experiments to distinguish between reactants and products), there is no vertical displacement between the reactant and the product PES. The reaction coordinate may be taken as the difference between the internal coordinates of the reactants and the

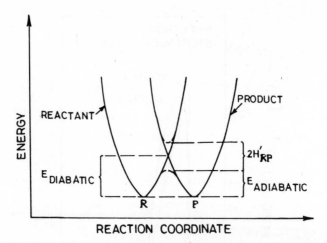

Fig. 2. A section of the potential energy surface for an electron exchange reaction. The reaction coordinate is the difference in the Fe—O distance between ferrous and ferric ions. The dashed lines correspond to adiabatic surfaces. The energies of activation (E) and the magnitude of the matrix element H'_{AB} are also shown.

products. In the case of the $Fe(H_2O)_6^{3+} - Fe(H_2O)_6^{2+}$ electron exchange reaction, the reaction coordinate is the difference between the two ion oxygen distances, $r_{Fe^{2+}-O} - r_{Fe^{3+}-O}$. The difference in energy between the intersection of the two PESs and the bottom of either of the two PESs is $E_{Diabatic}$. The hamiltonian matrix element $H_{RP}(r) = \int \Phi_R H \Phi_P \, d\tau$ gives the separation between the intersection point of the two PESs and the local maximum of the lower adiabatic surface. The full electronic hamiltonian is given by H. The energy of activation for crossing over the adiabatic surface is shown in Fig. 2. as $E_{Adiabatic}$.

The transtition probability per unit time, $w_{vR \to wP}$, for crossing from the reactant state Ψ_{vR} to the product state Ψ_{wP} is given in the first order perturbation theory by

$$w_{vR \to wP} = 4\pi^2 H^2_{vR \to wP} \; \rho(E_{wP})/h \tag{3}$$

The matrix element between the reactant and the product vibronic states is $H_{vR \to wP}$. Condon factorization is used to decompose the vibronic matrix element into $H_{RP} \cdot S_{vR \to wP}$, where H_{RP} is the electronic matrix element and $S_{vR \to wP}$ is the Franck-Condon factor. The density of product states at the product potential energy E_{wP} is $\rho(E_{wP})$. The dependence of the transition probability on the distance separating the reactants is mainly through H_{RP}. Additional distance dependence comes about through solvent reorganisation and the work terms.

In electron exchange reactions involving transition metal complexes such as ML_6^{2+} and ML_6^{3+}, where M is the metal and L the ligand, the electronic contributions to the activation process are through the electronic matrix element which has been discussed above. Vibrational contributions to the activation process are due to the inner sphere breathing modes involving the M-L vibrations and the long wavelength solvent modes. The expression derived for the electron exchange rate constant [13] that includes both the inner sphere and the solvent vibrations is given below.

$$\hat{k}_{el} = \frac{H_{RP}^2}{hQ_R} (\pi^3/E_{Solv} RT)^{1/2} \sum_{v,w} \hat{k}_{vR,wP} \qquad (4)$$

where

$$\hat{k}_{vR,wP} = \exp(-E_{vR}/RT) \mid S \mid_{vR,wP}^2 \exp[-(E_{Solv} + \Delta\varepsilon_{vRwP}/4)^2/E_{Solv}RT] \qquad (5)$$

Here, $E_{vR} = vhv_R$ is the energy of the reactant vibrational state with vibrational quantum number v, w the quantum number of the product state and Q_R is the vibrational partition function. The energy sharing process between the inner sphere and the solvent modes is taken into account through $\Delta\varepsilon_{vR,wP} = \dot{E}_{wP} - E_{vR}$, which is the energy exchanged between the inner sphere and the solvent modes. The total activation energy required for the reaction may be achieved by a number of combinations of inner sphere and the solvent modes.

In a semiclassical approach that includes the results of Brunschwig et al [14, 15], the local rate constant $\hat{k}_{el} = \hat{k}_{el}(r)$ is given by

$$\hat{k}_{el}(r) = \frac{2P_{RP}}{(1 + P_{RP})} \quad v_{eff} \Gamma_n \exp(-E_{Diabatic}/RT) \qquad (6)$$

where, v_{eff} is the mean frequency corresponding to oscillations in either the reactant or the product potential energy well, Γ_n is a measure of nuclear tunneling across the potential energy barrier and $2P_{RP}/(1 + P_{RP})$ is the thermally averaged transmission coefficient. The Landau-Zener transmission probability P_{RP} for crossing from one diabatic surface to another is given by

$$P_{RP} = 1 - \exp[-4\pi^2 H_{RP}^2/(hu \mid S_R - S_P \mid)] \qquad (7)$$

Here H_{RP} is the hamiltonian matrix element between the reactants and the products separated by a distance r, u the average forward velocity of the reactants in the transition region, and S_R and S_P are the slopes of the reactant and the product surfaces in the transition region. An expression for the tunneling factor Γ_n has been obtained by Brunschwig et al [15] using Holstein's theory [16] and is given by

$$\Gamma_n = \exp\{-4E_{in}(r)[\tanh(y/4) - (y/4)]/hv_{in}\}/[2\sinh(y/2)/y]^{1/2} \qquad (8)$$

where $y = hv_{in}/k_B T$ and v_{in} is the average symmetrical mode frequency that is associated with the inner sphere activation energy E_{in}. The total activation energy has an additional contribution from the solvent reorganisation energy E_{Solv} which can be estimated either from the two sphere model of Marcus [17] or from the ellipsoidal model of Cannon [18]. At large separations of the reactants, the two sphere model is appropriate, but at small separations, where part of the reactants overlap, the ellipsoidal model is better suited and is used.

The semiclassical model has yielded results which are in close agreement with the quantum mechanical results over a wide temperature range [15]. The major distance dependance of the electron exchange rate comes about through P_{RP} and E_{Solv}. The remaining factors are taken to be independent of the separation between the reactants, although this assumption could introduce a minor error in the estimate of the bulk rate constant. These effects may however play a significant role in the temperature dependence of the rate constant.

3. THE STRUCTURAL EFFECTS OF THE MEDIUM

The dominant effect of the condensed medium, which is a molecular liquid in the present study, is due to the close packing of the molecules in the medium which makes the approach of the reactants to reactive separations in the liquid very different from the gas phase encounters. The packing causes specific work to be done in the medium to bring the reactants to reactive separations. Although the long range interactions (Coulombic and dipolar) among the reactants and between the reactants and the solvent particles play an important role, the major contribution is due to the local arrangements among the medium molecules when the reactants are separated by a few molecular diameters. Before going into the theory of molecular fluids, two recent examples of the effect of a medium on the gas phase PESs are considered.

Several methods are available for estimating the influence of a medium on the potential energy curve between two reactants. Monte Carlo and Molecular Dynamics simulations or the integral equations of classical statistical mechanics are the more common routes. The results obtained from two non-empirical calculations are given in Fig. 3. The effect of a polar medium on the potential energy of a diatomic molecule, adapted from the work of Chiles et al [19] is shown in Fig. 3a. Curve A is the potential energy of an isolated molecule (i.e., in the gas phase). Curves B and C are obtained when the molecule is placed in polar media. Two major effects of the medium are seen here. Firstly, there is a

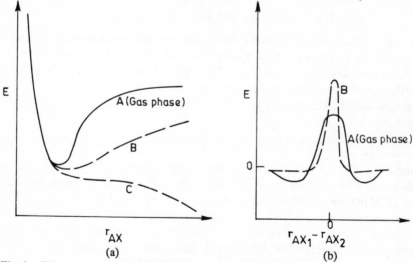

Fig. 3. Effects of solvation on potential energy surfaces. (a) The potential energy curve for a diatomic molecule AX in the gas phase (curve A), polar solvent (curve B), and highly polar solvent (curve C); (b) The potential energy diagram for a collinear reaction $X_2 + AX_1 \rightarrow X_2A + X_1$, when X_1 is identical to X_2. Curve A is the gas phase result and curve B (dashed) corresponds to a polar solvent.

broadening of the effective potential (i.e. the potential in the condensed medium or the potential of mean force) near the minimum occurring in the gas phase potential, and secondly, at large separations, the effective potential is lower than the gas phase potential due to the solvation of the individual ions. In highly polar media, the isolated atoms/ions may be stabilised to a greater extent than the united atoms (i.e. the molecule) and in such a situation, the minimum in the effective potential near the atom-atom contact distance disappears. Such a situation is common in the case of heteronuclear molecules like HCl and NaCl which exist only as dissociated ions in highly polar media such as water. Calculations on H_2 in a medium of Drude oscillators were performed using the Path Integral Monte Carlo method [19, 20].

The schematic results in Fig. 3a correspond to the equilibrium or the structural effect of a polar medium on the potential energy curve for the association reaction of the type $X + A = XA$. In Fig. 3b, the effect of a medium on a more general reaction, based on the work of Chandrasekhar, Smith and Jorgensen [21] is shown. Activation controlled reactions in the gas phase as well as in the condensed medium show a maximum in the plot of the potential energy of the reactants along a suitably chosen reaction coordinate. The energy of the highest point in such a plot is referred to as the energy of the activated complex. A symmetric PES is the characteristic of all exchange reactions whenever the reactants and the products are identical. The local minima in the gas phase PES in Fig. 3b on either side of the central maximum are due to the formation of local structures such as ion-dipole complexes. The change in the structure of the PES in going to the condensed medium is caused by the average local arrangements of the solvent molecules around the reactants. In the detailed Monte Carlo simulations carried out by Chandrasekhar et. al [21] on the S_N2 reaction

$$Cl^- + CH_3Cl' \rightarrow ClCH_3 + Cl'^-$$

the symmetric gas phase minima disappeared in aqueous solution as illustrated by the dotted curve, which is the effective potential between Cl^- and CH_3Cl in aqueous solution. The disappearance of the local minima in the solution phase implies that the separated reactants as well as the ion-dipole complexes are solvated nearly to the same extent. The increase in the activation energy in the solution medium is caused by the increased work needed to bring the reactants to the symmetric transition state. The equilibrium effects of the medium on the energetics of the reaction can thus be quite dramatic and we now turn to a theoretical framework used for describing these equilibrium effects.

A convenient description of the equilibrium structure of molecular fluids is in terms of the equilibrium distribution functions. The position and orientation of a nonlinear molecule i is determined by the coordinates of its center of mass, R_i, and the Euler angles $\Omega_i = (\phi_i, \theta_i, \psi_i)$ with respect to a coordinate frame. The intermolecular forces between two such molecules depend on their relative separation as well as orientation. The potential energy of a system containing N such molecules may be written as $V_N(R^N, \Omega^N)$. The set of coordinates of all the molecules is represented by R^N, and Ω^N is the set of all molecular solid angles.

The molecular pair distribution function in a translationally invariant one component molecular fluid is given by [22]

$$g(1, 2) = g^{(2)}(R_{12}, \Omega_1, \Omega_2)$$

$$= \frac{8\pi^2}{\rho^2 \Xi} \sum_{N=2}^{\infty} \frac{z^N q^N_{rot}}{(N-2)!} \int\!\!\int \cdots \int\!\!\int \exp[-\beta V_N(R^N, \Omega^N)] \cdots$$

$$dR_3 dR_4 \ldots dR_N \, d\Omega_3 d\Omega_4 \ldots d\Omega_N \tag{9}$$

Here R_{12} is the distance between molecules 1 and 2, ρ the bulk density of the system, z the activity, q_{rot} the rotational partition function of an isolated molecule, Ξ the grand partition function, and $\beta = 1/k_B T$. The integration is over the coordinates and orientations of all molecules other than 1 and 2. A direct estimation of $g(1, 2)$ is not readily possible, although a knowledge of this will enable us to calculate the thermodynamic and structural properties. Using a spherical harmonic expansion for $g(1, 2)$, it is possible to calculate thermodynamic properties by low order perturbation theory [23]. Even if a more compact formalism were available for $g(1, 2)$, the orientational dependance of the potential energy between molecules is not readily available. A more convenient way is to write the pair potential as a sum of site-site pair potentials ($u_{\alpha\beta}$) as shown below:

$$U(1, 2) = \sum_{\alpha=1}^{n_\alpha} \sum_{\beta=1}^{n_\beta} u_{\alpha\beta}(r_{\alpha\beta}) \tag{10}$$

The distance between site α on molecule 1 and site β on molecule 2 is $r_{\alpha\beta}$. The summation is over all sites on molecules 1 and 2. The site-site total correlation function $h_{\alpha\beta}(r_{\alpha\beta}) = g_{\alpha\beta}(r_{\alpha\beta}) - 1$ is defined in terms of the molecular pair correlation function $h(1, 2) = g(1, 2) - 1$ by the equation [24]

$$h_{\alpha\beta}(r) = \int\!\!\int_{r=r_{\alpha\beta}} h(1, 2) \, d\Omega_1 d\Omega_2 \tag{11}$$

The internal energy and the mean squared force of the molecular fluid can be directly calculated in terms of all $g_{\alpha\beta}(r)$s, while the pressure and the mean squared torque require the full $g(1, 2)$ [23]. The site-site distribution functions $g_{\alpha\beta}(r_{\alpha\beta}) = g_{\alpha\beta}(r)$ are really the zeroth moments of the function $g(1, 2)$, i.e. $g_{000}(r)$ which is the lowest term in the spherical harmonic expansion of $g(1, 2)$. For homonuclear diatomic molecules, the first and the second moments of $g(1, 2)$, i.e. $g_{100}(r)$ and $g_{200}(r)$ have been calculated using the site-site superposition approximation. A comparison of the estimated values of $g_{100}(r)$ from this scheme with those of computer simulations for the same model potential shows reasonable agreement (i.e. within about 20%) over the distance range of the first few molecular diameters [23].

The theory of site-site (or atom-atom) distribution functions (SSDFs) is rather well developed and several computational schemes are available for computing the SSDFs in molecular liquids. The site-site Ornstern-Zernike (SSOZ) or the reference interaction site model (RISM) integral equation was introduced by Chandler and Anderson [25]. The sites on molecules A and B are shown schematically below:

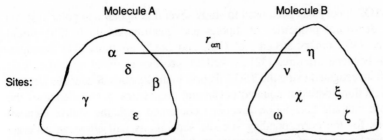

The SSOZ equation may be written in the following form by using the Fourier transforms of $c_{\alpha\eta}(r)$ (the site-site direct correlation function) and $h_{\alpha\eta}(r)$ [25–28].

$$\hat{H} = \hat{W}\hat{C}(I - \hat{W}\hat{C})\,\hat{W} \qquad (12)$$

Here, $\hat{H}$, $\hat{W}$ and $\hat{C}$ are matrices whose elements are defined by

$$(\hat{H})_{\alpha\eta}(k) = \frac{4\pi}{k}\,(\rho_\alpha\rho_\eta)^{1/2} \int_0^\infty dr\, r\, \sin(kr)\, h_{\alpha\eta}(r) \qquad (13)$$

$$(\hat{C})_{\alpha\eta}(k) = \frac{4\pi}{k}\,(\rho_\alpha\rho_\eta)^{1/2} \int_0^\infty dr\, r\, \sin(kr)\, c_{\alpha\eta}(r) \qquad (14)$$

$$(W)_{\alpha\eta}(k) = w_{\alpha\eta}(k) = \frac{\sin(kl_{\alpha\eta})}{kl_{\alpha\eta}} \qquad (15)$$

Here, the distance in coordinate space is denoted by r and k is the magnitude of the wave vector. The particle number density of site α is ρ_α, $w_{\alpha\eta}$ the intramolecular correlation function, I the unit matrix, and $l_{\alpha\eta}$ the fixed intramolecular distance between sites α and η. When the sites α and η are on different kinds of molecules, then $w_{\alpha\eta}(k) = 0$. In order to solve the SSOZ equation, an additional relation between $\hat{H}$ and $\hat{C}$ is required. In the absence of an exact relation, several approximate relations between H and C are used. Two of the common approximations are the hypernetted chain (HNC) and the Percus-Yevick (PY) approximations which are shown below:

$$c_{\alpha\eta}(r) = \exp[\,\phi_{\alpha\eta}(r) + \gamma_{\alpha\eta}(r)] - \gamma_{\alpha\eta}(r) - 1 \qquad \text{(HNC)} \qquad (16)$$

$$c_{\alpha\eta}(r) = [\,1 + \gamma_{\alpha\eta}(r)\,]\,[\exp(\phi_{\alpha\eta}(r))] - 1 \qquad \text{(PY)} \qquad (17)$$

with
$$\gamma_{\alpha\eta}(r) = h_{\alpha\eta}(r) - c_{\alpha\eta}(r) \text{ and } \phi_{\alpha\eta}(r) = -\beta\, u_{\alpha\eta}(r) \qquad (18)$$

These equations may be solved iteratively or recursively using an initial choice of $h_{\alpha\eta}(r)$. The limitations of the above approximations are well known but the measures to go significantly beyond these approximations have been only partially successful. The ease in the computation of $h_{\alpha\eta}(r)$ and a fair agreement of these functions with the computer simulation data of molecular fluids of simple molecules (i.e. molecules containing 2 to 6 atoms) makes this approach a useful tool for estimating the structural and kinetic properties of polyatomic fluids.

The SSOZ theory has been used to study several nonpolar and polar systems [26–29]. Structural properties of dipolar and quadrupolar fluids [29], liquid acetonitrile [30], binary systems of CCl_4 and $SnCl_4$ mixtures [31], benzene-hexafluorobenzene mixtures [32] as well as gas-liquid critical properties [33] have been investigated using the SSOZ theory. In the kinetics of aqueous electron transfer reactions between aquated octahedral complexes, a knowledge of the appropriate site-site correlation functions combined with the matrix element evaluations for the corresponding site-site separations will allow an accurate semiclassical estimate of the rate constants. Such an investigation is in progress [34] and an alternative approach which has worked reasonably well, will be considered now.

The presence of a high degree of symmetry in octahedral complexes enables us to use the readily available data of the pair distributions of atomic fluids in the study of electron exchange kinetics. Proper consideration has to be however given to account for and average over the molecular nature of the reactants.

There are several methods to compute the equilibrium correlation functions of atomic fluids. Monte Carlo and Molecular Dynamics simulations, integral equation methods and perturbation theories are fairly successful in describing the equilibrium structure of simple liquids over a wide range of temperatures and densities [35–36]. For ionic solutions, integral equations with the hypernetted chain closure provide an accurate description of equilibrium properties up to 1M concentration [37]. The starting point in the calculation is an estimate of the pair potential between all the constituents. These potentials are not known exactly in solution media although the potentials of mean force between ions in water have been estimated in recent times [37]. The values of the potential between ions in solution when the ions are separated by a distance between R and $3R$ are not known accurately. Here R is the contact distance between the ions. Among the many factors that contribute to the potential is the solvent polarizability effect which is really a many body effect. This effect is not known to an accuracy better than 0.5 kcal · mol^{-1}. A useful empirical model potential between ions i and j when they are separated by a distance r in an aqueous solution has the following form [38]

$$u_{ij}(r) = e_i e_j /\varepsilon r + COR_{ij}(r) + CAV_{ij}(r) + GUR_{ij}(r) \qquad (19)$$

e_i and e_j are the charges on the ions i and j, and ε is the dielectric constant of the medium. The repulsive part of the potential which dominates at short distances is $COR_{ij}(r)$. This can be either an exponential or an algebraic function of the pair separation. The polarisation of the ionic cavities due to the electric fields around it results in a repulsive CAV_{ij} contribution whose leading term decays as r^{-4}.

The effects that are not fully understood are clubbed into a $GUR_{ij}(r)$ term (named after R.W. Gurney) which has to account for the molecular nature of the solvent as well as the polarisation caused by the ions in their neighbourhood. An illustration of the details of the GUR_{ij} potential is given in Fig. 4. Each of the two ions may be considered to be surrounded by an envelope or a cosphere of the solvent in which the properties of the solvent are different from the properties of the bulk solvent. The thickness of the cosphere is usually such that at least

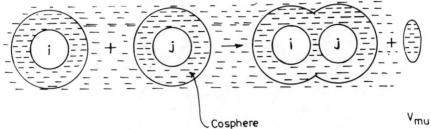

Fig. 4. Ions *i* and *j* approaching each other when the interionic separation is less than the sum of the cosphere radii. A volume V_{mu} is released to the bulk solvent.

one solvent shell surrounds the bare ions. If the ions approach each other so that the cospheres overlap, then the mutual overlap volume returns to the bulk or the normal state of the solvent. The GUR_{ij} potential is proportional to the overlap volume $V_{mu}(a, b, r)$, where *a* and *b* are the radii of the cospheres of ions *i* and *j* respectively. The potential is given by [38]

$$GUR_{ij}(r) = A_{ij} V_w^{-1} V_{mu}(a, b, r) \tag{20}$$

where

$$V_{mu}(r) = \pi \, [- (a^2 - b^2)/4r + 2(a^3 - b^3)/3 - (a^3 + b^3)r/2 - r^3/12] \tag{21}$$

Here V_w is the molar volume of the solvent in the normal state and A_{ij} is an adjustable parameter which is used to account for the specific ion-ion interactions. The four term potential mentioned above has been used to calculate the thermodynamic properties of 1–1, 1–2 and 2–1 electrolyte solutions. These predictions agree quite well with experimental as well the Monte Carlo simulation data. The hypernetted chain approximation is used to obtain the pair distribution functions. In the case of 2–2 aqueous electrolytes there are some discrepancies between the HNC and the MC distribution function data [39]. These discrepancies have been shown to be due to the neglected terms in the HNC approximation and their inclusion results in a corrected HNC equation whose results agree well with the MC data [39, 40]. The corrected HNC equation with a four term potential offers a computationally convergent and convenient scheme for predicting the structure and thermodynamics of electrolyte solutions.

In aqueous solutions involving charged octahedral complexes, the use of ion ion-pair potentials alone is not adequate to account for the dominant effect of the molecular or polyatomic nature of the reactants. The effect of polyatomicity on the distance of closest approach of two octahedral ions is shown in Fig. 5. When two octahedra approach each other along their four-fold axis, the distance of closest approach or the contact distance is the sum of the radii of the bare   ns plus two times the diameter of water molecules. This distance for the aquated $Fe^{2+} - Fe^{3+}$ octahedra is 6.9 Å. If the octahedra approach each other along their three-fold axes, then the distance of closest approach is reduced to 4.5 Å. For other approaches of the reactants, contact distances will range from 4.5 to 6.9 Å. The fact that only a small number of mutual configurations occur in the distance range of 4.5 to 6.9 Å has to be accounted for in some way if one has to retain the

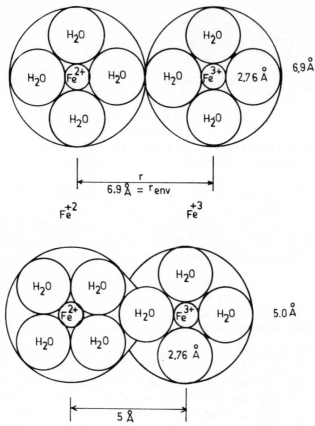

Fig. 5. Sections showing hydrated Fe^{2+} and Fe^{3+} octahedra. When the envelopes of the octahedra touch each other, the separation is $r = 6.9$ Å and when the octahedra penetrate without disrupting, they approach (along their three-fold axes) close to 5 Å.

use of central force models for interionic interactions. One such procedure for accounting for the smaller probability of penetrated configurations is the use of a switching function, $S_{ij}(r)$ which should be chosen such that it becomes zero for distances less than 4.5 Å and goes over to unity for distances beyond 6.9 Å. Several forms of the switching function have been used and it has been observed that the choice of the switching function has a very minor effect on the calculated results. Two switching functions that were used in the calculations are shown in Fig. 6. The expressions for the functions are also given in the figure. The contribution of these functions to the pair potential is to be treated as the effect of polyatomicity of the reactants and has to be added to eq. (19). This potential may be termed $MOL_{ij}(r)$ and is given by [9]

$$MOL_{ij}(r) = -k_B T \ln S_{ij}(r) \tag{22}$$

The parameters A_{ij} in the modified Eq. (19) were determined such that the distribution functions obtained from these potentials predict the thermodynamics

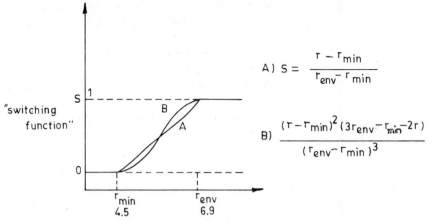

Fig. 6. Switching function S operating between r_{min} ($S = 0$) and r_{env} ($S = 1$). For $r < r_{min}$, $S = 0$ and $S = 1$ for $r \geq r_{env}$. Curve A is a linear function while curve B is a cubic.

of the reactants, which in the special case considered in the present work are the ferrous and ferric perchlorate solutions as well as their mixtures. These distribution functions that used no kinetic parameters are used in calculating the electron transfer rate constants. The results of the integrand for the rate constant [Eq. (2)] for two model potentials have already been shown in Fig. 1. Model 2 refers to the Gurney model for the interionic potential, while Model 1 uses a different procedure for taking into account the solvent molecularity [9]. Both models fit the kinetic data within a factor of 2 in the concentration range of 0 to 1 M. Extensions of such models to more general reactions will be described in the conclusion section.

4. CONTRIBUTIONS FROM SOLVATION DYNAMICS

In the case of reactions involving significant charge transfer or rearrangement, the contribution of the dynamics of the solvent to the reaction rate can be rate determining. As the reaction proceeds through charge rearrangement, the polarisation of the medium will respond to the rearrangement. If the medium response is slow, then the reaction rate will generally be reduced. Even in an elementary kinetics of a particle crossing a barrier when the particle motion is simultaneously coupled to a heat bath, Kramers [41] had shown that the rate constant for the passage over the barrier has a strong dependence on the coupling to the heat bath. The coupling (an elementary example of which is the friction coefficient in the Langevin equation) of the reaction coordinate to the heat bath is due to the correlated motion of the solvent as the reactants traverse a reaction path. For small values of this coupling, the flow of energy into the reactive trajectory is not very rapid and the transition state population is less than that predicted by the Boltzmann distribution and thus the resulting rate constants are small. At large values of coupling, the motion along the entire reaction path becomes diffusive, thereby slowing the reaction. In Fig. 7, the rate constant for a

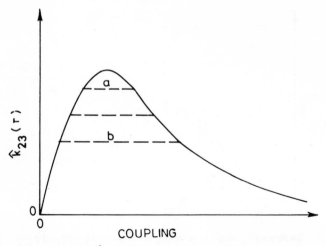

Fig. 7. The local rate constant $\hat{k}_{23}(r)$ as a function of the coupling to the medium. The dotted lines indicate various actual possibilities. Curve b corresponds to a situation wherein the transition state populations can not be maintained at either small or intermediate values of coupling.

general reaction as a function of coupling to the medium is shown. The determination of the value of this coupling for a given reaction condition is a very difficult task. The dependence of this coupling on temperature, pressure and the reactant concentrations can have a remarkable effect on kinetic parameters and this is observed in the unusual dependence of activation entropies and activation volumes on the reactant concentrations.

In the analysis by Kramers and extensions thereof [42, 43], values of the coupling appear directly in the rate expressions. When the polyatomicity of the medium is taken into account, the number of reactive modes and the dimensionality of the PES becomes unmanageably large and a kinetic steady state analysis may be used to include the effect of the coupling due to solvation dynamics. As a convenient starting point, the hydrodynamic and the dielectric friction may be separated [44, 45]. In charge transfer processes, the long wavelength fluctuations due to Coulombic and dipolar forces dominate in the solvent response or relaxation. The correlations induced by dispersive Lennard-Jones interactions decay more rapidly than those induced by lower order multipolar interactions and thus do not contribute in a major way either to the dielectric response or to the charge transfer kinetics. The dielectric relaxation times provide a good measure of the coupling of the reaction coordinate to the collective solvent modes. The local motions in the reactants such as the breathing modes in octahedral complexes, also provide an internal high frequency mode to reactive coupling. Both these effects were incorporated in the rate expression for the electron exchange kinetics as follows [9]:

$$\hat{k}_{AB}(r) = \exp\{-\beta A^*(r)\}/[2\{\tau_e(r) + \tau^*(r)\}] \tag{23}$$

Here $A^*(r)$ is the Helmholtz free energy of activation, $\tau_e(r) = 0.5/\hat{k}_{el}(r)$ is the characteristic time for the primary electron transfer event calculated from section 2, and $\tau^{*}(r)$ is the relaxation time for the activation process, which includes the dynamical solvent effects.

The relaxation time for the activation process has contributions from inner sphere vibrational modes (reactant breathing modes) whose relaxation time may be denoted by τ_{in} and from outer sphere long wavelength (solvent) modes with a relaxation time τ_{out}. Both these modes can simultaneously assist in the activation process and the slower of the two processes does not necessarily dominate the kinetic process. This is seen from the expression $\tau(r)$ below, which is valid when the activation energies for the inner and outer sphere activations are fairly large

$$\tau(r)^{-1} = \tau_{in}^{-1} + \tau_{out}^{-1} \tag{24}$$

It is possible now to calculate these relaxation times by the use of molecular theories as well as by the use of computer simulations. These may also be estimated from experimental data. In the early estimate of τ_{in}, the linewidth of the Raman spectrum of $Mg(H_2O)_6^{2+}$ was used [9]. This is a better measure of the correlation time than the reciprocal of the average of the symmetric mode vibrational frequencies for $Fe(H_2O)_6^{2+}$ and $Fe(H_2O)_6^{3+}$. A value of $\tau_{out} = 2$ ps was used as a measure of the polarisation relaxation time. In the neighbourhood of the ions, the polarisation relaxation is known to be faster than the dielectric relaxation of the bulk solvent. The dielectric relaxation time for water is 8 ps. There have been a number of efforts to calculate relaxation times analogous to τ_{out} using molecular theories [46, 47], but the inner sphere correlation times have not yet been calculated.

We have performed molecular dynamics simulations on a few model systems to assess the magnitude of solvent relaxation time [48, 49]. In these models, the system consists of an electron donor, an electron acceptor and a surrounding medium of 50 to 100 solvent particles. The reactants, i.e. the donor and the acceptor are maintained at a fixed separation of 5 Å, which was the "most reactive" distance in Fig. 1. The solvent consists of atomic as well as molecular species and all the particles interact with a Lennard-Jones plus Coulombic potential given by:

$$u_{ij}(r) = A_{ij}/r^{12} - B_{ij}/r^6 + q_i q_j/r \tag{25}$$

The charges on the particles or the sites in the molecules are denoted by q_i and q_j and the coefficients A_{ij} and B_{ij} are so chosen that the contact distance between the sites is $\sigma = 3.4$ Å and the depth of the Lennard-Jones potential $\varepsilon/k_B = 120$ K. The charges on the solvent have been chosen in the range $\pm 0.05e$ to $\pm 0.25e$, where e is the electronic charge. The charges on the reactants range from $\pm 0.1e$ to $\pm 0.5e$. The reduced density is in the range of 0.4 to 0.5. Using time steps in the range of 0.001 to 0.01 ps, Verlet algorithm was used to integrate the Newton's equations of motion. The temperature of the system was maintained at 298 K by either velocity rescaling or by the use of stochastic collisions. The charges on the reactants as well as the solvent have been initially kept small to minimise the possibility of charge clustering which could persist in the relatively small simulation cell if the charges were very large. This will necessitate the use of much smaller time steps and a careful monitoring of the displacements of the solvent particles.

To study the dynamical correlations due to fluctuations in the medium polarisation, electric field fluctuations in the medium in the vicinity of the reactants as well as at the location of the reactants are estimated. The points in space at which the electric fields are evaluated as a function of time are shown in Fig. 8. From the values of the electric fields (EFs), the electric field time correlation functions (EFTCFs) are obtained through:

$$C(t) = \langle \, EF(0) \cdot EF(t) \rangle / \langle \, EF(0)^2 \, \rangle \qquad (26)$$

where EF is the electric field at any one of the points in Fig. 8. An estimate of the electric field correlation time may be obtained from the initial slopes of the logarithm of the EFTCFs versus time. These slopes would actually be the electric field relaxation times if the EFTCFs were single exponentials. In the simulations

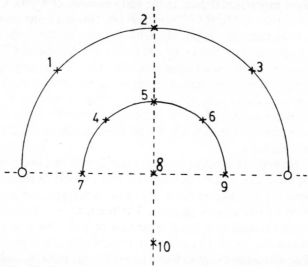

Fig. 8. A section of a Molecular Dynamics simulation cell showing the points in the cell at which the time dependence of the electric fields are calculated. The positions of the ions are denoted by small circles.

performed, the EFTCFs show multiexponential behaviour. The relaxation times in atomic solvents range from 2 to 10 ps and the relaxation behaviour is not very sensitive to the specific location of the point in the vicinity of the reactants. In the case of dipolar solvents, the relaxation times are much smaller, i.e. about 1 ps. For large values of τ_{out}, the value of the total relaxation time $\tau^{\neq}(r)$ is unaffected, whereas for small values of τ_{out} the total relaxation process is significantly altered.

The rate constants for the electron exchange reaction between ferrous and ferric ions as a function of concentration are explained rather well by the theory outlined above. The activation parameter $\Delta S^{\neq}$ obtained from the temperature dependence of the rate constant is shown in Fig. 9. The dotted curve labelled DH is obtained by using the Debye-Hückel $g(r)s$. All other models use the HNC approximation for calculating the distribution functions. Models 1 and 3 use the Gurney potentials while model 2 uses the granular potential obtained by using the PY hard sphere solutions [9]. This model uses $-K_B T \ln [g_{ij}^{PY}(r)]$ in place of $GUR_{ij}(r)$. There is no significant difference between the results from the Gurney and the granular models and the agreement between theory and experiments is

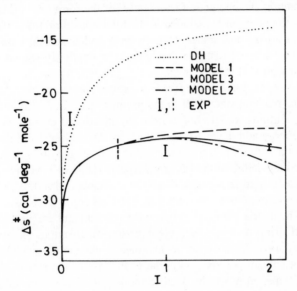

Fig. 9 Entropy of activation ΔS^* for the electron exchange reaction as a function of ionic strength. The dashed vertical bar at $I = 0.55$ M is the experimental value for the ferrous-ferric electron exchange. Other experimental data are for vanadous-ferric electron exchange. The theoretical curves for various models [one using DH and three using HNC theory for $g_{23}(r)$] are labelled as Model 1, Model 2 and Model 3 (see text for details).

very good beyond $I = 0.5$ M. The disagreement at low values of ionic strength is indeed surprising since the structural factors can be calculated accurately at low concentrations. While the values of $g_{23}(r)$ need to be checked against simulation data, the temperature dependence of $\tau(r)$ as well as its concentration dependence has not yet been estimated theoretically and an estimation of the same may partially explain the remaining discrepancy.

5. CONCLUSION

In this section, the generalisations arising out of the methods described in the earlier sections are outlined. For electron exchange and electron transfer reactions with activation energies greater than 10 $k_B T$, a separate treatment of the electronic factors, work terms and the solvation effects is expected to be valid to a high degree of accuracy. At moderate to high temperatures, a classical description of the solvent medium is adequate. High energy fluctuations in the medium are expected to be relatively small and the following generalisation of Eq. (2) may be used.

$$k_{AB} = \int d^3r \, g_{AB}(\mathbf{r}) f(\mathbf{r})/\tau(\mathbf{r}) \tag{27}$$

where the terms in the equation have a meaning similar to that of Eq. (2). The term $f(\mathbf{r})$ contains the energetic factors only [of the form $\exp(-\beta\Delta A^*)$] and the dynamics of the medium is included in the total relaxation time, $\tau(\mathbf{r})$. The form of $\tau(\mathbf{r})$ needs to be determined in each case and a special case is given in Eq. (23). The vectorial distance dependence is explicitly shown on the right hand side through $\mathbf{r}$. It is to be noted that $g_{AB}(\mathbf{r})$ depends on the approach of the reactants to a separation r while $f(\mathbf{r})$ is to be determined by the changes as one goes from the reactant state A, B to the product state A^+, B^- (refer to Fig. 2).

The contributions to $f(\mathbf{r})$ come from the electronic energy, intramolecular vibrational energy and the energy of solvation. An estimation of this factor will be needed for a very limited range of $\mathbf{r}$ values. For large values of $\mathbf{r}, f(\mathbf{r})$ goes to zero and the knowledge of the PES over a wide range of $\mathbf{r}$ will not be required. Only in a nearly rigid framework of all the reactants and mildly polar solvents, significant contributions to the bulk rate seem to come from distances greater than 10 Å. The matrix elements between the reactant and the product states may be estimated using ab initio or a combination of ab initio and semiempirical quantal calculations [50]. Newer techniques are becoming available to include the effects of solvent polarisation in the evaluation of the matrix elements [51] and these will also improve the detailed modelling of these reactions.

Significant progress has been made in the last decade in the rapid estimation of molecular correlation functions. Simulation methods are even now very time consuming and approximation methods such as the RISM (reference interaction site model) method or perturbation theory are very useful. While improvements in the site-site integral equation methods have been proposed [52], evaluation of the site-site correlation functions with six to ten sites on each molecule is becoming feasible [34]. Alternatives such as reference linearised hypernetted chain (RLHNC) have also been used for finding out the extent of solvent structural effects on the kinetic parameters of reactions [53].

Progress has also been significant in the analysis of the solvent dynamical effects. Important advances have been made in the development of molecular theories [47, 54, 55], and supporting data are being generated from computer experiments [49, 56–58]. Generalised Smoluchowski equation for density fluctuations in a polar medium including a molecular cavity has been solved to obtain the longitudinal and the transverse polarisation relaxation times of the medium [47]. The decay is nonexponential just as in the case of simulation studies. A molecular theory for a medium containing two cavities (reactants) has not been developed yet. In such a calculation, the dependence of the relaxation times on the distance separating the reactants can be assessed. An estimation of the dependence of $\tau(\mathbf{r})$ on temperature and on reactant concentrations may be crucial for explaining the anomalous behaviour of the kinetic activation parameters. An alternative formulation will be needed if we have to take into account the time dependent friction $\zeta(t)$. If $\zeta(t)$ does not decay to zero rapidly, a description in terms of relaxation times may not be adequate.

Solvent relaxation in a TIP4P model for water (transferable intermolecular potential with four sites on each H_2O) around a dipolar cavity was studied using molecular dynamics simulations and the results indicated that relaxation in the molecular system is slower than that predicted by continuum models [56]. In our work, we are investigating the dynamics of solvation around two reacting cavities as a function of the separation between the cavities [48, 49]. Special attention is given for analysing whether the solvent far from the reacting sites relaxes faster than the solvent in the vicinity of the reactants. To understand the mechanism of the coupling of the reaction to the heat bath, a number of simulations have been forthcoming [57, 58]. For example, time dependent friction (or the memory kernel) $\zeta(t)$ is evaluated for a number of systems by obtaining the force-force autocorrelation functions. The generalised Langevin equation or the more recent techniques of nonequilibrium statistical mechanics [59] may provide a framework for going over from a steady state analysis to a dynamical theory of electron transfer rates in polar media.

While the article deals with a molecular modelling of electron transfer rate processes, such an attempt is necessary if one has to use the results from the gas phase PES as well as the liquid state distribution functions. The applicability of such a method can be tested against experimental data for well known electron transfer reactions such as those between MnO_4^- and MnO_4^{2-} and between Ru^{2+} and Ru^{3+}. If there is a formation of a bridge between the reactants, then the formulation of $\hat{k}_{AB}(r)$ has to be modified [60, 61] because the lifetime of the locally bridged intermediate will dominate over all other factors.

6. ACKNOWLEDGEMENT

The author would like to thank Prof. P.T. Narasimhan for continued encouragement, Prof. H.L. Friedman for introducing him to the theory of electrolyte solutions and P. Vijaya Kumar and D.H.S. Ram Kumar for useful discussions.

REFERENCES

1. W.L. Reynolds and R.W. Lumry, The Mechanism of Electron Transfer, Ronald Press: New York (1966).
2. R.D. Cannon, Electron Transfer Reactions, Butterworths: London (1980).
3. J. Ulstrup, Charge Transfer Processes in Condensed Media, Springer-Verlag: Berlin (1979).
4. B. Chance, D.C. DeVault, H. Fraunfelder, J.R. Schreiffer and N. Sutin, Tunneling in Biological Systems, Academic Press: New York (1969).
5. M.D. Newton and N. Sutin, Ann. Rev. Phys. Chem., **35**, 437 (1984).
6. E.M. Kosower and D. Huppert, Ann. Rev. Phys. Chem., **37**, 127 (1986).
7. B. Fain, Theory of Rate Processes in Condensed Media, Springer-Verlag: Berlin (1980).
8. F.K. Fong, Theory of Molecular Relaxation, John Wiley: New York (1975).

9. B.L. Tembe, H.L. Friedman and M.D. Newton, J. Chem. Phys., **78**, 1490 (1982).
10. J.P. Hansen and I.R. McDonald, Theory of Simple Liquids, Academic Press: New York (1976).
11. H.L. Friedman, A Course in Statistical Mechanics, Plenum Press: New York (1983).
12. R.D. Levine and R.B. Bernstein, Molecular Reaction Dynamics and Chemical Reactivity, Oxford University Press, New York (1987).
13. N.R. Kestner, J. Logan and J. Jortner, J. Phys. Chem. **78**, 2148 (1974).
14. M.D. Newton, Int. J. Quant. Chem. Symp., **14**, 363 (1980).
15. B.S. Brunschwig, J. Logan, N. Sutin and M.D. Newton, J. Am. Chem. Soc., **102**, 5798 (1980).
16. T. Holstein, Ann. Phys., **8**, 343 (1959).
17. R.A. Marcus, Ann. Rev. Phys. Chem., **15**, 155 (1964).
18. R.D. Cannon, Chem. Phys. Lett., **49**, 299 (1977).
19. R.A. Chiles, G.A. Jongeward, M.A. Bolton and P.G. Wolynes, J. Chem. Phys., **81**, 2039 (1984).
20. D. Thirumalai and B.J. Berne, Ann. Rev. Phys. Chem., **37**, 401 (1986).
21. J. Chandrasekhar, S.F. Smith and W.L. Jorgensen, J. Am. Chem. Soc., **106**, 3049 (1984).
22. K.E. Gubbins and C.G. Gray, Theory of Molecular Fluids, Oxford University Press: London (1986).
23. N. Quirke and D.J. Tildesley, Mol. Phys., **45**, 811 (1982).
24. J.S. Hoye and G. Stell, J. Chem. Phys., **65**, 18 (1982).
25. D. Chandler and H.C. Andersen, J. Chem. Phys., **57**, 1930 (1972).
26. D. Chandler, in The Liquid State of Matter, E.W. Montroll and J.L. Lebowitz, Editors, North Holland: Amsterdam (1982).
27. G.P. Morriss and D. MacGowan, Mol. Phys., **58**, 745 (1986).
28. D. Chandler, Mol. Phys., **47**, 871 (1982).
29. P.J. Rossky, Ann. Rev. Phys. Chem., **36**, 321 (1986).
30. K.J. Fraser, L.A. Dunn and G.P. Morriss, Mol. Phys., **61**, 775 (1987).
31. E. Enciso, C. Martin, M.B. Dearman and J.C. Dore, Mol. Phys. **60**, 541 (1987).
32. O. Steinhausser, I. Hausleithner and H. Bertnagolli, Chem. Phys., **111**, 371 (1987).
33. P.A. Monson, Mol. Phys., **62**, 65 (1987).
34. D.H.S. Ram Kumar, A.P. Kudchadker and B.L. Tembe, to be published.
35. D.A. MacQuarrie, Statistical Mechanics, Harper and Row, New York (1976).
36. D. Chandler, Statistical Mechanics, Oxford University Press, London (1988).
37. H.L. Friedman, Ann. Rev. Phys. Chem., **32**, 179 (1981).
38. P.S. Ramanathan and H.L. Friedman, J. Chem. Phys. **54**, 1086 (1971).
39. P.J. Rossky, B. Dudowicz, B.L. Tembe and H.L. Friedman, J. Chem. Phys., **73**, 3372 (1980).
40. B. Russel and P.J. Rossky, J. Chem. Phys. **79**, 1419 (1983).
41. H.A. Kramers, Physica (The Hague), **7**, 284 (1940).
42. J.L. Skinner and P.G. Wolynes, J. Chem. Phys., **69**, 2143 (1978).
43. B. Carmeli and A. Nitzan, J. Chem. Phys., **80**, 3596 (1984).
44. T.W. Nee and R. Zwanzig, J. Chem. Phys., **52**, 6353 (1970).
45. G. Van der Zwan and J.T. Hynes, J. Phys. Chem., **89**, 4181 (1985).
46. D.F. Calef and P.G. Wolynes, J. Chem. Phys., **78**, 470 (1983).
47. B. Bagchi, Ann. Rev. Phys. Chem., **40**, 115 (1989).
48. P. Vijaya Kumar and B.L. Tembe, Proc. Indian Acad. Sci. Chem. Sci., **100**, 305 (1988).

49. P. Vijaya Kumar and B.L. Tembe, Proceedings of the Discussion Meeting on Solvation Dynamics and Charge Transfer, Indian Institute of Science, Bangalore; World Scientific, Singapore, in press.
50. P. Siddarth and R.A. Marcus, J. Phys. Chem., **94**, 2985 (1990).
51. H.J. Kim and J.T. Hynes, J. Phys. Chem., **94**, 2736 (1990).
52. D. Chandler, R. Silbey and B.M. Ladanyi, Mol. Phys., **46**, 1335 (1982).
53. T. Morita, B.M. Ladanyi and J.T. Hynes, J. Phys. Chem., **93**, 1386 (1989).
54. P.G. Wolynes, J. Chem. Phys., **86**, 5133 (1987).
55. M.D. Newton and H.L. Friedman, J. Chem. Phys., **88**, 4460 (1988).
56. O.A. Karim, A.D.J. Haymet, M.J. Banet and J.D. Simon, J. Phys. Chem., **92**, 3391 (1988).
57. S.-B. Zhu, J. Lee and G.W. Robinson, J. Chem. Phys., **88**, 7088 (1988).
58. S.-B. Zhu, J. Lee and G.W. Robinson, J. Chem. Phys., **90**, 7127 (1989).
59. H. Grabert, Projection Operator Techniques in Nonequilibrium Statistical Mechanics, Springer-Verlag, Berlin (1982).
60. R.A. Marcus and R. Almeida, J. Phys. Chem., **94**, 2973 (1990).
61. K.V. Mikkelson and M.A. Ratner, J. Chem. Phys., **90**, 4237 (1989).

7. Dynamics of Gas-Surface Scattering

K.L. Sebastian

Department of Applied Chemistry
Cochin University of Science and Technology
Cochin, India

Abstract

Study of gas-surface interactions is of great interest in different fields. In this article we briefly outline the different experimental techniques that are used for the study of the interactions, pointing out certain interesting current experiments. Then we review the progress that has been made in the theory of such interactions. First we give a description of the theory of elastic, diffractive scattering from the surface. The utility of close coupling calculations, the currently popular fast Fourier transform technique, and semiclassical wave packet propagation are described. Often the scattering involves energy exchange between the projectile and the solid. Thus one can have various inelastic processes like phonon excitation and rotational, vibrational or electronic excitation of the projectile. The scattering may involve non-adiabatic processes too. For example, it may lead to creation of electron-hole excitations in the metal, which has been suggested as a possible mechanism of sticking of light atoms. Considerable effects of non-adiabaticity are manifested in scattering processes leading to the exchange of an electron between the projectile and the solid. We touch upon the theory of all the above processes, stressing the progress that has been made in the recent past.

1. INTRODUCTION

The interaction between a gas atom or molecule and a surface is important in several fields. Heterogenous catalysis, hypersonic flight, crystal and thin film growth are just a few such examples. However, inspite of its obvious importance, microscopic studies of such interactions have become possible only during the last two decades. Earlier, such studies were hindered by the difficulty of attaining and maintaining ultrahigh vacuum. Nowadays, studies of interaction of gases with well characterized single crystal surfaces are possible, using a wide variety of experimental techniques.

One now has several techniques for the characterization of surfaces. Of these, the most important is low energy electron diffraction (LEED). This depends on the fact that electrons having an energy less than about 100 eV have wave lengths roughly of the order of interatomic spacing in crystals. Further they penetrate only about 20–100 layers of the crystal. Because of these reasons, their diffraction has become a very important tool in the study of crystal surfaces. It has been used to study the structures of a wide variety of surfaces, with or without adsorbed atoms. Other techniques, like emission of electrons caused by X-rays or UV radiation (X-ray or Ultraviolet Photoelectron spectroscopy), Auger electron spectroscopy (AES), and X-ray absorption fine structure, have also been used. All these have led to very valuable information on interatomic distances, adsorption sites, phase transitions etc. Of more recent origin is electron energy loss spectroscopy which studies the inelastic scattering of electrons from surfaces. This can give information on the nature of the surface chemical bond. See reference 1 for details and interesting applications of these techniques. Another recent technique is inverse photoemission, i.e. emission of photons as a result of bombardment with low energy electrons, which gives information on the unoccupied orbitals [1].

Field ion microscopy and field electron emission [2] are among the oldest tools of a surface chemist. They are able to give an almost atomic level image of surfaces of those metals which can withstand the high electric field that has to be applied. However, these techniques have the defect of distorting the surface and hence are not currently advocated. Other techniques, that have been used are: work function measurements, thermal desorption, electron or photon induced desorption, ion or metastable atom scattering and IR spectroscopy. The construction of the scanning tunneling microscope (STM) [3] has been a very exciting development. It gives information on the electronic topography of surface and adsorbed layers. It has been used to directly image the chemical bonds of the Si (100) – (2 × 1) surface [4]. It has also been used to study surface reconstruction and doping effects on chemical reactivity [3]. Though upto now the studies have been confined to metal or semiconductor surfaces [5], organic crystals and polymers can also be studied [6]. Vibrational spectroscopy using STM is a very exciting possibility that is being currently investigated.

The most useful technique for the study of the interaction of atoms and molecules with surfaces is the scattering of molecular beams. In this, one shoots a beam of molecules of well defined energy on to a surface and studies the outcoming particles. A variety of different processes can occur as a result of the collision with the surface. Trapping of the molecule to give a physisorbed state, sticking to give a chemisorbed state, rotational, vibrational and/or electronic excitation, dissociation, excitation of phonons, dissociative chemisorption, charge transfer between the molecule and the surface are some of the different processes that might happen. As is currently popular in gas phase crossed beam experiments, one should be carrying out state to state studies. Thus techniques like laser induced fluorescence, multiphoton ionization, and IR emission have been used to monitor the population of different states after the scattering [7].

While we do not intend to cover all the important work done in this field, we give below, selected examples from recent literature which should give the reader a flavour for the types of things that are now possible. In a recent study [8], crossed molecular beams of CO and O_2 were allowed to be incident on the Rh (111) surface. The molecules adsorb and react to give CO_2, which desorbs. Angular distribution and translational and vibrational energy distributions of the desorbing CO_2 were measured. Angular distribution was found to deviate from cosine, (cosine would have been the result if CO_2 had attained equilibrium with the surface) and energy distributions were non-Boltzmann. These indicate that CO_2 has not attained equilibrium with the surface. The same reaction has been studied on Pt (111) and Pd (111) [9]. A theoretical study of this reaction is an interesting challenge. In another investigation [10], time of flight and laser induced fluorescence have been used to obtain translational energies and vibrational and rotational populations of NO, photodesorbed from Pt (111). Again, distributions were found to be non-Boltzmann. This has been interpreted in terms of a desorption mechanism involving a temporary negative ion resonance. In a recent publication, [11] the probability of dissociative chemisorption of methane on Pt (111) was reported to depend upon the velocity component normal to the surface, vibrational energy and the surface temperature. The authors concluded that none of the existing models [12] could explain the experimental observations satisfactorily.

In the following, we review certain aspects of the theory of scattering of atoms, molecules and ions from the surface of a solid. Recent reviews on the topic are by Singh and Deb [13] and Gerber [14].

2. ELASTIC SCATTERING OF ATOMS AND MOLECULES

The scattering of He and H_2 from the surface of LiF was studied as early as 1930 and had provided evidence for the de-Broglie wave particle hypothesis. More recently, He scattering has become a standard tool for the determination of surface structure. The technique has the advantage of being non-destructive. Further, as the atom is reflected from the topmost layer of the solid, the scattering is a sensitive probe of the interaction potential between the projectile and the topmost layer of the solid. In comparison, in LEED, a reflected electron would feel the effect of many layers of atoms, as it would penetrate some depth into the solid before being reflected. However, the He scattering experiment is much more difficult to carry out than other diffraction experiments (LEED, X-ray, or neutron).

With the recent progress in computer algorithms and computer power, it has become possible to carry out essentially exact calculations on diffractive scattering. The most important of the calculational techniques is the close coupling method, which is described below. Other techniques that have been used are given in section 2.2

2.1 Close Coupling method

The method is quite well known in gas phase collision theory. We assume the solid surface to have a rigid structure, with all the atoms remaining stationary at their equilibrium positions. Note that this rules out the possibility of energy exchange between the solid and the atom incident on it. We take our co-ordinate system in such a fashion that the Z-axis is perpendicular to the surface of the solid, which is assumed to occupy the half space $z < 0$ and the atom incident on it from above (see Fig. 1).

We denote the position vector of the atom by **r** and its components by x, y and z. The interaction potential $V(x, y, z)$ depends only on the position of the

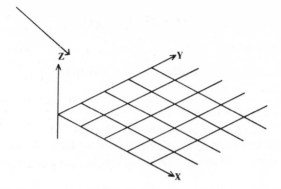

Fig. 1.   Scattering from the surface of a crystal. The crystal occupies the region $z < 0$.

atom. For simplicity, we take the solid to be simple cubic and denote the periodicities in the two directions parallel to the surface (X- and Y-directions) by a and b. Thus one has

$$V = (x + na, y + mb, z) = V(x, y, z) \tag{1}$$

for any integers n and m. Equation (1) is an expression of the periodicity of the potential $V(x, y, z)$.

Equation (1) implies that the potential may be expanded as a Fourier series as in (2).

$$V(x, y, z) = \sum_{n}\sum_{m} V_{nm}(z) \exp (i\mathbf{G}_{nm} \cdot \mathbf{R}) \tag{2}$$

In the above, $\mathbf{G}_{nm} = 2\pi (n\hat{\mathbf{i}}/a + m\hat{\mathbf{j}}/b)$, where $\hat{\mathbf{i}}$ and $\hat{\mathbf{j}}$ are unit vectors in the X- and Y-directions; $R = x\hat{\mathbf{i}} + y\hat{\mathbf{j}}$ is the component of the position vector $\mathbf{r}$ of the atom in the surface plane; n and m are allowed to have all integral values between $-\infty$ and ∞. All points whose position vectors are $\mathbf{G}_{nm}$, with n and $m \in \{-\infty, \infty\}$ form a lattice, referred to as the reciprocal lattice. The scattering is described by the Schrödinger equation

$$[- (\hbar^2/2\mu) \nabla^2 + V(x, y, z)] \, \psi \, (x, y, z) = E \, \psi \, (x, y, z) \tag{3}$$

μ is the mass of the atom and E is its energy. The equation has to be solved with appropriate boundary conditions (see below).

Let $\mathbf{k}$ denote the incident wave vector of the atom and $\mathbf{K}$ denote its component parallel to the surface. k is related to the energy by $E = k^2 \hbar^2/2\mu$. Because of the periodicity of the potential, given in equation (1), we look for solution of (3) of the form

$$\psi(x, y, z) = \sum_{n_1,m_1} \psi_{n_1 m_1}(z) \exp [i(\mathbf{K} + \mathbf{G}_{n_1 m_1}) \cdot \mathbf{R}] \tag{4}$$

Substituting equation (4) into equation (3) and multiplying the resultant equation by $\exp [i\mathbf{G}_{nm} \cdot \mathbf{R}] \, d\mathbf{R}$ and integrating over a unit cell of the surface leads to

$$\left[- \frac{d^2}{dz^2} + V_{nm}(z)\right] \psi_{nm}(z) + (2\mu/\hbar^2) \sum_{n_1,m_1} V_{nm,n_1 m_1}(z) \, \psi_{n_1 m_1}(z)$$

$$= [k^2 - (K + G_{nm})^2] \, \psi_{nm}(z) \qquad (5)$$

$V_{nm, n_1 m_1}(z)$ is defined by

$$V_{-n-m, n_1 m_1}(z) = 1/(ab) \int V(x, y, z) \exp [i(G_{n_1-n, m_1-m} \cdot \mathbf{R})] \, d\mathbf{R}$$

We define $\kappa_{nm}^2 = [k^2 - (K + G_{nm})^2]$. If κ_{nm} is real, then $\psi_{nm}(z)$ behaves like $\exp (\pm i\kappa_{nm} z)$ for large positive z. Then one says that the (nm)th channel is open. On the other hand, if κ_{nm} is imaginary, $\psi_{nm}(z)$ decays like $\exp (- \mid \kappa_{nm} \mid z)$ and the (nm)th channel is said to be closed. Therefore, the above set of differential equations (5) have to be solved, subject to the following boundary conditions.

$$\psi_{n_1 m_1}(z) \to 0 \text{ for } z \to \infty \text{ for the closed channels, and}$$

$$\psi_{n_1 m_1}(z) \to \kappa_{n_1 m_1}^{-1/2} \exp [- i\kappa_{n_1 m_1} z] \, \delta_{n_1 0} \delta_{m_1 0}$$

$$+ \kappa_{n_1 m_1}^{-1/2} \exp [- i\kappa_{n_1 m_1} z] \, S_{n_1 m_1, 00} \qquad (6)$$

for open channels.

$$\psi_{n_1 m_1}(z) \to 0 \text{ for } z \to \infty,$$

as the atom cannot penetrate into the solid. The quantity $S_{n_1 m_1, 00}$ defined by the above equations is referred to as an element of the scattering matrix.

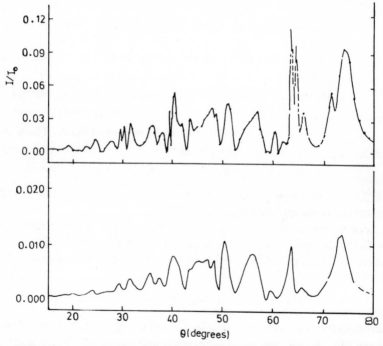

Fig. 2   Helium scattering from a monolayer of Xe on graphite. I/I_0 is plotted against the angle of incidence. Top: converged close coupled calculation. Bottom: experimental results (reprinted with permission from [17]).

The probability of scattering into the $(n_1 m_1)$th direction is given by $P_{n_1 m_1} = |S_{n_1 m_1,00}|^2$. The above equations are solved by numerical techniques quite well-known in gas phase scattering theory. The computational effort involved scales like N^3, where N is the total number of channels used in the calculation. The method has been successfully employed for the scattering of He atoms from the surface of GaAs, Xe adsorbed on graphite, LiF (001) etc. [15–17]. For a comparison of the theory and experiment see Fig. 2.

2.2 Other Methods

(a) The fast Fourier transform (FFT) method, introduced by Kosloff and Kosloff [18, 19] has become very popular in the past few years for the treatment of gas-surface scattering. The idea is to solve the time dependent Schrödinger equation,

$$i\hbar \, \partial\Psi(\mathbf{r}, t)/\partial t = H \, \Psi(\mathbf{r}, t) = [-(\hbar^2 / 2\mu) \, \nabla^2 + V(x, y, z)]\Psi(\mathbf{r}, t) \qquad (7)$$

numerically. At an initial time t_0, the wave function $\Psi(\mathbf{r}, t_0)$ is taken to be a wave packet approaching the surface. By solving the above equation numerically, one can obtain the wave function at any desired later time t and hence extract any information regarding the scattering process. In order to solve the equation, one has to choose a grid of points in space on which the values of the wave function at any given instant are to be calculated. The effect of ∇^2 on $\Psi(\mathbf{r}, t)$ is calculated using an FFT technique. If N_g is the number of grid points, the computational effort scales as $N_g \ln N_g$. The method has been successfully applied to the scattering of He from $\overset{\cdot}{W}(110)$ [20]. The results are in good agreement with the coupled channel calculations. The main advantages of this method are:

1. Computational effort is less in comparison with the close coupling calculations.
2. It can be used to study scattering from surfaces which are not periodic, for example, scattering from an amorphous solid.
3. The method can be modified to take excitations of the solid into account.

As the number of open channels increases, the close coupling calculations become more and more time consuming. This does not happen in the FFT method.

(b) Semiclassical Gaussian wave packet method [21–23]: In this method, one assumes that the wave function at any instant of time can be represented as the sum of a finite number of Gaussians, whose positions and widths are time dependent. A given Gaussian would have the form

$$G(\mathbf{r}, t) = \exp\{i/\hbar(\mathbf{r} - \mathbf{r}_t) \cdot \mathbf{A}_t \cdot (\mathbf{r} - \mathbf{r}_t) + \mathbf{p} \cdot (\mathbf{r} - \mathbf{r}_t) + \gamma_t\}$$

$\mathbf{r}_t$, $\mathbf{p}_t$ and γ_t are parameters in the function and determine the location, speed of movement, phase and normalization of the Gaussian. $\mathbf{A}_t$ is a complex matrix giving the distribution and spread of the packet. Equations can be derived for the time evolution of these quantities. These are simple differential equations similar to those in classical mechanics. They may be solved to obtain the wave function at any time. By analysing the Gaussians after the scattering is over, scattering probabilities can be calculated. See the review by Gerber et al for more details.

The method has been successfully applied to the diffraction of He from the (001) surface of LiF [22].

(c) In addition to the above, other methods that have been used for the calculation of scattering probabilities are:
1. distorted wave Born approximation [23],
2. semiclassical methods of Miller [24] and Marcus [25] and
3. the sudden approximation [26].

(see Gerber [14] and the references therein for details on these methods).

3. INELASTIC SCATTERING OF ATOMS AND MOLECULES

The scattering of an atom or a molecule from a solid is often an inelastic process. In the scattering, the projectile, or the target may get excited and then one says that the process is inelastic. For example, as a result of the collision with the surface, a molecule may get rotationally, vibrationally or electronically excited. There is also the possibility that the solid may get vibrationally (creation of phonons) or electronically (creation of electron-hole excitations) excited.

3.1   One Phonon Excitation

Just as the small amplitude vibrations of a polyatomic molecule may be described in terms of normal modes, the vibrations of a solid may be described in terms of its normal modes. Excitation of these normal modes are referred to as creation of phonons. In the scattering of an atom from the surface of a solid, the atom may undergo a change in its wave vector parallel to the surface by G_{nm} as in the earlier section, in addition to which it may cause the excitation of a phonon, with wavevector Q. Thus, if K_i and K_f are the components of the incident and final wavevectors of the atom parallel to the surface, and E_i and E_f are the energies of the incident and scattered beams, then

$$K_i + G_{nm} - Q = K_f \tag{8}$$

and

$$E_i = E_f + \hbar\omega(Q) \tag{9}$$

$\hbar\omega(Q)$ is the energy of the phonon that is created. By measuring the energy lost by the atom as a function of its change in the parallel momentum, it is possible to obtain dispersion curves (ω versus Q curves) for the phonons created. These curves have been theoretically calculated and compared with experiment. Such studies have been performed by Toennies [27, 28] using a time of flight technique for the scattering of He from alkali halides and noble metals. Similar studies are also available for rare gas monolayers on a metal support [29]. Calculation of the intensities of the inelastically scattered beams have been carried out using the distorted wave Born approximation (DWBA) [30]. In this, one first solves the Schrödinger equation exactly for the static solid (i.e. one in which the atoms are not allowed to vibrate) using the close coupling method and then treats the interaction between the atom and the surface vibrations perturbatively (Figs. 3 and 4).

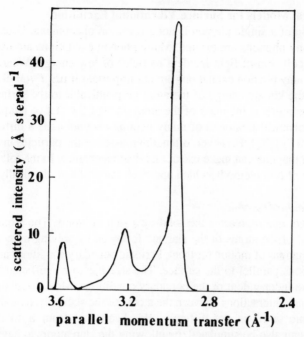

Fig. 3 Theoretical results for the He scattering from LiF(001). $E_i = 17$ meV. $\theta_i = 63.2°$ and $\theta_f = 26.8°$ (taken from [27], with permission from Kluwer Academic Publishers).

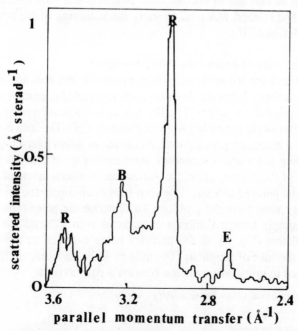

Fig. 4 Experimental results for the system in Fig. 3 (taken from [27], with permission from Kluwer Academic Publishers).

3.2 Classical Models for Surface Vibrational Excitation

The excitation of a single phonon is not a common phenomena. Usually, in the collision, many phonons are excited. Many phonon excitations are unimportant only for the collision of light incident particles of low energy. Weare [31] has shown that many phonon excitations are not important if $\mu E_\perp T_s /(Mk\theta_D^2) < 0.01$, where $E_\perp$ is the kinetic energy of the atom perpendicular to the surface, T_s, the surface temperature, μ the mass of the atom and θ_D, the Debye temperature. A quantum mechanical treatment of many phonon excitations is a difficult many body problem [32, 33]. However, often, the masses of the particles involved are large enough that one can make use of classical mechanics. In the following, we give outlines of two methods, which approach the problem classically.

3.2.1 Molecular Dynamics

In this method, one represents the solid by a slab of atoms. The motions of the projectile and of the atoms of the slab are followed by solving numerically the Newton's equations of motion for them. Periodic boundary conditions are imposed in the directions parallel to the surface. The slab has to be sufficiently big that the results are independent of the boundary conditions. Most calculations make use of harmonic interactions between the atoms of the slab [34], though inclusion of anharmonic terms is not difficult [35]. Scattering from a solid at finite temperature can also be simulated, by allowing the slab atoms to have different positions and velocities with probabilities proportional to $\exp(-H_s/kT)$, where H_s is the classical Hamiltonian for the solid. The calculations, however, are time-consuming as one has to average over positions and momenta of all the slab particles. The method was used to study the scattering of Ne atoms from LiF (001) by McClure [36].

3.2.2 The Generalized Langevin Equation Approach

This is another tool for the study of energy transfer in the collision of atoms/molecules with surfaces. It has also been successfully applied to reactive scattering and reactions happening on surface [37]. The approach was developed by Adelman and Doll [38], following the earlier work of Zwanzig [39]. The idea is to divide the solid into two zones, the primary zone, consisting of atoms interacting directly with the colliding atom and a secondary zone consisting of atoms interacting with the atoms of the primary zone, the interactions between atoms of the solid being taken to be purely harmonic. One then tries to eliminate the co-ordinates of the secondary zone from the problem. To illustrate the procedure, consider the following simple model: Collision of an atom with a "solid" of just two harmonic oscillators (Fig. 5) all the particles being assumed to move in one dimension, for the sake of simplicity. The masses of the harmonic oscillators are taken to be equal to unity. We write the Newton's equations as

$$\mu \ddot{y} = - \partial V(x_1, y)/\partial y, \tag{10}$$

$$\ddot{x}_1 = - \omega^2 x_1 - \Omega^2 x_2 - \partial V(x_1, y)/\partial x_1, \tag{11}$$

$$\ddot{x}_2 = - \omega^2 x_2 - \Omega^2 x_1. \tag{12}$$

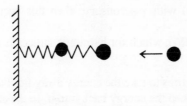

Fig. 5 Collision of an atom with a "solid" of two harmonic oscillators.

$V(x_1, y)$ is the interaction potential between the incident atom with position at y and the first atom of the solid, located at x_1. We imagine that the first oscillator forms the primary zone and the second the secondary zone. Solving equation (12), we get

$$x_2(t) = x_2^0 \cos(\omega t) + (p_2^0/\omega) \sin(\omega t) - \Omega^2 \int_0^t \beta(t - s) x_1(s) \, ds \quad (13)$$

In the above, $\beta(t) = \sin(\omega t)/\omega$. Equation (13) on substitution into equation (11) gives

$$\ddot{x}_1 = - \omega^2 x_1 - \partial V(x_1, y)/\partial x_1$$

$$+ \Omega^4 \int_0^t \beta(t - s) x_1(s) ds + R_1(t) \quad (14)$$

with

$$R_1(t) = \Omega^2 [x_2^0 \cos(\omega t) + p_2^0 \sin(\omega t)/\omega] \quad (15)$$

$R_1(t)$ depends on the initial position and momentum of the second oscillator. If the solid is at a temperature T, then these initial quantities have to be thought of as random variables, with probability distributions dependent on temperature. This means that x_2^0 and p_2^0 are independent Gaussian random variables with mean zero and hence $R_1(t)$ is a stationary random force with mean zero. Performing an integration by parts on the right hand side of (14), it may be rewritten as

$$\ddot{x}_1 = - \omega^2 x_1 - \partial V(x_1, y)/\partial x_1 - \int_0^t \Delta(t - s) \dot{x}_1(s) \, ds + R(t) \quad (16)$$

$R(t)$ also is a random force. Equation (16) together with equation (10) forms the basis of the generalized Langevin equation (GLE) approach. Even though equation (16) was derived for a secondary system consisting of only one atom, the form of the equation remains unaltered for a secondary system consisting of an infinite number of atoms.

Note that equation (16) means that the effect of the secondary zone is to exert two types of forces on the primary system.

1. A frictional force, which has memory, and is represented by

$$\int_0^t \Delta(t - s) x_1(s) ds.$$

If $\Delta(t - s) = 2\gamma\delta(t - s)$ with γ a constant, then this becomes $\gamma\dot{x}_1(t)$, the usual frictional force.

2. A random force $R(t)$, which for harmonic lattices is a Gaussian with mean zero. That is $\langle R(t) \rangle = 0$.

The frictional force tries to take the energy away from the primary zone while the random force can feed the energy back into it. In the absence of the colliding particle, this drain and inflow of energy have to balance so that the primary zone is maintained at a temperature T. This implies that the random force, the frictional force and the temperature are related. This relationship can be shown to be

$$\Delta(t) = kT \langle R(t)R(0) \rangle \tag{17}$$

In scattering from a three dimensional solid, things are obviously more complicated, in that the primary zone may need many co-ordinates for its description.

For actual applications, one has to know the kernel, $\Delta(t)$ and the random force $R(t)$. If these were to be exactly calculated, then one would have the same amount of computational complexity as the original problem. The usually adopted procedure is to employ simple expressions for $\Delta(t)$ with some adjustable parameters, chosen best to reproduce known information on surface and bulk vibrational properties. The calculation of $R(t)$ and the frictional force are then not time consuming. The procedure is to generate the random force on a computer and to solve the equations of the type (10) and (16) numerically for a large number of realizations of the random force. The method has been applied to the scattering of Ar and Xe from Pt (111) by Tully [37] (Figs. 6 and 7). Tully has also studied the thermal desorption of these atoms. This is more difficult to

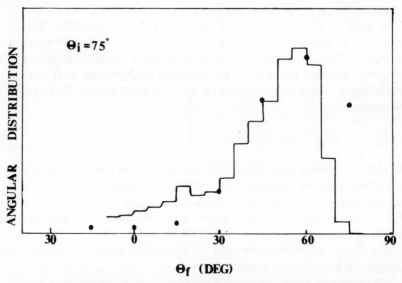

Fig. 6 Angular distribution of Ar scattered from Pt (111) with $T_s = 700$ K and $E_i = 6$ kJ/mol. Points are experimental results and solid line GLE results (taken from [37], with permission from American Chemical Society).

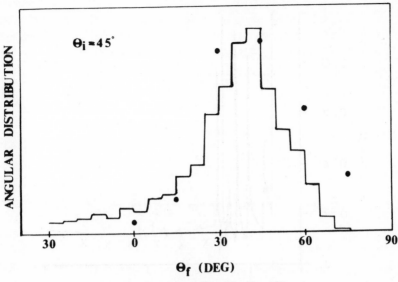

Fig. 7   Same as Fig. 6 for $\theta_i = 45°$.

study as this is a slow process. The procedure has also been applied to the reaction of a gas phase oxygen atom with a carbon atom adsorbed on Pt (111).

4.   ROTATIONAL EXCITATION OF MOLECULES
As a result of the collision with a surface, the molecule can get rotationally, vibrationally and electronically excited. For incident energies less than 1 eV, electronic excitation is very improbable. The final rotational state distribution can be determined using laser induced fluorescence or time of flight measurements. Rotational excitation in the scattering of HD from Pt (111) has been studied by Sibener et al [40]. They have been able to observe resonances in the scattering. These are due to states in which the molecule has been excited to such rotational states that it does not have enough energy in translational motion perpendicular to the surface to escape from the potential well in the vicinity of the surface (Fig. 8). If one assumes the surface to be rigid, then the coupled channels method can be easily extended to treat rotational/vibrational excitations of the molecule. Phonon participation is more difficult to treat, but can be done if one assumes the validity of classical mechanics and makes use of the GLE approach. Methods in which the centre of mass motion of the molecule is treated through the GLE approach and rotational motion quantum mechanically have also been developed [41].

5.   VIBRATIONAL EXCITATION OF MOLECULES
In contrast to rotational transitions, vibrational transitions in collisions with surfaces have been much less studied experimentally. IR spectroscopic study of vibrationally excited CO and CO_2 produced by molecular beam scattering from poly-crystalline surfaces have been studied by Fenn et al [42]. They find that the final vibrational populations are determined by an adsorption-desorption

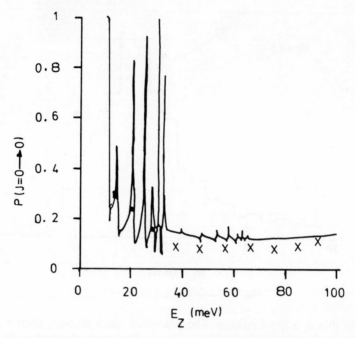

Fig. 8   Rotational transition probabilities for the scattering of HD from Ag (111). The sharp variations are due to resonances (taken from [40] with permission from American Institute of Physics).

mechanism. Vibrational excitation of NO scattered from Ag (111) has been attributed to an electronic mechanism, involving the de-excitation of thermal e-h excitations in the solid [43]. Theoretical studies on O_2 scattering from Ag (111) in which an electron is temporarily transferred to the molecule to form a temporary negative ion are available [44]. See the papers of Holloway and the review by Gadzuk [45]. Interaction of the oscillating dipole moment with the conduction electrons of metal has been suggested as the mechanism for de-excitation of the vibrations of excited CO and CO_2 from silver surfaces [46].

6.   NON-ADIABATIC PROCESSES

In the scattering from metal surfaces, there is the possibility that the metal is excited electronically in the collision. This is a non-adiabatic process, as there is transfer of energy between the nuclear and electronic degrees of freedom [47–48]. It is also possible for the energy of the electron-hole (e-h) excitations to be transferred to the molecule, causing it to be vibrationally excited [49–50] or even to dissociate. An incident molecule may lose all its translational energy that it gets stuck on the surface [51–52].

Non-adiabatic phenomena also occur in the scattering of atoms/ions like Na/Na$^+$ from the surface of metals [53–61]. In the following, we discuss the theory of these phenomena. A recent review of the topic is by Brako and Newns [56].

6.1 Charge exchange scattering

The scattering of atoms/ions from metal surfaces has been studied theoretically by several authors [53–57, 60, 61]. Let us consider the scattering of a sodium atom from the surface of a metal. In the scattering the atom may lose an electron and thereby become Na^+. It is possible to measure experimentally the fraction of ions that have been produced. To calculate this theoretically, one can adopt a simple jellium model description for the solid. That is, we assume that the ion cores of the metal are smeared out into a continuous positive background with a step at the surface. To describe the motion of the electrons in the solid, a single particle approximation, in which the electrons move in an effective potential $V_{ef}(z)$ can be used. This may be taken to be the potential calculated under the local density approximation. The Schrödinger equation determining the electronic states in the metal is thus

$$[(-\hbar^2/2m)\nabla^2 + V_{ef}(z)]\psi_k = \varepsilon_k\psi_k \qquad (18)$$

There is set of continuous eigenvalues, starting from $V_{ef}(\infty)$ upwards (Fig. 9). In a similar fashion, ψ_a, the orbital from which the electron is removed (3s in the case of Na) obeys

$$[(-\hbar^2/2m)\nabla^2 + V_a(r)]\psi_a = \varepsilon_a\psi_a \qquad (19)$$

$V_a(r)$ is the potential due to ion core of Na. ε_a is the energy of the orbital ψ_a and is equal to $-I$, where I is the ionization potential of the atom.

Fig. 9 The wave functions ψ_a and ψ_k, and the effective potential $V_{ef}(z)$.

If the atom is kept fixed at a distance R from the surface of the metal, there will be interaction between ψ_k and ψ_a. This will shift the energy of the orbital ψ_a, and further its energy will acquire a finite width, provided it lies in the continuum of metal states. That is, the orbital becomes a resonance and if we put an electron in it, the electron will not stay there for ever, but will hop in to the metal. The energy of ψ_a is also shifted by the image interaction. This is by an amount $e^2/(4R)$ for not too small R. The reason for this is that the formation of an ion is energetically favoured near the metal, because the ion would be stabilized by the image interaction. This means that the ionization potential of the atom is reduced by $e^2/(4R)$. So the effective energy of the orbital ψ_a is $-I + e^2/(4R)$. Figure 10 shows how $\varepsilon_a(R)$ varies with R. The expression $e^2/(4R)$ has to be modified for small R (in comparison with the Fermi screening length) but the qualitative behaviour is unchanged. The figure also shows the broadening of the energy of the orbital. The broadening depends on R and increases as one approaches the surface. Thus, for example, in Na scattering from $W(100)$, $\varepsilon_a(R)$ is always greater than ε_F. So when the atom is near the surface, the electron leaves the atom causing it to ionise. The majority of atoms do not pick up the electron on their way back and hence they come out as ions.

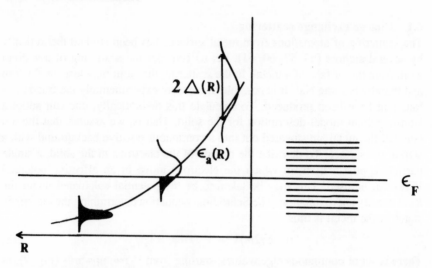

Fig. 10 $\varepsilon_a(R)$ plotted against R. Also shown is the broadening of the atomic level and how the width $\Delta(R)$ changes with R. In the figure, for large R, $\varepsilon_a < \varepsilon_F$ and as R decreases, $\varepsilon_a(R)$ increases and crosses the Fermi energy.

In order to calculate the probability of ionization, one can adopt the following approach. For atoms incident with kinetic energies > 10 eV, one can treat ionic motion classically. The resultant trajectory may be used to find how ε_a and Δ (the width of the ionic orbital) change with time during the collision process. Under certain approximations, the time-dependent Schrödinger equation may be solved numerically [60, 61]. If the width of the band of the metal is large in comparison to Δ, then approximate analytical expression for the occupation number of the orbital ψ_a may be found. Taking the ion to be far away from the metal at the time $t = -\infty$ and the collision to be over at $t = \infty$, the occupation number of the orbital ψ_a is [53]

$$\langle n_a(\infty) \rangle = \langle n_a(-\infty) \rangle \exp\left[-\int_{-\infty}^{\infty} 2\Delta(\tau)\,d\tau\right] + \pi^{-1}\int_{-\infty}^{\infty} d\varepsilon\, f(\varepsilon, T)$$

$$\times \left|\int_{-\infty}^{\infty} d\tau [\Delta(\tau)]^{1/2}\, g(\tau)\, \exp(-i\varepsilon\tau)\right|^2 \qquad (20)$$

In the above, $f(\varepsilon, T)$ is the Fermi-Dirac distribution function,

$$f(\varepsilon, T) = [\exp\{(\varepsilon - \varepsilon_F)/kT\} + 1]$$

and

$$g(\tau) = \exp\left[-\int_{\tau}^{\infty} d\tau\, \{i\varepsilon_a(\tau) + \Delta(\tau)\}\right].$$

This expression has been successfully applied to the description of the temperature dependence of the neutral fraction in the scattering of Na from W(110) (Fig. 11) [53].

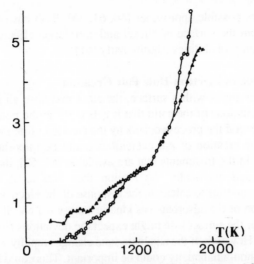

Fig. 11 Experimental neutral flux (arbitrary units) for Na scattered from $W(110)$, from [36c]. $\theta_i = 60°, E_i = 30$ eV (o) and 60 eV (Δ) (reprinted with permission from [53]).

The above approach assumes that all the effects of electron repulsions can be put into a one particle theory. If one wishes to incorporate at least the coulomb repulsion between the up and down spin electrons in ψ_a, then the problem is much more difficult to handle and time-dependent Hartree-Fock and a generalisation of the coupled cluster approach to time-dependent problems have

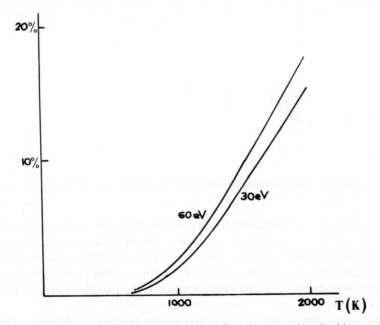

Fig. 12 Theoretical results for the system in Fig. 11 (reproduced with permission from [53]).

been suggested as possible approaches [60, 61, 56]. Both have been applied to Li$^+$ scattering from the surface of Nickel and correlation effects were found to alter neutralization probabilities significantly [61].

6.2 Sticking Due to Electron-Hole Pair Creation

In the collision of atoms with a surface, the atom may lose all its translational energy to the excitations of the solid that it gets stuck in the potential well near the surface. In general the process occurs by the creation of phonons. It has been suggested that the creation of e-h excitations could be important, at least for light atoms [47]. In the treatments that are available [51, 52], the motion of the adsorbate is treated classically. Its motion then acts as a time-dependent perturbation and one tries to calculate the response of the electronic system. Due to the slow motion of the adsorbate (its kinetic energy ~ 1 eV, if it moves in the potential well near the surface) we might expect the deviations from the adiabatic limit to be small. However, if the adiabatic state changes rapidly with the position of the adsorbate, non-adiabaticity could be important. This could lead to creation of e-h excitations and hence sticking [48]. This mechanism has been suggested to operate for adsorbates having an affinity level close to the Fermi energy of the metal. As the adsorbate approaches the surface, its affinity level is generally shifted downwards (Fig. 13) and it may move below the Fermi level. This leads to the partial occupation of the affinity level in the adiabatic state. If the affinity level is narrow when it crosses the Fermi level, then the system may not be able to follow the adiabatic state and non-adiabaticity could become important.

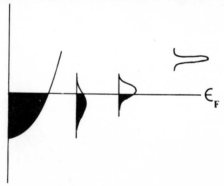

Fig. 13   Substrate and adsorbate density of states. The blackened area indicates the occupancy of adsorbate state.

Schönhammer and Gunnarsson [48] have developed an approach in which they approximate e-h excitations as bosons. Assuming the atom to follow a classical trajectory, they reduce the problem to a set of forced harmonic oscillators, from which they calculate the sticking probability as the probability that an excitation with energy > initial kinetic energy of the particle is created in the solid (Fig. 14).

These calculations as well as others [63] suggest that there could be significant contributions to sticking from this mechanism. On the experimental side, however, there is, as yet, no evidence supporting this.

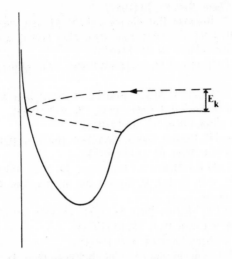

Fig. 14   Adiabatic potential energy curve and motion of the incoming atom on it. E_k is the initial kinetic energy of the atom.

7. ACKNOWLEDGEMENTS

This work was supported by the Department of Science and Technology, Government of India. I thank K. Sumithra for help in the preparation of the manuscript.

REFERENCES

1. G. Ertl and H. Küppers, Low energy electrons and surface chemistry, VCH Verlagsgesellschaft mbH, Weinheim (1985).
2. G.A. Somorjai, Principles of Surface Chemistry, Prentice-Hall, (New Jersey) (1972).
3. G. Binnig, H. Roherer, R.B. Gerber and E. Wiebel, Phys. Rev. Lett. **49**, 57 (1982).
4. R.J. Hamers, Ph. Avouris and F. Bozso, Phys. Rev. Lett. **59**, 2071 (1987).
5. Ph. Avouris, J. Phys. Chem. **94**, 2246 (1990).
6. T. Sletor and R. Tycko, Phys. Rev. Lett. **60**, 1418 (1988).
7. B. Pullman, J. Jortner, A. Nitzan and R.B. Gerber (eds), Dynamics on surfaces, D. Reidel Co., Boston (1984).
8. J. Segner, C.T. Campbell, G. Doyen and G. Ertl, Surf. Sci. **138**, 505 (1984); T. Matsushima and H. Asada, J. Chem. Phys. **85**, 1658 (1986).
9. S.A. Buntin, L.J. Richer, D.S. King and R.R. Cavanagh, J. Chem. Phys. **91**, 6429 (1989).
10. A.C. Luntz and D.S. Bethune, J. Chem. Phys. **90**, 1274 (1989).
11. H. Winters, J. Chem. Phys. **64**, 3495 (1975); S.G. Brass and G. Ehrlich, Phys. Rev. Lett. **57**, 2532 (1986); M.B. Lee, Q.Y. Yang and S.T. Ceyer, J. Chem. Phys. **87**, 2724 (1984).
12. J.A. Barker and D.J. Auerbach, Surf. Sci. Repts. **4**, 1 (1985). (see references 312 to 330 in this paper for experimental details).
13. H. Singh and B.M. Deb, Pramana-J Phys. **27**, 337 (1986).

14. R.B. Gerber, Chem. Rev. **87**, 29 (1987).
15. A.T. Yinnon, S. Bosanac, R.B. Gerber and J.N. Murrell, Chem. Phys. Lett. **58**, 364 (1978); R. Laughlin, Phys. Rev. **B25**, 2222 (1982); J.M. Hutson and C. Schwartz, J. Chem. Phys. **79**, 5179 (1983).
16. G. Wolken in Dynamics of Molecular Collisions, W.H. Miller, Ed. Plenum 1976, part A, p-121.
17. U. Garibaldi, A.C. Levi, R. Spadacini and G. Tommei, Surf. Sci. **48**, 649 (1975).
18. R. Kosloff and D. Kosloff, J. Chem. Phys. **79**, 1823 (1983).
19. R. Kosoloff, J. Phys. Chem. **92**, 2087 (1988).
20. A.T. Yinnon and R. Kosloff, Chem. Phys. Lett. **102**, 216 (1983).
21. E.J. Heller, J. Chem. Phys. **62**, 1544 (1975).
22. G. Drolshagen and E.J. Heller, J. Chem. Phys. **79**, 2072 (1983); J. Chem. Phys. **82**, 226 (1985); R.B. Gerber, R. Kosloff and M. Bermann, Computer Physics Reports, **5**, 59 (1986).
23. G. Armand and J.R. Manson, Phys. Rev. Lett. **93**, 1389 (1979).
24. W.H. Miller, Adv. Chem. Phys. **25**, 69 (1974).
25. R.A. Marcus, J. Chem. Phys. **54**, 3965 (1971).
26. R.B. Gerber, A.T. Yinnon, and J.N. Murrell, Chem. Phys. **31**, 1 (1978).
27. J.P. Toennies in "Dynamics of Gas-Surface Interactions", G. Benedek and U. Valbusa, Eds., Springer-Verlag, Berlin, 208 (1982).
28. G. Brusdeylins, R.B. Doak and J.P. Toennies, Phys. Rev. Lett. **46**, 437 (1981).
29. K.D. Gibson, S.J. Sibener, B.M. Hall, D.L. Mills and J.E. Black, J. Chem. Phys. **83**, 4256 (1985).
30. J.P. Toennies in "Dynamics on Surfaces", B. Pullman and R.B. Gerber, (Eds.) D. Reidel Pub. Co., Boston, 1 (1984).
31. J.H. Weare, J. Chem. Phys. **61**, 2900 (1974).
32. S.A. Adelman and J.D. Doll, J. Chem. Phys. **61**, 4242 (1974).
33. S.A. Adelman and J.D. Doll, J. Chem. Phys. **63**, 4908 (1975); **64**, 2375 (1976).
34. J.A. Barker, D.R. Dion and R.P. Merrill, Surf. Sci. **95**, 15 (1980).
35. E. Kolodeny, A. Amirav, R. Elber and R.B. Gerber, Chem. Phys. Lett. **113**, 303 (1984).
36. J.D. McClure, J. Chem. Phys. **57**, 2810 (1972).
37. J.C. Tully, Acc. Chem. Res. **14**, 188 (1981).
38. S.A. Adelman and J.D. Doll, J. Chem. Phys. **61**, 4242 (1974).
39. R. Zwanzig, J. Chem. Phys. **32**, 1173 (1960).
40. K.B. Whaley, C.F. Yu, C.S. Hogg, and S.J. Sibener, J. Chem. Phys. **83**, 4235 (1985).
41. D.C. Clary and A. E. DePristo, J. Chem. Phys. **81**, 5167 (1984).
42. D.A. Mantall, S.B. Rijali, G.L. Haler and J.B. Fenn, J. Chem. Phys. **78**, 4250 (1983).
43. C.T. Rettner, F. Fabre, J. Kimman and D.J. Auerbach, Phys. Rev. Lett. **55**, 1904 (1985).
44. P.J. Van den Hoek, C.M. Horn and A.W. Kleyn, Surf. Sci. **198**, L335 (1988).
45. J.W. Gadzuk, Ann. Rev. Phys. Chem. **39**, 395 (1988); D. Halstead and S. Holloway, J. Chem. Phys. **88**, 7197 (1988). S. Holloway, J. Vac. Sci. Technol. **A5(4)**, 476 (1987).
46. J. Misewich, P.L. Houston and R.P. Merril, J. Chem. Phys. **82**, 1577 (1985).
47. G.P. Brivio and T.B. Grimley, J. Phys. **C10**, 2351 (1977).
48. J.K. Norskov and B.I. Lundqvist, Surf. Sci. **89**, 251 (1979).
49. J.W. Gadzuk, J. Chem. Phys. **79**, 6341 (1983).

50. D.M. Newns, Surf. Sci. **171**, 600 (1986).
51. R. Brako and D.M. Newns, Solid State Commun. **33**, 713 (1980).
52. K. Schönhammer and O. Gunnarsson, Phys. Rev. **B22**, 1629 (1980).
53. R. Brako and D.M. Newns, Physica Scripta, **T6**, 5 (1983).
54. A. Modinos, Prog. in Surface Sci. **26**, 19 (1987).
55. Z. Gortel and M. Tsukada, Phys. Rev. **B39**, 11259 (1989).
56. R. Brako and D.M. Newns, Rep. Prog. Phys. **52**, 655 (1989).
57. S. Tsuneyuki, N. Shima and M. Tsukada Surf. Sci. **186**, 26 (1987).
58. E.G. Overbosch, B. Raser, A.D. Tanner and J. Los, Surf. Sci. **92**, 310 (1980).
59. H. Schall, W. Huber, H. Hoermann, W. Maus-Friedrichs and V. Kempter, Surf. Sci. **210**, 163 (1989).
60. T.B. Grimley, V.C. Jyothi Basu and K.L. Sebastian, Surf. Sci. **124**, 305 (1983).
61. K.L. Sebastian, Phys. Rev. **B31**, 6976 (1985).
62. J.A. Barker, D.R. Dion and R.P. Merrill, Surf. Sci. **95**, 15 (1980).
63. Z. Kirson, R.B. Gerber, A. Nitzan and M.A. Ratner, Surf. Sci. **137**, 527 (1984).

8. Physics and Chemistry of Surfaces: Nonlinear Laser Techniques

Kankan Bhattacharyya

Physical Chemistry Department
Indian Association for the Cultivation of Science
Jadavpur, Calcutta, India

Abstract

The novel applications of surface second harmonic generation (SHG) to study surface phenomena has been discussed. SHG is dipole forbidden in the bulk of a liquid or in any centrosymmetric media. However, SHG is possible at the surface of a liquid or more generally at any interface. This unique surface selectivity renders it a very powerful technique to study the orientation, concentration and dynamics of various species at the interfacial region.

1. INTRODUCTION

Physics and chemistry in two dimensions has long been a subject of active interest. Net forces that occur at a surface can give rise to high surface viscosity which drastically affect molecular motions on the surface. Also, the net alignment of solvent molecules at the surface could cause an unusual local polarity which would markedly influence the dynamics and equilibria. The selective adsorption of different species gives rise to surface concentrations which are vastly different from those in the bulk. Thus both the dynamics and equilibria at the surface are expected to be considerably different from that in the bulk. Although there have been considerable speculation about the behaviour of chemical species at interfaces until recently very few techniques were at the disposal of surface scientists to selectively study the various surface layers. Over the last decade there has been an explosive growth in surface science with the development of a wide assortment of new techniques based on ion, electron and photon spectroscopies. A testimony to this growth is the fact that surface science has been chosen as the theme of the most recent Solvay Conference [1]. In this article we wish to give an overview of some recent applications of a novel nonlinear laser technique, surface second harmonic generation (SSHG). This technique has certain special advantages over others [2]. SHG is electric dipole forbidden in the bulk of any liquid or in any centrosymmetric medium and therefore is truely surface selective. Moreover, it does not require vacuum and hence is convenient particularly for liquid surfaces.

Another advantage in this method is that by utilising ultrashort lasers one can study the dynamics at surfaces in the time scale not accessible in any other technique. Thus, since early eighties a wide variety of surfaces have been studied using this technique [2–27, 29–45]. Already using this technique a substantial amount of new information has been obtained regarding the spectroscopy [6], orientation [4–5, 18, 21–24], chemical reactions [19, 25–26], nonlinear polarisabilities [18], two dimensional phase transition [20], dynamics [30–33], surface enhancement [34–37], electrochemical reactions [3, 10, 37–40] and biological processes [40–44]. A number of reviews of this emerging technique have already appeared in the literature. The most recent among them are by Shen [2] and Richmond et al [3]. Although this new technique can in principle be applied to any surface, in the present article we will concentrate mainly on liquid surfaces.

2. BACKGROUND THEORY

Before elaborating on the actual results obtained by SSHG we will digress a bit to outline the underlying principles. In general the response of a molecular system to the electric field (E) of the radiation can be described [2] by expanding the electronic polarisation (P) as

$$P = \chi^{(1)}E + \chi^{(2)} : EE + \chi^{(3)} : EEE + \dots \tag{1}$$

The nonlinear terms in eq. (1) become important only at very high incident fields as in lasers. The second harmonic generation is governed by the second order nonlinear susceptibility $\chi^{(2)}$. Since the latter is a third rank tensor of even parity, in a centrosymmetric system or isotropic media (e.g. bulk of a liquid) $\chi^{(2)}$ vanishes. This is why SHG is forbidden in the bulk of a liquid. At an interface, however, the inversion symmetry is broken and hence SHG is possible in the interfacial region between two centrosymmetric media. This unique surface selectivity renders SHG an extremely sensitive and versatile technique to study surfaces.

In general, $\chi^{(2)}$ has twenty seven elements. But using the symmetry properties of the surface (e.g. rotation about the surface normal) one can show that a number of them vanish and several are equal to one another [27]. If 'z' denotes the surface normal the only nonvanishing elements of $\chi^{(2)}$ are, $\chi^{(2)}_{zzz}$, $\chi^{(2)}_{xzx} (= \chi^{(2)}_{yzy})$ and $\chi^{(2)}_{zxx} (= \chi^{(2)}_{zyy})$. Thus the components of the second order nonlinear polarisation can be written in the case of surfaces as,

$$P^{(2)}_x = 2\chi^{(2)}_{xzx} E'_z E'_x$$

$$P^{(2)}_y = 2\chi^{(2)}_{yzy} E'_z E'_y$$

$$P^{(2)}_z = 2\chi^{(2)}_{zxx}(E'^2_x + E'^2_y) + \chi^{(2)}_{zzz}E'^2_z \tag{2}$$

where the prime denotes the input radiation fields in the surface layer. These input fields are related to but different from the components of the incident radiation field and they are calculated from the Fresnel coefficients and the appropriate boundary conditions [2, 4–6].

In the absence of local fields $\chi^{(2)}$ can be expressed as,

$$\chi^{(2)} = N_s \langle \alpha^{(2)} \rangle \tag{3}$$

where N_s is the number of molecules at the surface, $\alpha^{(2)}$ denotes the second order nonlinear polarisability and the angular bracket denotes an orientational average. If the second order polarisability $\alpha^{(2)}$ is dominated by a single element $\alpha^{(2)}_{\xi\xi\xi}$ one can write explicitly,

$$\chi^{(2)}_{zzz} = N_s \langle \cos^3 \theta \rangle \alpha^{(2)}_{\xi\xi\xi}$$

$$\chi^{(2)}_{xzx} = \chi^{(2)}_{zxx} = N_s \langle \cos \theta \sin^2 \theta \rangle \alpha^{(2)}_{\xi\xi\xi} \tag{4}$$

where θ is the angle between the molecular ξ-axis and the positive surface normal 'z'.

The polarisations described in eq. (4) give rise to a second harmonic (SH) field. The explicit forms of the SH fields are obtained by using them as a nonlinear source term in the appropriate Maxwell's equation [2]. The actual expressions of the SH fields E_p, with polarisation parallel and E_s, perpendicular to the plane of incidence are,

$$E_s = C \frac{P_y^{(2)}}{k_{1z} + k_{2z}} \tag{5a}$$

$$E_p = \frac{[(k_{2z}/k^{(1)}) P_x^{(2)} + (\varepsilon_2 k_{2x}/\varepsilon' k^{(1)}) P_z^{(2)}]}{\varepsilon_2 k'_{1z} + k_{2z}} \tag{5b}$$

where ε' is the dielectric constant at the interface between two media '1' and '2', k the wave vector (or its components) in indicated media and 'C', a constant.

3. APPLICATIONS

In a typical surface SHG experiment one measures three properties of the second harmonic light generated at the surface. They are the polarisation, phase and intensity. From the polarisation one can infer the relative orientation of the adsorbed species at the interface, the phase gives the absolute orientation while the intensity is related to the interfacial populations. In the following sections, we will illustrate the applications of this technique using some recent results.

3.1 Polarisation of SH Light and Relative Orientation

The polarisation (Φ) of the SH light is given by the ratio of $E_s(2\omega)$ and $E_p(2\omega)$. Using the equations discussed above one can show that Φ is related to the ratio (Θ) of the two orientational averages, e.g.

$$\Theta = \frac{\langle \cos^3 \theta \rangle}{\langle \cos \theta \sin^2 \theta \rangle} \tag{7}$$

From the experimental value of Φ one can calculate Θ. For solid surfaces it is reasonable to assume that all the adsorbed molecules make the same angle θ with the surface normal. Then, the right hand side of eq. (7) reduces to $\cot^2 \theta$ and it becomes easy to determine Θ for the solid surface.

The situation is entirely different for liquid surfaces. To illustrate, let us consider the case of substituted phenols adsorbed at the surface of aqueous solutions. Although it is expected that the polar OH group will point towards water the different orientations of the molecule should not differ in energy appreciably. Hence, there is almost equal probability of the molecule to make any angle with the normal between 0° and 90°. If this be the case one has to integrate the right side of eq. (7) from 0° and 90° and this results in the final polarisation of 54°. In fact for the series of phenol derivatives studied by us the polarisation of the SH light is 50° ± 5°. This indicates that the phenol derivatives exhibit a very broad distribution of orientation. A very interesting application of orientation has been done by Shen and coworkers which indicated that the orientation of adsorbed molecules undergoes a sharp change during a two dimensional phase transition [20].

3.2 Phase of SH Light and Absolute Molecular Orientation

The polarisation measurement suffers from an important difficulty that it cannot distinguish between a molecule pointing up and another pointing down. The reason is that if an adsorbed molecule is made upside down θ changes to $\pi-\theta$ and then both the numerator and the denominator of eq. (7) change sign keeping the ratio Θ unchanged. We will now outline a scheme to ascertain the absolute orientation of the adsorbed molecules.

If one considers only one element of $\chi^{(2)}$ (e.g. $\chi^{(2)}_{xzx}$) it is obvious that it changes sign when the molecule is inverted. Thus, if one measures the absolute sign or phase of $\chi^{(2)}_{xzx}$ one can infer the absolute orientation. From equations (3) and (5) it is evident that the phase (or sign) of $\chi^{(2)}_{xzx}$ is given by that of the surface SH field E_s with polarisation perpendicular to the plane of incidence (xz, in this case). Following the scheme of Wynne and Bloembergen [46] the phase of E_s and hence of $\chi^{(2)}_{xzx}$ is determined through an interference experiment. For this purpose, SH radiation is generated in a reference crystal by the fundamental beam reflected from the surface. The superposition of the two SH radiation fields, one generated at the surface under study and the other at the reference crystal, produces an interference pattern. The interference pattern is obtained because the refractive index of the medium and hence the velocity of light at the fundamental frequency (ω) is different from that at the second harmonic frequency (2ω). By varying the distance between the surface and the reference crystal the phase of the SH light generated by the reference crystal can be systematically changed with respect to that of the other SH light. As the reference crystal is moved away from the sample by δl, the fundamental travels a greater distance. Taking into account the dispersion of the ambient air one can show that the translation causes the phase of the reference SH wave to change by

$$\delta\phi = (2\omega/c)[n(\omega) - n(2\omega)]\delta l$$

$$= - (2\omega/c) \, \Delta n \, \delta l \tag{8}$$

where ω represents fundamental frequency and $\Delta n = n(\omega) - n(2\omega)$ denotes the difference in refractive indices of air at ω and 2ω respectively. Thus by scanning the position of the reference, a modulation of the SH intensity is observed. In order to obtain the absolute phase of the surface nonlinear susceptibility of the sample, comparison is made with a calibrated standard. For this purpose, a bulk right handed quartz crystal was used for which the sign of $\chi^{(2)}_{xxx}$ is known to be negative [23].

As discussed in our recent works [23–24] the absolute sign of $\chi^{(2)}$ in case of phenol is negative. This indicates that the molecular ξ-axis makes an angle greater than 90° with the surface normal. From theoretical calculations it is known that in the case of phenol the molecular ξ-axis is directed from the ring to the OH group. Thus it is concluded that the OH group is pointing downwards towards water which is consistent with the traditional chemical notions. More recently, the absolute orientation of water molecules at the surface of water has been determined using the phase measurements [23]. The results indicate that the protons predominantly point down on the liquid side which is consistent with a recent molecular dynamics simulation of the water surface [47].

3.3   Intensity Measurements: Chemistry at Interfaces

3.3.1   *Steady State Experiments*
For a surface chemist, the most important quantity is, however, the interfacial population, N_s. From the above discussion it follows that the surface second harmonic field amplitude (E) is linearly proportional to $\chi^{(2)}$ and hence to N_s. Thus $E(2\omega)$ is a direct measure of N_s. In principle, for liquid surfaces, N_s (more precisely the surface excess) can be determined using the Gibbs' adsorption isotherm [27] which relates N_s to the concentration gradient of surface tension. Unfortunately, for many solutes, particularly for submonolayer coverages the surface tension does not change detectably. For such systems, surface SHG is by far superior to conventional surface tension measurements. This has been illustrated by our recent work [25] where it was found that under the condition when the intensity of surface SH light changed by a factor of eighty, the change of surface tension was almost undetectable. Such a sensitivity enables a study of many surface phenomena using surface SHG which cannot be detected by conventional methods. For example, using SSHG we have shown for the first time that small aromatic ions do not stay at the surface of water and the equilibrium in the surface region is vastly different from that in the bulk [25–26]. The superior sensitivity of this technique has allowed stringent tests of the various adsorption isotherms [22, 25–26, 45] and also, to reinvestigate some of the age old problems of surface chemistry. For instance, one now knows the precise length of the hydrocarbon chain needed to keep a p-alkyl phenolate ion floating at the surface of water solution [26] or how molecular orientation changes during a two dimensional phase transition [20].

A very interesting application of SSHG can be made using the resonance enhancement of second harmonic generation. The quantum mechanical expression for $\chi^{(2)}$ is of the following form [2]:

$$\sum_{a,b} \frac{\langle \psi_g | \mu | \psi_a \rangle \langle \psi_a | \mu | \psi_b \rangle \langle \psi_b | \mu | \psi_g \rangle}{(\Delta E_{ag} - h\nu_L - i\Gamma)(\Delta E_{bg} - 2h\nu_L - i\Gamma')} \tag{9}$$

where g denotes the ground state and a, b the intermediate states and v_L the laser frequency. Evidently, when energy of the laser photon (hv_L) or that of two of them ($2hv_L$) becomes equal to the energy gap (ΔE) the magnitude of $\chi^{(2)}$ is very high. This is called one or two photon resonance enhancement of SHG, respectively. If there are more than one spectroscopically distinct species at the surface one can suitably tune the laser frequency such that the resonance condition is satisfied for one of the species but not for others. Thus one can selectively probe one adsorbed species in presence of another. This has been recently utilised to probe selectively the population of small aromatics in presence of small amounts of surfactants [21]. It has been found that a small amount of a surfactant enhances the interfacial population. It may be mentioned that though, similar cooperative effects on adsorption on solid surfaces induced by surfactants had been known for quite sometime there has been no report on such cooperative effects on liquid surfaces.

3.3.2 *Time Resolved Studies: Dynamics at Surfaces*
The study of chemical dynamics in liquid solutions constitutes one of the most active areas of research in chemical physics [48]. With the advent of ultrashort lasers there has been tremendous interest to understand how the dynamics of chemical processes depends on the environment. A very interesting question which has been asked recently is whether the dynamics at the surfaces is different from that in the bulk of the same liquid. Unfortunately, before the advent of the SSHG technique it was not possible to answer this question because no other spectroscopic technique is surface selective. Recently, time resolved SSHG studies have been made to study the dynamics of photoinduced melting of semiconductor surfaces [30], changes of electrodes following a transient potential jump [31], photoisomerisation [32] and energy transfer [33] in the surface layer of aqueous solutions. In the time resolved studies the samples are excited by a pump beam which is followed by a probe beam. Usually, the pump and probe beams are of different wavelengths and are incident on the sample at different angles so that SHG induced by the pump can be spectrally or spatially separated from that due to the probe beam. At a time before the arrival of the pump beam the SSHG signals are due to the ground state molecules. Following the excitation, transient species with different nonlinear polarizabilities are produced which cause a change in the SHG signal. As the molecules gradually revert back to the ground state the SSHG signal comes back to its initial value. Thus, the time resolved SSHG experiments are similar to ground state recovery experiments. Using this method it has been shown that the photoisomerisation of a cyanine dye (DODCI) is significantly slower at the surface compared to that in the bulk [32]. Again in the case of energy transfer from Rhodamine 6G (R6G) to DODCI it has been found that while the life time of the donor (R6G) reduces by a factor of three at the surface the reduction is only by 17% [33] at the bulk of the same solution. The faster rate of energy transfer at the surface can be attributed to selective enrichment at the surface leading to a greater local concentration of the acceptor at the surface. Quantitative explanation of the difference in chemical dynamics at the surface from that in the bulk of the same

solution is definitely going to be a challenging problem and will await further investigations.

3.3.3 Biological Systems

Biological membranes are essentially naturally oriented dipole layers and as such are capable of producing strong SHG signals. Thus, SSHG technique should be extremely useful for the study of biological systems. This simple fact has been realized only very recently [41–44]. Huang et al. has studied bacteriorhodopsin molecule in purple membrane (PM)–PVA films bleached by cw light source using surface SHG [44]. They found that the dipole moment of the retinyl chromophore in bR_{570} is 1.7 times larger in PM than in free chromophore and that the M_{412} species remains unprotonated.

3.4 Surface Enhancement of SHG Signals

Like surface enhanced Raman signal (SERS) SHG efficiency of many species increases vastly on adsorption on certain surfaces. The main advantage of surface enhanced SHG over SERS is while the latter is restricted to only Ag, Au and Cu surfaces the former is observed for a variety of surfaces [34–37]. Of particular interest is the very large enhancement of SSHG signal for the centrosymmetric molecule pyrazine adsorbed on Ag surface [34]. Since pyrazine is inherently centrosymmetric it should not give SHG signal. The observation of the SSHG signal in this case indicates that on adsorption on Ag surface the centre of symmetry is destroyed. More recently Van Dyne et al. has developed a microscopic imaging technique based on surface SHG [36].

4. CONCLUSION

Because of their obvious implications in a wide variety of disciplines ranging from catalysis, semiconductor surfaces to biomembranes, surface science has grown enormously over the last decade. In this short article we have tried to emphasise, rather than to review, the usefulness of the novel technique based on surface SHG. A considerable amount of knowledge has already been gathered using this technique, which proves beyond doubt its potentiality. One can foresee much more exciting experiments to be performed particularly on biomembranes and chemical dynamics in two dimensions. To summarise, this new technique coupled with the recent developments of ultrashort lasers of high peak power is bound to usher in a new era in surface science.

5. ACKNOWLEDGEMENTS

The author is greatly indebted to Professor K.B. Eisenthal for introducing him to this field and to Dr. T.F. Heinz for numerous stimulating discussions. It is a pleasure to thank all the coworkers namely Drs. J.M. Hicks, K. Kemnitz, E.V. Sitzmann, R. Bowmann, M.C. Goh and G.R. Pinto and Mr. A. Castro.

REFERENCES

1. "Solvay Conference on Surface Science", ed. F.W. de Wette, Springer Series in Surface Science, vol. 14 (Springer-Verlag, 1988).
2. Y.R. Shen, *Nature*, 1989, **337**, 519; in "The Principles of Nonlinear Optics" (Wiley, 1984).
3. G.L. Richmond, J.M. Robinson and V.L. Shanon, Prog. Surf. Sci. 1988, **1**, 1.
4. H.W.K. Tom, T.F. Heinz and Y.R. Shen, Laser Chem., 1983, **3**, 279.
5. T.F. Heinz, H.W.K. Tom and Y.R. Shen, Phys. Rev., 1983, **A28**, 1883.
6. T.F. Heinz, C.K. Chen, D. Ricard and Y.R. Shen, Phys. Rev. Lett., 1982, **48**, 478.
7. T.L. Mazely and W.M. Hetherington III, J. Chem. Phys., 1987, **86**, 3640.
8. D.F. Voss, M. Nagumo, L.S. Goldberg and K.A. Bunding, J. Phys. Chem., 1986, **90**, 1834.
9. G. Marowsky, A. Giersulski and B. Dick, Opt. Commun., 1985, **52**, 339.
10. G.L. Richmond, *Langmuir*, 1986, **2**, 132.
11. P. Di Lazarro, P. Mahatoni and F. De Martini, Chem. Phys. Lett., 1985, **114**, 103.
12. N.E. Van Wyck, E.W. Koenig, J.D. Bynes and W.M. Hetherington III, Chem. Phys. Lett., 1985, **122**, 153.
13. Z. Chen, W. Chen, J. Zheng, W. Wang and Z. Zhang, Opt. Commun., 1985, **54**, 305.
14. H.W.K. Tom, C.M. Mate, X.D. Zhu, J.E. Crowell, T.F. Heinz, G.A. Somorjai and Y.R. Shen, Phys. Rev. Lett., 1985, **52**, 348.
15. T.T. Chen, K.U. Von Raben, D.V. Murphy, R.K. Chang and B.L. Laube, Surface Science, 1984, **143**, 369.
16. R.M. Corn, M. Romagnoli and M.D. Levenson, J. Chem. Phys., 1984, **81**, 4127.
17. C.K. Chen, T.F. Heinz, D. Ricard and Y.R. Shen, Phys. Rev., 1983, **B27**, 1965.
18. T. Rasing, Y.R. Shen and M.W. Kim, Chem. Phys. Lett., 1986, **130**, 1.
19. G. Berkovic, T. Rasing and Y.R. Shen, J. Chem. Phys., 1986, **85**, 7374.
20. T. Rasing, Y.R. Shen, M.W. Kim, S. Grubb and J. Bock, Phys. Rev. Lett., 1985, **55**, 2903.
21. T. Rasing, Y.R. Shen, M.W. Kim, P. Valint and J. Bock, Phys. Rev., 1985, **A31**, 537.
22. J.M. Hicks, K. Kemnitz, K.B., Eisenthal and T.F. Heinz, J. Phys. Chem., 1986, **90**, 560.
23. K. Kemnitz, K. Bhattacharyya, J.M. Hicks, G.R. Pinto, K.B. Eisenthal and T.F. Heinz, Chem. Phys. Lett., 1986, **131**, 285.
24. M.C. Goh, J.M. Hicks, G.R. Pinto, K. Kemnitz, K. Bhattacharyya, K.B. Eisenthal and T.F. Heinz, J. Phys. Chem., 1988, **92**, 5074.
25. K. Bhattacharyya, E.V. Sitzmann and K.B. Eisenthal, J. Chem. Phys., 1987, **87**, 1442.
26. K. Bhattacharyya, E.V. Sitzmann, A. Castro and K.B. Eisenthal, J. Chem. Phys., 1988, **89**, 3376.
27. G. Marowsky, A. Gierulski, G.A. Reider and A.J. Schmidt, Appl. Phys., 1984, **B34**, 69.
28. A.W. Adamson, "Physical Chemistry of Surfaces", 4th ed. (Wiley, New York, 1982).
29. K. Bhattacharyya, E.V. Sitzmann and K.B. Eisenthal, (to be communicated).
30. C.V. Shank, R. Yen and C. Hirliman, Phys. Rev. Lett., 1983, **51**, 900.
31. V. Shanon, D.A. Koos, J.M. Robinson and G.L. Richmond, Chem. Phys. Lett., 1987, **142**, 323.

32. E.V. Sitzmann and K.B. Eisenthal, J. Chem. Phys., 1988, **92**, 4579.

33. E.V. Sitzmann and K.B. Eisenthal, J. Chem. Phys. , 1989, **90**, 2831.

34. T.F. Heinz, C.K. Chen, D. Ricard and Y.R. Shen, Chem. Phys. Lett., 1981, **83**, 180.

35. G.T. Boyd, Th. Rasing, J.R.R. Leite and Y.R. Shen, Phys. Rev., 1984, **B30**, 519.

36. K.L. Haller, L.A. Blum, R.I. Atkem, E.J. Zeeman, G.C. Schatz and R.P. Van Duyne, J. Chem. Phys., 1989, **90**, 1237.

37. C.K. Chen, T.F. Heinz, D. Ricard and Y.R. Shen, Chem. Phys. Lett., 1981, **83**, 455.

38. G.L. Richmond, Chem. Phys. Lett., 1984, **106**, 26.

39. V.L. Shanon, D.A. Koos and G.L. Richmond, J. Chem. Phys., 1987, **87**, 1440.

40. H.M. Rojhantalab and G.L. Richmond, J. Phys. Chem., 1989, **93**, 3269.

41. I. Freund, M. Deutsch and A. Sprecker, J. Biophys., 1986, **50**, 693.

42. O.A. Aktsipetrov, N.N. Akhmediev, N.N. Vsevolodov, D.A. Esikov, D.A. Shutov, Sov. Phys. — *Doklad.* (Engl. Transl.), 1987, **32**, 219.

43. J. Huang, A. Lewis and Th. Rasing, J. Phys. Chem., 1988, **92**, 1756.

44. J.Y. Huang, Z. Chen and A. Lewis, J. Phys. Chem., 1989, **93**, 3314.

45. A. Castro, S. Ong and K.B. Eisenthal, Chem. Phys. Lett., 1989, **163**, 412.

46. J.J. Wynne and N. Bloembergen, Phys. Rev., 1968, **128**, 606.

47. M. Matsumoto and Y. Kataoka, J. Chem. Phys., 1988, **88**, 3233.

48. B. Bagchi, Annu. Rev. Phys. Chem., 1989, **40**, 115.

9. Quantum Fluid Dynamical Approach to Chemical Dynamics

Swapan K. Ghosh

Heavy Water Division
Bhabha Atomic Research Centre
Bombay, India

Abstract

Some recent developments in the theoretical foundations of quantum fluid dynamical formalism for many-electron systems are discussed. The time-dependent systems characterised by scalar as well as vector potentials are shown to be amenable to a density-description using single particle charge and current densities as basic variables. Using this time-dependent density functional formalism, a fluid dynamical transcription in three dimensional space is obtained for the electron fluid. The scope of the fluid analogy is further broadened through the definition of several thermodynamic-like quantities of chemical significance. The applicability of the density based description to the study of chemical dynamics is discussed.

1. INTRODUCTION

In recent years, two important approaches in applied quantum mechanics, viz. quantum fluid dynamics [1–3] (QFD) and density functional theory [4–6] (DFT) have emerged as conceptually simple and highly successful tools in various branches of physics and chemistry [7, 8]. Our objective here is to present glimpses of recent developments in these two valuable approaches, highlighting the applicability to the study of the dynamics of many-particle systems. The close interconnections of QFD and DFT have been explored throughout this paper in order to unify, interlink and strengthen the theoretical foundations of these two formalisms, which finally aim at an alternative quantum mechanics in three-dimensional (3-D) space [9].

Quantum fluid dynamics is a theory in which quantum phenomena are described and interpreted in a "classical" language through hydrodynamic equations of motion characteristic of a classical fluid. This theory involves a transcription of the time-dependent (TD) Schrodinger equation which enables one to view the electron cloud as a "classical" fluid moving under the action of classical Coulomb forces augmented by the forces of quantum origin. Starting with the earliest attempt of Madelung [10], QFD was rejuvenated by the pioneering works of Bohm [11] and Takabayashi [12] in the fifties and have since then achieved tremendous success [1, 3] in the study of time evolution of quantum systems in terms of the density quantities in three dimensional space rather than the wavefunction in configuration space.

The basic variables of QFD in 3-D space are the single particle density $\rho(\mathbf{r}, t)$ and the current density $\mathbf{j}(\mathbf{r}, t)$. The appeal of this formalism as an attractive alternative to the conventional approach rests on the tremendous simplification due to reduction in dimensionality [13], the density based formalism provides over the wavefunction approach where the difficulty in solving the Schrödinger equation increases very rapidly with the number of electrons. Moreover, various interpretive models [9] that can be built in terms of the density quantities provide a better conceptual visualisation. An additional advantage of the density is that it is a fundamental physical observable and is amenable to experimental determination [14], thus permitting the accuracy of quantum mechanical calculations to be tested directly.

QFD is closely linked with density functional theory, another approach for the formulation of quantum mechanics in 3-D space. Starting with the pioneering works of Hohenberg, Kohn and Sham [4, 5], who laid the foundations for its strict mathematical formulation and thus provided a formal justification for the use of density as a basic variable, DFT provides an alternative route to the calculation of the properties of inhomogeneous electron systems in a formally exact manner and enables one to incorporate the electron correlation effects within a single-particle framework. DFT is now extended in scope through the generalisations to excited states [15], time dependent phenomena [16–21] as well as magnetic fields [21–23]. The two approaches QFD and DFT for TD situations are now jointly called quantum fluid density functional theory [24, 25] (QFDFT) which has recently been employed to the study of collision phenomena [24, 25]. The formalisms however had so far been mostly restricted to scalar potentials alone and situations involving vector potentials, e.g. when a magnetic field (static or TD) is applied, have attracted attention only recently. The extension to include magnetic fields [21–23] broadens the scope of QFDFT by covering a very important class of TD problems, viz. the interaction of electromagnetic radiation with matter.

A chemical reaction involves an encounter of atoms and molecules and consequent rearrangement of the nuclear configuration into a new one corresponding to reactants and products respectively. The conventional approach for studying the dynamics of this transformation involves a quantum mechanical calculation of the interatomic potentials for various configurations, followed by the computation of quasiclassical trajectories [26, 27] based on this potential energy surface. Much detailed information and insight can however be obtained by following the time evolution of the electron distribution [28] during the course of the reaction, since it is this quantity which governs the reaction. For this purpose, QFD is ideally suited since it provides a pair of important fluid dynamical equations, viz. the continuity and the Euler equation characterising the time dependence of the charge and current densities respectively. This study can enable one to visualise the transformation of the system from its initial to its final configuration and thus provide a detailed understanding of the mechanism of the encounter, including the associated quantum effects.

Due to the availability of Lasers as well as related sophisticated experimental techniques, studies of state to state chemistry in molecular beams [29] are now being possible. The reactants can now be prepared in a particular state and the post collision product state can be analysed experimentally [30]. On the theoretical side, the electron density contours [31], quantum mechanical streamlines [32] corresponding to the current density etc., obtained through the solutions of equations of QFD, can reveal a great deal of information not only for initial and final states but also for the activated complex formation and hence the inherent mechanism of the state to state transformation. One significant feature of the study of streamlines involves the detection of presence and location of vortices [33], which are known to play an important role in collision processes [34, 35].

Although the QFD transcription is straightforward for a single-particle microscopic quantum system, which would be presented in Section 2, the many-particle Schrödinger equation is not directly amenable [2] to a 3-D formulation. The TDDFT, however, provides a route to the QFD description in 3-D space, which forms the subject matter of Section 4, while in Section 3 we present a review of DFT and its generalisation to time dependent situations involving magnetic field as well. It is shown that QFD equations can be obtained either from the one-particle TDDFT equations directly or from consideration of an associated stochastic Brownian motion model approach, following the early work of Nelson [36].

The central theme in the QFD picture is that the electron cloud is viewed as a fluid. While the QFD equations represent the balance equations [3, 37] governing the dynamics, to ascribe a deeper meaning to this fluid analogy, it would be worthwhile to look for other equations of classical fluid theory corresponding to the electron fluid. One difficulty in obtaining this extension arises because several equations for a classical fluid involve temperature, whereas one normally ascribes a zero temperature to a pure microscopic quantum system. However, even at this zero external temperature, the electron is in motion and has a kinetic energy (KE). This inherent KE which is of purely quantum origin, has led to the definition of an electronic temperature [38] which is in general local (varying in space) and is only a quantum and internal temperature. The concept of this electron temperature has opened up the possibility of introducing other equations of classical fluid theory for the electron fluid [39]. This also provides an integral equation approach [39] for the calculation of electron density of many-electron systems. The scope of these formalisms have been further broadened due to their recent generalisations to time dependent situations [25]. All these aspects are discussed in Section 5, while in Section 6, we offer a few concluding remarks.

2. QUANTUM FLUID DYNAMICS OF A SINGLE PARTICLE QUANTUM SYSTEM

For a single electron bound by an external potential $V(\mathbf{r}, t)$ one starts with the time-dependent Schrödinger equation (TDSE)

$$[- (\hbar^2/2m)\nabla^2 + V]\psi(\mathbf{r}, t) = i\hbar(\partial\psi/\partial t) \qquad (1)$$

and substitutes, following Madelung [10], the polar form of the wavefunction

$$\psi(\mathbf{r}, t) = \rho^{1/2}(\mathbf{r}, t) \exp [iS(\mathbf{r}, t)/\hbar] \tag{2}$$

to obtain a pair of hydrodynamical equations, viz. the continuity equation

$$(\partial\rho/\partial t) + \nabla \cdot \mathbf{j}(\mathbf{r}, t) = 0 \tag{3}$$

and the Euler type equation of motion

$$m(d\mathbf{v}/dt) = - \nabla(V + V_{qu}) \tag{4}$$

with $(d\mathbf{v}/dt) = (\partial\mathbf{v}/\partial t) + (\mathbf{v} \cdot \nabla)\mathbf{v}$. Here, $\mathbf{v}(= \nabla S/m)$ is the velocity field, ρ is the electron density, $\mathbf{j}(= \rho\mathbf{v})$ is the current density and V_{qu} is the quantum potential [11] defined respectively as

$$\rho = \psi^*\psi; \mathbf{j} = (- i\hbar/2m) (\psi^*\nabla\psi - \psi\nabla\psi^*) \tag{5}$$

$$V_{qu} = - (\hbar^2/2m)\nabla^2\rho^{1/2}/\rho^{1/2} \tag{6}$$

Equations (3) and (4) form the basis of QFD. But for the additional quantum potential term, these hydrodynamic equations are purely classical in appearance. When the external potential is time independent, the classical force acting on an element of the electron cloud is exactly balanced by the corresponding quantum force resulting into zero velocity field and consequently a stationary state [40].

The velocity field $\mathbf{v}$ is actually the real part of a more generalised quantum mechanical local velocity field $\mathbf{u}$ defined [1, 32] through the momentum operator as

$$\mathbf{u} = - (i\hbar/m) \nabla\psi/\psi = \mathbf{v} + \mathbf{v}_{im}; \mathbf{v}_{im} = - (\hbar/2m)\nabla \ln \rho \tag{7}$$

Both the real and imaginary velocity fields are however irrotational in nature [1, 3].

QFD can be generalised to include the effect of the magnetic vector potential. Thus, for the additional scalar and vector potentials $\phi(\mathbf{r}, t)$ and $\mathbf{A}(\mathbf{r}, t)$ respectively, the TDSE given by

$$\{(1/2m) [- i\hbar\nabla + (e/c)\mathbf{A}]^2 + V - e\phi\} \psi(\mathbf{r}, t) = i\hbar(\partial\psi/\partial t) \tag{8}$$

would lead to the continuity equation (3) and the equation of motion

$$m(d\mathbf{v}/dt) + \{e\mathbf{E} + (e/c)\mathbf{v} \times \mathbf{B}\} = - \nabla(V + V_{qu}) \tag{9}$$

where the electric and the magnetic fields $\mathbf{E}$ and $\mathbf{B}$ are given by

$$\mathbf{E} = - \nabla\phi - c^{-1}(\partial\mathbf{A}/\partial t); \qquad \mathbf{B} = \nabla \times \mathbf{A} \tag{10}$$

and the velocity field is $\mathbf{v} = m^{-1} (\nabla S + (e/c)\mathbf{A})$. The current density $\mathbf{j}$ would thus contain the additional term $(e/mc)\mathbf{A}\rho$. There are many interesting consequences of this extension especially when spin is taken into account, which have been discussed by Ghosh and Deb [2].

For a many electron system, analogous fluid dynamical equations have been obtained [2] but the corresponding Schrödinger fluid is a fluid in configuration space which loses the physical clarity, thereby becoming essentially a device to supplement the mathematical formalism.

The semblance of a classical picture can however be maintained if the QFD for a many electron system is formulated in terms of the physical observables in 3-D space, viz. the electron density $\rho(\mathbf{r}, t)$ and the current density $\mathbf{j}(\mathbf{r}, t)$ defined in terms of the many electron wavefunction $\psi(\mathbf{r}_1, \mathbf{r}_2, \mathbf{r}_3, \ldots \mathbf{r}_N, t)$ as

$$\rho(\mathbf{r}, t) = \int d\tau \, \psi^* \sum_k \delta(\mathbf{r} - \mathbf{r}_k) \, \psi \qquad (11a)$$

$$\mathbf{j}(\mathbf{r}, t) = (- i\hbar/2m) \int d\tau \, \psi^* \, \{\sum_k [\nabla_k \delta(\mathbf{r} - \mathbf{r}_k)$$

$$+ \, \delta(\mathbf{r} - \mathbf{r}_k)\nabla_k] \, \psi + (e/mc)A\rho\} \qquad (11b)$$

Success in formulating QFD in 3-D space for a many electron system has been achieved using the framework of single particle self consistent field theories, such as Hartree, Hartree-Fock [41], natural orbital partitioning [2], etc. However, the most general formally exact description is possible using a TD density functional framework [3, 17], which is discussed in the following section.

3. DENSITY FUNCTIONAL THEORY AND ITS TIME DEPENDENT GENERALISATION

Density functional theory was formally born with two remarkable theorems proved by Hohenberg and Kohn [4], justifying the use of a single particle density as the basic variable in the quantum mechanical description of the ground state of a many-electron system. While their first theorem proves that the external scalar potential $V(\mathbf{r})$ characterising an N-electron system is uniquely determined by the electron density $\rho(\mathbf{r})$, and thus ensures that *sufficient* information is contained in the density function, the second one leads to methods for the direct calculation of $\rho(\mathbf{r})$. Thus, for a given $V(\mathbf{r})$, minimization of the energy functional $E[\rho]$ given by

$$E[\rho] = \int dr \, V(\mathbf{r}) \, \rho(\mathbf{r}) + F[\rho] \qquad (12)$$

subject to the normalization condition

$$\int d\mathbf{r} \, \rho(\mathbf{r}) = N \qquad (13)$$

as a constraint, leads to the Euler equation

$$\mu = (\delta E/\delta\rho) = V(\mathbf{r}) + \delta F/\delta\rho \qquad (14)$$

where μ is a Lagrange multiplier interpreted as the chemical potential of the electron cloud [42]. The universal functional $F[\rho]$ consists of contributions from kinetic and electron-electron interaction energies. Separating out the classical Coulomb energy of the electron distribution given by

$$E_{coul}[\rho] = (e^2/2) \int dr \int dr' \, \rho(\mathbf{r}) \, \rho(\mathbf{r}') / | \mathbf{r} - \mathbf{r}' | \qquad (15)$$

one can write

$$F[\rho] = E_{coul}[\rho] + G[\rho] \qquad (16)$$

where $G[\rho]$ is another universal functional consisting of a KE functional $T[\rho]$ and the exchange-correlation (XC) energy functional $E_{xc}[\rho]$, both of which are approximated for practical use since exact forms are still not known. The Thomas-

Fermi (TF) theory [43] results if one replaces the KE functional by the TF expression, which corresponds to a locally homogeneous approximation.

On replacing $T[\rho]$ by $T_s[\rho]$, the KE of a system of noninteracting electrons of same density and incorporating the $(T - T_s)$ contribution through a modified E_{xc} term, one obtains from Eq. (14), the single particle Kohn-Sham (KS) equations [5]

$$[- (\hbar^2/2m)\nabla^2 + V_{eff}(\mathbf{r}; \rho)]\psi_k = \varepsilon_k \psi_k \qquad (17)$$

with

$$V_{eff}(\mathbf{r}; \rho) = V(\mathbf{r}) + e^2 \int d\mathbf{r}´\, \rho(\mathbf{r}´)/|\,\mathbf{r} - \mathbf{r}´\,| + \delta E_{xc}/\delta\rho \qquad (18)$$

and

$$\rho(\mathbf{r}) = \sum_k |\, \psi_k(\mathbf{r}) \,|^2 \qquad (19)$$

The set of equations (17)–(19) are to be solved self-consistently and the energy is to be calculated using the relation

$$E = \sum_k \varepsilon_k - E_{coul}[\rho] + E_{xc}[\rho] - \int d\mathbf{r}\, \rho(\mathbf{r})\, (\delta E_{xc}/\delta\rho) \qquad (20)$$

Although Hartree-like in simplicity, the KS equations incorporate the XC effects in a formally exact manner. In the absence of an exact knowledge of $E_{xc}[\rho]$, approximations are, however, to be employed. The KS scheme is the basis of the conventional DFT, although various improvements [44] along the lines of the TF theory have also been proposed.

The ground state wavefunction for scalar potential is real and as shown here, sufficient information is contained in the density $\rho(\mathbf{r})$. However, for vector potential and also general TD situations, the wavefunction is complex and two real quantities $\rho(\mathbf{r}, t)$ and the current density $\mathbf{j}(\mathbf{r}, t)$ are needed for a complete specification of the system, even if there is only a single particle.

For a system of N-electrons moving under the influence of their mutual Coulombic interaction alongwith the single-particle external potential due to the nuclei $V(\mathbf{r})$, an additional TD scalar potential $\phi(\mathbf{r}, t)$ and a TD vector potential $\mathbf{A}(\mathbf{r}, t)$, the objective of TDDFT is to describe the system with the density quantities $\rho(\mathbf{r}, t)$ and $\mathbf{j}(\mathbf{r}, t)$ defined in Eqs. (11) as basic variables. It has been proved recently by Ghosh and Dhara [21] that the current density $\mathbf{j}(\mathbf{r}, t)$ determines both the scalar and the vector potentials uniquely, if the potentials can be expanded into Taylor series with respect to the time coordinate around an initial time t_0.

One first derives an equation for the time evolution of the current density using the equation of motion for the current density operator, and after some algebraic manipulations using the Taylor expansion, concludes that two different sets of potentials $(\phi, \mathbf{A})$ and $(\phi', \mathbf{A}')$ differing by more than a gauge transformation cannot lead to identical $\mathbf{j}(\mathbf{r}, t)$. Therefore, a given current density $\mathbf{j}(\mathbf{r}, t)$ can result only from a *unique* set of scalar and vector potentials $\phi(\mathbf{r}, t)$ and $\mathbf{A}(\mathbf{r}, t)$ respectively satisfying the prescribed gauge. Thus $\mathbf{j}(\mathbf{r}, t)$ fixes the potentials and hence the Hamiltonian, which implies that all the properties of the system are unique functionals of the current density. The fact that $\mathbf{j}(\mathbf{r}, t)$ determines the density $\rho(r, t)$ uniquely is evident from the continuity equation (3) itself which can be directly employed to obtain $\rho(r, t)$ for a given $j(r, t)$ since $\rho(r, t_0)$ is known. The functionals involving the wavefunction ψ can therefore be treated as functionals of the current density $j(r, t)$ or more conveniently of both $j(r, t)$ and $\rho(r, t)$ but in general they do not seem to be determined uniquely from $\rho(r, t)$ alone.

The quantity $Q \equiv \int dt \langle \psi \mid -i\hbar(\partial/\partial t) + \hat{T} + U + V - e \sum_k \phi_k \mid \psi \rangle$ is clearly a functional of $\rho(r, t)$ and $j(r, t)$, where $\hat{T} = (1/2m) \sum_k [\hat{p}(r_k) + (e/c)A(r_k, t)]^2$ is the kinetic energy operator. For given $V(r)$, $\phi(r, t)$ and $A(r, t)$, the stationary condition $\delta Q_{(V)}[\rho(r, t), j(r, t)] = 0$, at $\rho = \rho_0$ and $j = j_0$, is obeyed at the correct solution point, which follows from the Dirac-Frenkel TD variational principle. Here $\{V\}$ indicates that all the potentials are held constant. After separating out the explicit potential dependent terms, one can write

$$Q [\rho, j] = F[\rho, j] + \int dt \int dr \, \{\rho(r, t) [V(r) - e\phi]$$

$$+ (e/c) A \cdot j_p + (e/2c) A \cdot j_d\}$$

$$= F[\rho, j] + \int dt \int dr \, \{\rho(r, t) [V(r) - e\phi]$$

$$+ (e/c) A \cdot j(r, t) - (e^2/2mc^2)A^2 \rho(r, t)\} \qquad (21)$$

where j_p and j_d are the paramagnetic and the diamagnetic contributions to the current density $j(r, t)$ given by

$$j = j_p + j_d \qquad (22a)$$

$$j_p = - (i\hbar/2m) \langle \psi \mid \sum_k [\nabla_k \delta(r - r_k) + \delta(r - r_k)\nabla_k] \mid \psi \rangle \qquad (22b)$$

$$j_d = (e/mc) \langle \psi \mid \sum_k A_k \delta(r - r_k) \mid \psi \rangle = (e/mc)A(r, t) \rho(r, t) \qquad (22c)$$

and $F[\rho, j]$ is the universal functional

$$F[\rho, j] = \int dt \langle \psi[\rho, j] \mid - (\hbar^2/2m) \sum_k \nabla_k^2$$

$$+ U - i\hbar(\partial/\partial t) \mid \psi[\rho, j] \rangle \qquad (23)$$

Although the variational principle $\delta Q = 0$ can be exploited for the calculation of densities, for practical implementation, the functional $F[\rho, j]$ is to be approximated. A TF type approximation would lead to the TD TF theory; however a better scheme follows if one considers a functional $Q^s[\rho, j]$ defined for a fictitious system of N noninteracting particles having the (V-representable) current density $j(r, t)$ and the corresponding electron density $\rho(r, t)$ [i.e. the solution of the continuity equation], which are identical to those of the actual system of interest (where interaction is present), i.e.

$$Q^s[\rho(r, t), j(r, t)] = \int dt \langle \psi_{\rho j}^s \mid - (\hbar^2/2m) \sum_k \nabla_k^2 - i\hbar(\partial/\partial t) \mid \psi_{\rho j}^s \rangle \qquad (24)$$

where $\psi_{\rho j}^s$ corresponds to a stationary point. The variation principle finally leads to a set of single-particle TD Schrödinger-like equations

$$\{(1/2m) [- i\hbar\nabla + (e/c)A_{eff}]^2 + V_{eff}(r, t)\}\psi_k(r, t) = i\hbar(\partial\psi_k(r, t)/\partial t) \qquad (25)$$

and the exact single-particle density $\rho(\mathbf{r}, t)$ and the current density $\mathbf{j}(\mathbf{r}, t)$ of the many-electron system can be obtained from

$$\rho(\mathbf{r}, t) = \sum_k \rho_k = \sum_k \psi_k^*(\mathbf{r}, t)\psi_k(\mathbf{r}, t) \tag{26}$$

and

$$\mathbf{j}(\mathbf{r}, t) = -(i\hbar/2m) \sum_k [\psi_k^*(\mathbf{r}, t) \nabla\psi_k(\mathbf{r}, t) - \psi_k(\mathbf{r}, t) \nabla\psi_k^*(\mathbf{r}, t)]$$
$$+ (e/mc)\rho(\mathbf{r}, t) A_{\text{eff}}(\mathbf{r}, t) \tag{27}$$

The effective scalar and vector potentials $V_{\text{eff}}(\mathbf{r}, t)$ and $\mathbf{A}_{\text{eff}}(\mathbf{r}, t)$ consist respectively of the external potentials $V(\mathbf{r}) - e\phi(\mathbf{r}, t)$ and $\mathbf{A}(\mathbf{r}, t)$ supplemented by internal contributions arising from the density and the current density distributions, viz.

$$V_{\text{eff}}(\mathbf{r}, t) = V(\mathbf{r}) - e\phi(\mathbf{r}, t) + (\delta U_{\text{int}}/\delta\rho) + (\delta E_{\text{xc}}/\delta\rho)$$
$$+ (e^2/2mc^2) [A_{\text{eff}}^2 - A^2] \tag{28}$$

and

$$\mathbf{A}_{\text{eff}}(\mathbf{r}, t) = \mathbf{A}(\mathbf{r}, t) + (c/e) (\delta U_{\text{int}}/\delta\mathbf{j}) + (c/e) (\delta E_{\text{xc}}/\delta\mathbf{j}) \tag{29}$$

The term U_{int} consists of the classical Coulomb energy $E_{\text{coul}}(\rho)$ defined in Eq. (15) and an analogous current-current interaction contribution, which although often ignored, can contribute to the vector potential. For E_{xc}, one has to use the generalization of the XC energy functional in the presence of a magnetic field [22, 23].

Equation (25) is to be solved for $\rho(\mathbf{r}, t)$ and $\mathbf{j}(\mathbf{r}, t)$ self-consistently with the help of Eqs. (26)–(29). The picture that emerges is that of a system of noninteracting particles moving in the effective scalar and vector potentials $V_{\text{eff}}(\mathbf{r}, t)$ and $\mathbf{A}_{\text{eff}}(\mathbf{r}, t)$ respectively. The calculated densities are however identical to those of the actual system of interest. For zero vector potential, the self-consistent equations become identical to the conventional time-dependent KS equations [5] for scalar potential alone. Also, for static scalar and vector potentials, one obtains the time-independent single-particle equations [22]. The present formulation satisfies the important property of gauge invariance which has been proved elsewhere [21].

4. QUANTUM FLUID DYNAMICS IN 3-D SPACE WITHIN A TIME DEPENDENT DENSITY FUNCTIONAL FRAMEWORK

The TDDFT developed in the preceding Section provides a formally exact description of quantum mechanics of many-electron systems subjected to TD electric and magnetic fields in terms of the single particle density variables $\rho(\mathbf{r}, t)$ and $\mathbf{j}(\mathbf{r}, t)$. Since these quantities are also the key variables in the hydrodynamic formulation, one can easily obtain the QFD equations in 3-D space within the framework of TDDFT. The fluid dynamical version of the TD TF theory is in fact already established [45]. A more general exact equation, however, follows from the equation of motion in terms of the current density operator $\hat{\mathbf{j}}(t)$, viz.

$$i\hbar(\partial/\partial t)\,\mathbf{j}\,(\mathbf{r},\,t) = \langle\,\psi(t)\,|\,i\hbar(\partial/\partial t)\hat{\mathbf{j}}\,(t) + [\hat{\mathbf{j}}\,(t),\hat{H}\,(t)]\,|\,\psi(t)\,\rangle \qquad (30)$$

which can be rewritten as

$$(\partial/\partial t)\mathbf{j}(\mathbf{r},\,t) = \mathbf{P}_{\{V\}}[\rho(\mathbf{r},\,t),\,\mathbf{j}(\mathbf{r},\,t)] \qquad (31)$$

where the vector $\mathbf{P}_{\{V\}}$ is a functional of $\rho(\mathbf{r},\,t)$ and $\mathbf{j}(\mathbf{r},\,t)$ for specified $\{V\}$ and is given by

$$\mathbf{P}_{\{V\}}[\rho,\,\mathbf{j}] = -\,(i/\hbar)\,\langle\,\psi(t)\,|\,[\hat{\mathbf{j}}_0,\hat{H}_0]\,|\,\psi(t)\,\rangle\,-\,(\rho/m)\,[\nabla V + e\mathbf{E}(\mathbf{r},\,t)]$$
$$-\,(e/mc)\,(\mathbf{j} \times \mathbf{B}) \qquad (32)$$

Here, $\mathbf{E}$ and $\mathbf{B}$ are the electric and magnetic fields given by Eq. (10) and $\hat{H}_0$ and $\hat{\mathbf{j}}_0$ correspond to the Hamiltonian and current density operators respectively without the potential terms. The continuity equation (3) and the equation of motion (31) describe the dynamics of the electron fluid [21].

One can also substitute the polar form of the orbitals, viz. $\psi_k = \rho_k^{1/2} \exp\,(iS_k/\hbar)$ into the single particle equation (25) and separate the real and imaginary parts to obtain the continuity equation (3) and the equation

$$-\,(\hbar^2/2m)\,[\nabla^2\,\rho_k^{1/2}/\rho_k^{1/2} + (1/2m)\,(\nabla S_k + (e/c)A_{\text{eff}})^2 + v_{\text{eff}} = -\,(\partial S_k/\partial t) \qquad (33)$$

Using the definition of the k-th orbital current density

$$\mathbf{j}_k = (\rho_k/m)\,(\nabla S_k + (e/c)A_{\text{eff}}]; \qquad \mathbf{j} = \sum_k \mathbf{j}_k \qquad (34)$$

Equation (33) leads to

$$(\partial\mathbf{j}/\partial t) + \nabla \cdot \sum_k (\mathbf{j}_k\mathbf{j}_k/\rho_k) + (e/m)\,[\rho\mathbf{E}_{\text{eff}} + (1/c)\,\mathbf{j} \times \mathbf{B}_{\text{eff}}]$$
$$= (1/m)\,\sum_k \rho_k\nabla Q_k \qquad (35)$$

where

$$Q_k = -\,(\hbar^2/2m)\,[\nabla^2\,\rho_k^{1/2}/\rho_k^{1/2}] \qquad (36)$$

denotes the quantum potential due to the kth orbital density. The effective electric and magnetic fields $\mathbf{E}_{\text{eff}}$ and $\mathbf{B}_{\text{eff}}$ are given by

$$\mathbf{E}_{\text{eff}}(\mathbf{r},\,t) = -\,(1/e)\nabla v_{\text{eff}}(\mathbf{r},\,t) - (1/c)\,(\partial/\partial t)A_{\text{eff}}(\mathbf{r},\,t) \qquad (37a)$$

$$\mathbf{B}_{\text{eff}}(\mathbf{r},\,t) = \nabla \times A_{\text{eff}}(\mathbf{r},\,t) \qquad (37b)$$

and consists of the external fields $\mathbf{E}(\mathbf{r},\,t)$, and $\mathbf{B}(\mathbf{r},\,t)$ augmented by internal contributions from density distributions. But for the appearance of Q_k and these internal contributions, Eq. (35) is completely classical. The rhs of Eq. (35) can also be written as $\nabla \cdot \overleftrightarrow{T}_q$ where $\overleftrightarrow{T}_q$ is the quantum stress tensor defined by

$$\overleftrightarrow{T}_q = (\hbar/2m)^2\,[\nabla(\nabla\rho) - \sum_k (\nabla\rho_k\nabla\rho_k/\rho_k)] \qquad (38)$$

A comprehensive stress tensor has also been defined [40] in terms of the quantum, XC and the electrostatic stress tensors. The latter can be expressed in terms of electric fields arising from nuclear and electronic charge distribution and have the same form as that of Maxwell's stress tensor in classical electrodynamics. Equation (35) can also be written in tensorial form as the

Navier-Stokes equation of fluid dynamics. Various other implications of the stress tensor concept have been highlighted by Bamzai and Deb [9].

The physical picture associated with the TDDFT formalism corresponding to Eq. (25) is that of N noninteracting particles moving in an effective potential V_{eff} satisfying the Schrödinger euqation. The corresponding QFD picture is that of an electron fluid, the dynamics of which is governed by the classical fluid like equations with an additional quantum potential contribution. While the derivation presented has been obtained by a mathematical reformulation of the Schrödinger like single particle equation (25) of TDDFT, there is another appealing approach to arrive at the same directly from the physical picture itself. For this purpose, one considers the particles to move in a deterministic force field defined by V_{eff} with an additional stochastic force. This approach is complementary to that of Madelung and starts from the classical stochastic theory of Brownian motion.

Following Nelson [36], consider the position $\mathbf{r}(t)$ of the particle to be a random variable and write

$$d\mathbf{r}(t) = \mathbf{b}(\mathbf{r}, t)\, dt + d\mathbf{w}(\mathbf{r}, t) \tag{39}$$

where $\mathbf{b}(\mathbf{r}, t)$ is the drift and $d\mathbf{w}$ is a random variable. The probability density $\rho(\mathbf{r}, t)$ associated with $\mathbf{r}(t)$, satisfies the forward and backward Fokker-Planck equations

$$(\partial\rho(\mathbf{r}, t)/\partial t) = -\nabla \cdot [\rho(\mathbf{r}, t)\mathbf{b}(\mathbf{r}, t)] + (1/2)D\,\nabla^2\,\rho(\mathbf{r}, t) \tag{40}$$

$$(\partial\rho(\mathbf{r}, t)/\partial t) = -\nabla \cdot [\rho(\mathbf{r}, t)\mathbf{b}^*(\mathbf{r}, t)] - (1/2)D\,\nabla^2\,\rho(\mathbf{r}, t) \tag{41}$$

with $\mathbf{b}^*(\mathbf{r}, t)$ as the backward drift.

Addition of the equations (40) and (41) leads to the continuity equation (3), where the velocity field $\mathbf{v}$ of the probability current is defined as

$$\mathbf{v} = (1/2)\,(\mathbf{b} + \mathbf{b}^*) \tag{42}$$

Defining the stochastic or osmotic velocity field $\mathbf{u}(\mathbf{r}, t)$ as

$$\mathbf{u} = (1/2)\,(\mathbf{b} - \mathbf{b}^*) \tag{43}$$

one can express the mean acceleration $\mathbf{a}$ in terms of these two velocities as

$$\mathbf{a} = [(\partial/\partial t) + (\mathbf{v} \cdot \nabla)]\mathbf{v} + (\mathbf{u} \cdot \nabla)\mathbf{u} + (1/2)\,D\nabla(\nabla \cdot \mathbf{u}) \tag{44}$$

Considering now the validity of Newton's equation of motion $\mathbf{F} = m\mathbf{a}$, where $\mathbf{F}$ is the external force corresponding to the potential V_{eff}, we obtain the equation of motion

$$[(\partial/\partial t) + (\mathbf{v} \cdot \nabla)]\mathbf{v} = \mathbf{F}/m + [(\mathbf{u} \cdot \nabla)\mathbf{u} + (1/2)D\nabla(\nabla \cdot \mathbf{u})] \tag{45}$$

Using the relation between $\mathbf{b}$ and $\mathbf{b}^*$, and choosing the diffusion constant to be given by $D = \hbar/m$, one obtains $\mathbf{u} = (\hbar/2m)\nabla\rho/\rho$, which can be compared with the imaginary velocity field defined in Eq. (7). Substituting these expressions for D and $\mathbf{u}$, Eq. (45) can easily be shown to lead to the QFD equation (4) or (9), depending on whether V_{eff} consists of only scalar potential or scalar and vector potentials both. Writing the equations for each particle and combining them, one arrives at the QFD equation of Eq. (35).

The closer link between DFT and QFD discussed in this Section, provides not only a transparent physical picture but also leads to alternative calculational methods in terms of real density quantities rather than the complex wavefunction.

5. THERMODYNAMIC TRANSCRIPTION OF THE FLUID ANALOGY TO THE ELECTRON CLOUD

The fluid dynamical equations considered so far characterize the dynamical evolution for density and current density. For static case, they would imply that the net force acting at each point of the electron fluid is zero [40], i.e. the classical electrostatic force is exactly balanced by quantum forces. Further insight into this fluid analogy can be obtained by deriving other equations of classical fluid theory through the definition of a local temperature for the electron cloud to characterise the distribution function. Ghosh et. al. [38] has defined a local electronic temperature $T(r)$ for the ground state of a many-electron system in terms of its KE density $\varepsilon_{kin}(r, \rho)$, by analogy to the ideal gas law, viz.

$$\varepsilon_{kin}(r, \rho) = (3/2)\rho(r)k_B T(r) \tag{46}$$

where k_B is the Boltzmann constant. This concept of temperature is reminiscent of an effective temperature introduced for a quantum liquid by Born and Green [46] and by Mazo and Kirkwood [47] who showed that all the quantum effects can be transferred to a properly defined effective temperature and thus a quantum liquid can be treated as a classical one. In the same spirit, Ghosh and Berkowitz [39] have shown that classical fluid-like equations can be written to describe a quantum system and the quantum effects are incorporated through the local temperature. By writing [39] the density in terms of the classical formula

$$\rho(r) = [\beta(r)/2\pi]^{-3/2} \exp [\beta(r) \{\mu - \varphi_{eff}(r)\}] \tag{47}$$

where $\beta(r) = [k_B T(r)]^{-1}$, μ is the chemical potential, $\varphi_{eff}(r)$ is an effective potential [39] related to the Kohn-Sham potential and the density functional version of the quantum potential, $v_q = \delta T_s/\delta\rho$. In terms of the intrinsic potential

$$u(r) = (\delta F/\delta\rho) = \mu - v_{ext}(r) \tag{48}$$

where $v_{ext}(r)$ is the external potential, one can define [39] the correlation function $h(r, r')$ by

$$\{\delta\rho(r)/\delta u(r')\} = \beta(r')\rho(r) [\delta(r - r') + \rho(r')h(r, r')] \tag{49}$$

and also the direct correlation function $c(r, r')$ by

$$\{\delta u(r)/\delta\rho(r')\} = \beta^{-1}(r') [\delta(r - r')/\rho(r) - c(r, r')] \tag{50}$$

Using the identity

$$\int dr'' \{\delta\rho(r)/\delta u(r'')\}\{\delta u(r'')/\delta\rho(r')\} = \delta(r - r') \tag{51}$$

we obtain the Ornstein-Zernike equation

$$h(r, r') = c(r, r') + \int dr'' \, h(r, r'')\rho(r'')c(r'', r') \tag{52}$$

Considering the linear response, one also obtains the Yvon equation

$$\Delta\rho(r) = \beta(r)\rho(r)\Delta u(r) + \rho(r) \int dr' \, \beta(r')h(r, r')\Delta u(r')\rho(r') \qquad (53)$$

and another integro-differential equation for density

$$\nabla \ln \rho(r) = \beta(r)\nabla u(r) + \int dr' \, h(r, r')\rho(r')\beta(r')\nabla' u(r') \qquad (54)$$

which corresponds to BBGKY hierarchy for classical fluids. Another equation of importance is the compressibility equation

$$N\{\delta\mu/\delta\rho(r)\} = \beta^{-1}(r)[1 - \int dr' \rho(r')c(r, r')] \qquad (55)$$

where $\{\delta\mu/\delta\rho(r)\}$ can be called the local hardness [48]. Various local force laws showing the balance of classical and quantum forces have also been derived [49]. There also follows the local density functional virial equation of state [50]. Other equations of practical significance are the hyper-netted-chain and Percus-Yevick approximations which have been derived [39] using functional integration techniques and provide an integral equation scheme for the calculation of electron density. The underlying philosophy throughout has been to obtain a quantum "thermodynamics" of a microscopic system using the concept of local temperature.

The concept of the electronic temperature that has been defined through the electronic KE density also enters [38] naturally through a Lagrange multiplier while defining a six dimensional phase space (PS) distribution function [51] $f(r, p)$ corresponding to a density $\rho(r)$ through the maximization of an information entropy $S = -k_B \iint dr dp \, f [\ln f - 1]$, subject to the constraints of correct density $\rho(r) = \int dp f(r, p)$; and correct KE density $\varepsilon_{kin}(r; \rho) = \int f(r, p)(p^2/2) \, dp$. Apart from having an interpretive significance, this locally Maxwellian PS function given by

$$f(r, p) = [\beta(r)/2\pi]^{3/2}\rho(r) \exp [-\beta(r)p^2/2] \qquad (56)$$

provides a scheme for obtaining the momentum density, Compton profile [52] as well as the first order reduced density matrix and a new exchange energy functional [53] from the position space electron density.

The PS approach is used not only as a calculational tool, e.g. for establishing a bridge between the position space and momentum space, but also can be very helpful in understanding the connections between classical and quantum mechanics. Here a dynamical variable is represented by an ordinary function of r and p and the quantum mechanical averages are evaluated just like in classical case. Another distinctive feature is that both the state and the transition can be handled in an equivalent manner. The PS formalism is also useful in deriving the equations of quantum fluid dynamics [54], which has been discussed by Deb and Ghosh [3]. The advantage here is that one can easily deal with mixed states corresponding to a finite temperature.

Very recently, Deb and Chattaraj [25] have proposed a dynamical extension of the thermodynamic like concepts discussed here. The dynamics of many electron systems have been studied in terms of a space-time dependent temperature, entropy density and chemical potential $\mu(r, t)$ for the entire time evolving system. Since the time evolution of the system is envisaged in terms of the classical flow of a quantum fluid, they have suggested that the flow of $\mu(r, t)$

may be utilised to define microscopic rate constant. They have also proposed equations for entropy production and other equations of nonequilibrium thermodynamics corresponding to the electron fluid.

6. CONCLUDING REMARKS

The motivation and essence of the QFD approach involve conceptual simplicity, rigorous but transparent physics and computational economy. The major conceptual advantage of the fluid dynamical approach is that it offers a consistent "classical" view of quantum systems. From the discussion presented here, it is clear that a many electron system can be viewed as a fluid in 3-D space. Moreover, the continuous nature of the density distribution gives it a more fluid like character than a classical fluid. The dynamics of the electron fluid is governed by classical hydrodynamical equations and the quantum property enters through the quantum force alone.

Within the QFD viewpoint, chemical bond formation may be looked upon as due to collision of two fluid drops and a dissociation reaction as the splitting of a single drop into fragments. Such models have been highly successful in understanding nuclear reactions, nuclear fission etc. The generalised TDDFT providing a theoretical framework for direct calculation of $\rho(\mathbf{r}, t)$ and $\mathbf{j}(\mathbf{r}, t)$, and its associated QFD would enable one to study the interaction of radiation with matter. It would thus provide insight into collective excitations, photoabsorption, multiphoton dissociation, and various non-linear dynamical phenomena.

An important advantage of studying a quantum system in terms of the hydrodynamical quantities, viz. the electron density, current density, stress tensor etc is that these are all local quantities and thus much finer details may be revealed in contrast to the global ones. The understanding of chemical binding is considerably enhanced through studies of contour maps of electron density and also the simple model of binding in terms of stress tensor [9]. Study of the time evolution of these quantities as the nuclei approach each other in a chemical encounter would lead to new insights into the understanding of the mechanisms of reactions especially the quantum effects—resonances, tunnelling etc. Quantum stress tensor has already been of much interest in the study of nuclear reactions.

A joint attack through TDDFT and QFD in terms of $\rho(\mathbf{r}, t)$ and $\mathbf{j}(\mathbf{r}, t)$ opens the possibility of numerous practical applications in chemical dynamics. The recent work of Deb and Chattaraj [25] deals with a number of interesting aspects of the collision phenomena using a dynamical extension of the local thermodynamic picture within the frameworks of TDDFT and QFD. These developments broaden the scope of QFD and are thus significant in the context of search for the possibility of an alternative quantum mechanics in terms of density quantities rather than the wavefunction.

The implications of the study of dynamical behaviour of current density have not yet been fully explored. The fluid streamlines obtained by integrating the velocity field (both real and imaginary) can provide important information. A significant feature of the streamlines is the presence of vortices or quantum whirlpools [55, 56] which provide considerable insight into collision phenomena and hence play an important role in chemical dynamics especially when the vortices are close to the activated state. The vorticity is quantised and is useful in studying the magnetic properties.

Apart from these important unique features, QFD and DFT can provide practical schemes for improvement in the conventional quasiclassical trajectory approaches as well. It has been known [57] that the inclusion of correlation energy is important in obtaining an accurate potential energy surface. The tremendous advantage of a density based prescription is that the correlation effects can be incorporated in the KS scheme exactly (in principle) while still maintaining the simplicity of a Hartree like picture. Although exact form of the correlation energy functional is not yet known, even the available approximations can lead to improved results. In addition to the study of reactions at the molecular level, these approaches can be equally applicable to condensed phase reactions. A unified scheme has been recently proposed [58] by combining DFT and molecular dynamics, that profoundly extends the range of applicability of both concepts. This work has been of much current interest in the study of dynamics in condensed phases.

The applicability of QFD is not restricted to microscopic quantum systems alone. It provides an interesting general procedure for incorporating quantum effects within a classical framework by taking into account contribution from a quantum potential. Thus the quantum enhancement in a thermally activated barrier crossing process [59] influenced by solvent friction in condensed phase, which is of importance in electron or proton transfer processes [60] involving ultrafast dynamics [61] can be studied using a QFD approach generalised to dissipative systems [3]. The advantage of the QFD approach lies in the fact that the transition from microscopic to macroscopic phenomena is rather smooth since QFD provides essentially a macro-description of a micro-system [3, 62].

7. ACKNOWLEDGEMENTS

It is a pleasure to thank Dr Pratim Chattaraj and Alok Samanta for helpful discussions.

REFERENCES

1. S.K. Ghosh and B.M. Deb, Phys. Rep., **92**, 1 (1982).
2. S.K. Ghosh and B.M. Deb, Int. J. Quantum Chem., **22**, 871 (1982).
3. B.M. Deb and S.K. Ghosh, in, The Single Particle Density in Physics and Chemistry, ed. N.H. March and B.M. Deb, Academic Press, London (1987).
4. P. Hohenberg and W. Kohn, Phys. Rev., **136**, B864 (1964).
5. W. Kohn and L.J. Sham, Phys. Rev., **140**, A1133 (1965).
6. R.G. Parr and W. Yang, Density Functional Theory of Atoms and Molecules Oxford University Press, New York (1989).
7. N.H. March and B.M. Deb, Editors, The Single Particle Density in Physics and Chemistry. Academic Press, London (1987).
8. R.M. Dreizler and J da Providencia, Editors, Density Functional Methods in Physics, Plenum Press, New York (1985).
9. A.S. Bamzai and B.M. Deb, Rev. Mod. Phys., **53**, 96, 593 (1981).

10. E. Madelung, Z. Phys., **40**, 322 (1926).
11. D. Bohm Phys. Rev., **85**, 166, 180 (1952).
12. T. Takabayashi, Prog. Theo. Phys. Japan, **8**, 143 (1952).
13. R. Erdahl and V.H. Smith Jr, Editors, Density Matrices and Density Functionals. D. Reidel, Dordrecht (1987).
14. P. Becker, Editor, Electron and Magnetisation Densities in Molecules and Crystals, NATO Adv. Study Inst. Ser. B, Vol. 48, Plenum Press, New York (1980).
15. A.K. Theophilou, J. Phys., **C12**, 5419 (1979).
16. V. Peuckert, J. Phys., **C11**, 4945 (1978).
17. B.M. Deb and S.K. Ghosh, J. Chem. Phys., **77**, 342 (1982).
18. L.J. Bartolotti, Phys. Rev., **A24**, 1661 (1982).
19. E. Runge and E.K.U. Gross, Phys. Rev. Lett., **52**, 997 (1984).
20. A.K. Dhara and S.K. Ghosh, Phys. Rev., (Rapid Commun) **A35**, 442 (1987).
21. S.K. Ghosh and A.K. Dhara, Phys. Rev., **A38**, 1149 (1988).
22. G. Vignale and M. Rasolt, Phys. Rev. Lett., **59**, 2360 (1987).
23. S.K. Ghosh and A.K. Dhara, Phys. Rev., **A40**, 6103 (1989).
24. B.M. Deb and P.K. Chattaraj, Chem. Phys. Lett., **148**, 550 (1988)
25. B.M. Deb and P.K. Chattaraj, Phys. Rev., **A39**, 1696 (1989).
26. W.H. Miller, Editor, Dynamics of Molecular Collisions, Part A and B, Plenum Press, New York (1976).
27. R.D. Levine and R.B. Bernstein, Molecular Reaction Dynamics and Chemical Reactivity, Oxford Univ. Press, New York (1987).
28. R. Daudel, J. Molec. Struct. THEOCHEM., **103**, 269 (1983).
29. R.B. Bernstein, Chemical Dynamics via Molecular Beam and Laser Techniques, Oxford Univ Press, New York (1982).
30. I.W.M. Smith, Editor, Physical Chemistry of Fast Reactions, Vol. 2, Plenum Press, New York (1980).
31. B.M. Deb, Editor, The Force Concept in Chemistry, Van Nostrand Reinhold Co, New York (1981).
32. J.O. Hirschfelder, A.C. Christoph and W.E. Palke, J. Chem. Phys., **61**, 5435 (1974).
33. J.O. Hirschfelder, C.J. Goebel and L.W. Bruch, J. Chem. Phys., **61**, 5456 (1974).
34. J.O. Hirschfelder and K.T. Tang, J. Chem. Phys., **64**, 760 (1976).
35. J.O. Hirschfelder, in The New World of Quantum Chemistry, ed. B. Pullman and R.G. Parr, D. Reidel, Dordrecht (1976), p. 81.
36. E. Nelson, Phys. Rev., **150**, 1079 (1966).
37. J. Arponen, R.F. Bishop, E. Pajanne and N.I. Robinson, Phys. Rev., **A37**, 1065 (1988).
38. S.K. Ghosh, M. Berkowitz and R.G. Parr, Proc. Natl. Acad. Sci. USA, **81**, 8028 (1984).
39. S.K. Ghosh and M. Berkowitz, J. Chem. Phys., **83**, 2976 (1985).
40. B.M. Deb and S.K. Ghosh, J. Phys., **B12**, 3857 (1979).
41. C.Y. Wong, J. Math. Phys., **17**, 1008 (1976).
42. R.G. Parr, Ann. Rev. Phys. Chem., **34**, 631 (1983).
43. N.H. March, Adv. Phys., **6**, 1 (1957).
44. B.M. Deb and S.K. Ghosh, Int. J. Quantum Chem., **23**, 1 (1983); R.G. Parr and S.K. Ghosh, Proc. Natl. Acad. Sci., **83**, 3577 (1986).
45. J.A. Ball, J.A. Wheeler and E.L. Firemen, Rev. Mod. Phys., **45**, 333 (1973).
46. M. Born and H.S. Green, A General Kinetic Theory of Liquids, Cambridge Univ. Press, Cambridge (1949).

47. R.M. Mazo and J.G. Kirkwood, J. Chem. Phys., **28**, 644 (1958).
48. M. Berkowitz, S.K. Ghosh and R.G. Parr, J. Am. Chem. Soc., **107**, 6811 (1985).
49. S.K. Ghosh, J. Chem. Phys., **87**, 3513 (1987).
50. S.K. Ghosh and R.G. Parr, J. Chem. Phys., **82**, 3307 (1985).
51. S.K. Ghosh, Proc. Indian Acad. Sci. (Chem. Sci.), **99**, 21 (1987).
52. R.G. Parr, K. Rupnik and S.K. Ghosh, Phys. Rev. Lett., **56**, 1555 (1986).
53. S.K. Ghosh and R.G. Parr, Phys. Rev., **A34**, 785 (1986).
54. P. Carruthers and F. Zachariasen, Rev. Mod. Phys., **55**, 245 (1983).
55. E.A. McCullough, Jr. and R.E. Wyatt, J. Chem. Phys., **54**, 3578 (1971).
56. A. Kuppermann, J.T. Adams and D.G. Truhlar, VII Int. Conf. Physics of Electronic and Atomic Collisions, Belgrade, Yugoslavia, p. 149.
57. N. Sathyamurthy, Chem. Phys., **62**, 1 (1981).
58. R. Car and M. Parrienello, Phys. Rev. Lett., **55**, 2471 (1985).
59. P. Hanggi, J. Stat. Phys., **42**, 105 (1986).
60. A. Samanta, S.K. Ghosh and H.K. Sadhukan, Chem. Phys. Lett., **168**, 410 (1990).
61. G.R. Fleming and A.E. Siegman, Editors, Ultrafast Phenomena, Springer-Verlag, New York (1986).
62. H. Frohlich, Riv. Nuovo. Cimento., **3**, 490 (1973).

Subject Index

BC